D0299685

# Radiate Science knowledge with CGP...

OK, so there's a lot to learn in GCSE Combined Science — it is worth two GCSEs, after all.

Not to worry. This chunky CGP book explains all the facts, theory and practical skills you'll need, with essential exam practice questions on every page. It's a beautiful thing.

## How to access your free Online Edition

This book includes a free Online Edition to read on your PC, Mac or tablet.
To access it, just go to **cgpbooks.co.uk/extras** and enter this code...

4031 0285 9138 8776

By the way, this code only works for one person. If somebody else has used this book before you, they might have already claimed the Online Edition.

# CGP — still the best! ☺

Our sole aim here at CGP is to produce the highest quality books — carefully written, immaculately presented and dangerously close to being funny.

Then we work our socks off to get them out to you
— at the cheapest possible prices.

# Contents

Published by CGP

From original material by Richard Parsons.

Editors: Mary Falkner, Emily Forsberg, Paul Jordin, Rachael Marshall, Chris McGarry, Ciara McGlade, Sarah Oxley, Rachael Rogers, Frances Rooney, Sophie Scott and Hayley Thompson

Contributor: Paddy Gannon

ISBN: 978 1 78294 574 1

With thanks to Katherine Faudemer, Emily Howe and Karen Wells for the proofreading.

With thanks to Jan Greenway and Ana Pungartnik for the copyright research.

Percentile growth chart on page 21 copyright © 2009 Royal College of Paediatrics and Child Health.

Definition of health on page 39 from: Preamble to the Constitution of the World Health Organization as adopted by the International Health Conference, New York, 19 June – 22 July 1946; signed on 22 July 1946 by the representatives of 61 States (Official Records of the World Health Organization, no. 2, p. 100) and entered into force on 7 April 1948.

Hazard symbols are public sector information published by the Health and Safety Executive and licensed under the Open Government Licence. http://www.nationalarchives.gov.uk/doc/open-government-licence/version/3/.

Graph to show trend in Atmospheric $CO_2$ Concentration and global temperature on page 143 based on data by EPICA community members 2004 and Siegenthaler et al 2005.

Every effort has been made to locate copyright holders and obtain permission to reproduce sources. For those sources where it has been difficult to trace the originator of the work, we would be grateful for information. If any copyright holder would like us to make an amendment to the acknowledgements, please notify us and we will gladly update the book at the next reprint. Thank you.

Printed by Elanders Ltd, Newcastle upon Tyne.
Clipart from Corel®

Text, design, layout and original illustrations © Coordination Group Publications Ltd (CGP) 2016
All rights reserved.

Photocopying more than one chapter of this book is not permitted. Extra copies are available from CGP.
0800 1712 712 • www.cgpbooks.co.uk

# The Scientific Method

This section isn't about how to 'do' science — but it does show you the way most scientists work.

## Scientists Come Up With Hypotheses — Then Test Them

1) Scientists try to explain things. They start by observing something they don't understand.

2) They then come up with a hypothesis — a possible explanation for what they've observed.

3) The next step is to test whether the hypothesis might be right or not. This involves making a prediction based on the hypothesis and testing it by gathering evidence (i.e. data) from investigations. If evidence from experiments backs up a prediction, you're a step closer to figuring out if the hypothesis is true.

About 100 years ago, scientists hypothesised that atoms looked like this.

## Several Scientists Will Test a Hypothesis

1) Normally, scientists share their findings in peer-reviewed journals, or at conferences.

2) Peer-review is where other scientists check results and scientific explanations to make sure they're 'scientific' (e.g. that experiments have been done in a sensible way) before they're published. It helps to detect false claims, but it doesn't mean that findings are correct — just that they're not wrong in any obvious way.

3) Once other scientists have found out about a hypothesis, they'll start basing their own predictions on it and carry out their own experiments. They'll also try to reproduce the original experiments to check the results — and if all the experiments in the world back up the hypothesis, then scientists start to think the hypothesis is true.

4) However, if a scientist does an experiment that doesn't fit with the hypothesis (and other scientists can reproduce the results) then the hypothesis may need to be modified or scrapped altogether.

After more evidence was gathered, scientists changed their hypothesis to this.

## If All the Evidence Supports a Hypothesis, It's Accepted — For Now

1) Accepted hypotheses are often referred to as theories. Our currently accepted theories are the ones that have survived this 'trial by evidence' — they've been tested many times over the years and survived.

2) However, theories never become totally indisputable fact. If new evidence comes along that can't be explained using the existing theory, then the hypothesising and testing is likely to start all over again.

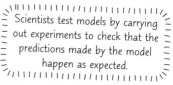

Now we think it's more like this.

## Theories Can Involve Different Types of Models

1) A representational model is a simplified description or picture of what's going on in real life. Like all models, it can be used to explain observations and make predictions. E.g. the Bohr model of an atom is a simplified way of showing the arrangement of electrons in an atom (see p.78). It can be used to explain trends down groups in the periodic table.

> Scientists test models by carrying out experiments to check that the predictions made by the model happen as expected.

2) Computational models use computers to make simulations of complex real-life processes, such as climate change. They're used when there are a lot of different variables (factors that change) to consider, and because you can easily change their design to take into account new data.

3) All models have limitations on what they can explain or predict. E.g. ball and stick models (a type of spatial model) can be used to show how ions are arranged in an ionic compound. One of their limitations is that they don't show the relative sizes of the ions (see p.85).

## I'm off to the zoo to test my hippo-thesis...

The scientific method has developed over time, and many people have helped to develop it. From Aristotle to modern day scientists, lots of people have contributed. And many more are likely to contribute in the future.

# Communication & Issues Created by Science

Scientific developments can be great, but they can sometimes raise more questions than they answer...

## It's Important to Communicate Scientific Discoveries to the General Public

Some scientific discoveries show that people should change their habits, or they might provide ideas that could be developed into new technology. So scientists need to tell the world about their discoveries.

Gene technologies are used in genetic engineering, to produce genetically modified crops. Information about these crops needs to be communicated to farmers who might benefit from growing them and to the general public, so they can make informed decisions about the food they buy and eat.

## Scientific Evidence can be Presented in a Biased Way

1) Reports about scientific discoveries in the media (e.g. newspapers or television) aren't peer-reviewed.

2) This means that, even though news stories are often based on data that has been peer-reviewed, the data might be presented in a way that is over-simplified or inaccurate, making it open to misinterpretation.

3) People who want to make a point can sometimes present data in a biased way. (Sometimes without knowing they're doing it.) For example, a scientist might overemphasise a relationship in the data, or a newspaper article might describe details of data supporting an idea without giving any evidence against it.

## Scientific Developments are Great, but they can Raise Issues

Scientific knowledge is increased by doing experiments. And this knowledge leads to scientific developments, e.g. new technologies or new advice. These developments can create issues though. For example:

Economic issues: Society can't always afford to do things scientists recommend (e.g. investing in alternative energy sources) without cutting back elsewhere.

Social issues: Decisions based on scientific evidence affect people — e.g. should alcohol be banned (to prevent health problems)? Would the effect on people's lifestyles be acceptable...?

Personal issues: Some decisions will affect individuals. For example, someone might support alternative energy, but object if a wind farm is built next to their house.

Environmental issues: Human activity often affects the natural environment — e.g. genetically modified crops may help us to produce more food — but some people think they could cause environmental problems (see p.37).

## Science Can't Answer Every Question — Especially Ethical Ones

1) We don't understand everything. We're always finding out more, but we'll never know all the answers.

2) In order to answer scientific questions, scientists need data to provide evidence for their hypotheses.

3) Some questions can't be answered yet because the data can't currently be collected, or because there's not enough data to support a theory.

4) Eventually, as we get more evidence, we'll answer some of the questions that currently can't be answered, e.g. what the impact of global warming on sea levels will be. But there will always be the "Should we be doing this at all?"-type questions that experiments can't help us to answer...

Think about new drugs which can be taken to boost your 'brain power'.

THE GAZETTE
BRAIN-BOOSTING DRUGS MAKE A MOCKERY OF EXAMS

THE POST
GENIUS PILLS TO BECOME THE NEW COFFEE

- Some people think they're good as they could improve concentration or memory. New drugs could let people think in ways beyond the powers of normal brains.

- Other people say they're bad — they could give you an unfair advantage in exams. And people might be pressured into taking them so that they could work more effectively, and for longer hours.

## Tea to milk or milk to tea? — Totally unanswerable by science...

Science can't tell you whether or not you should do something. That's for you and society to decide. But there are tons of questions science might be able to answer, like where life came from and where my superhero socks are.

# Risk

By reading this page you are agreeing to the risk of a paper cut or severe drowsiness...

## Nothing is Completely Risk-Free

1) A hazard is something that could potentially cause harm.

2) All hazards have a risk attached to them — this is the chance that the hazard will cause harm.

3) The risks of some things seem pretty obvious, or we've known about them for a while, like the risk of causing acid rain by polluting the atmosphere, or of having a car accident when you're travelling in a car.

4) New technology arising from scientific advances can bring new risks, e.g. scientists are unsure whether nanoparticles that are being used in cosmetics and suncream might be harming the cells in our bodies. These risks need to be considered alongside the benefits of the technology, e.g. improved sun protection.

5) You can estimate the size of a risk based on how many times something happens in a big sample (e.g. 100 000 people) over a given period (e.g. a year). For example, you could assess the risk of a driver crashing by recording how many people in a group of 100 000 drivers crashed their cars over a year.

6) To make a decision about activities that involve hazards, we need to take into account the chance of the hazard causing harm, and how serious the consequences would be if it did. So if an activity involves a hazard that's very likely to cause harm, with serious consequences if it does, it's considered high-risk.

## People Make Their Own Decisions About Risk

1) Not all risks have the same consequences, e.g. if you chop veg with a sharp knife you risk cutting your finger, but if you go scuba-diving you risk death. You're much more likely to cut your finger during half an hour of chopping than to die during half an hour of scuba-diving. But most people are happier to accept a higher probability of an accident if the consequences are short-lived and fairly minor.

2) People tend to be more willing to accept a risk if they choose to do something (e.g. go scuba diving), compared to having the risk imposed on them (e.g. having a nuclear power station built next door).

3) People's perception of risk (how risky they think something is) isn't always accurate. They tend to view familiar activities as low-risk and unfamiliar activities as high-risk — even if that's not the case. For example, cycling on roads is often high-risk, but many people are happy to do it because it's a familiar activity. Air travel is actually pretty safe, but a lot of people perceive it as high-risk.

4) People may over-estimate the risk of things with long-term or invisible effects, e.g. ionising radiation.

## Investigations Can be Hazardous

1) Hazards from science experiments might include:

- Microorganisms, e.g. some bacteria can make you ill.
- Chemicals, e.g. sulfuric acid can burn your skin and alcohols catch fire easily.
- Fire, e.g. an unattended Bunsen burner is a fire hazard.
- Electricity, e.g. faulty electrical equipment could give you a shock.

Hmm... Where did my bacteria sample go?

2) Part of planning an investigation is making sure that it's safe.

3) You should always make sure that you identify all the hazards that you might encounter. Then you should think of ways of reducing the risks from the hazards you've identified. For example:

- If you're working with sulfuric acid, always wear gloves and safety goggles. This will reduce the risk of the acid coming into contact with your skin and eyes.
- If you're using a Bunsen burner, stand it on a heat proof mat. This will reduce the risk of starting a fire.

You can find out about potential hazards by looking in textbooks, doing some internet research, or asking your teacher.

---

## Not revising — an unacceptable exam hazard...

The world's a dangerous place, but if you can recognise hazards, decide how to reduce their risks, and be happy to accept some risks, you can still have fun. Just maybe don't go skydiving with a great white shark on Friday 13th.

# Designing Investigations

Dig out your lab coat and dust down your badly-scratched safety goggles... it's <u>investigation time</u>.

## *Investigations Produce Evidence to Support or Disprove a Hypothesis*

1) Scientists <u>observe</u> things and come up with <u>hypotheses</u> to explain them (see p.1).
   You need to be able to do the same. For example:

   > <u>Observation</u>: People have big feet and spots. <u>Hypothesis</u>: Having big feet causes spots.

2) To <u>determine</u> whether or not a hypothesis is <u>right</u>, you need to do an <u>investigation</u> to gather evidence. To do this, you need to use your hypothesis to make a <u>prediction</u> — something you think <u>will happen</u> that you can <u>test</u>. E.g. people who have bigger feet will have more spots.

3) Investigations are used to see if there are <u>patterns</u> or <u>relationships</u> between <u>two variables</u>, e.g. to see if there's a pattern or relationship between the variables 'number of spots' and 'size of feet'.

## *Evidence Needs to be Repeatable, Reproducible and Valid*

1) <u>Repeatable</u> means that if the <u>same person</u> does an experiment again using the <u>same methods</u> and equipment, they'll get <u>similar results</u>.

2) <u>Reproducible</u> means that if <u>someone else</u> does the experiment, or a <u>different</u> method or piece of equipment is used, the results will still be <u>similar</u>.

*Investigations include experiments and studies.*

3) If data is <u>repeatable</u> and <u>reproducible</u>, it's <u>reliable</u> and scientists are more likely to <u>have confidence</u> in it.

4) <u>Valid results</u> are both repeatable and reproducible AND they <u>answer the original question</u>. They come from experiments that were designed to be a FAIR TEST...

## *To Make an Investigation a Fair Test You Have to Control the Variables*

1) In a lab experiment you usually <u>change one variable</u> and <u>measure</u> how it affects <u>another variable</u>.

2) To make it a fair test, <u>everything else</u> that could affect the results should <u>stay the same</u> — otherwise you can't tell if the thing you're changing is causing the results or not.

3) The variable you CHANGE is called the INDEPENDENT variable.

4) The variable you MEASURE when you change the independent variable is the DEPENDENT variable.

5) The variables that you KEEP THE SAME are called CONTROL variables.

   > You could find how <u>temperature</u> affects the rate of an <u>enzyme-controlled reaction</u>. The <u>independent variable</u> is the <u>temperature</u>. The <u>dependent variable</u> is the <u>rate of reaction</u>. Control variables include the <u>concentration</u> and <u>amounts</u> of reactants, <u>pH</u>, the <u>time period</u> you measure, etc.

6) Because you can't always control all the variables, you often need to use a <u>control experiment</u>. This is an experiment that's kept under the <u>same conditions</u> as the rest of the investigation, but <u>doesn't</u> have anything <u>done</u> to it. This is so that you can see what happens when you don't change anything at all.

## *The Bigger the Sample Size the Better*

1) Data based on <u>small samples</u> isn't as good as data based on large samples. A sample should <u>represent</u> the <u>whole population</u> (i.e. it should share as many of the characteristics in the population as possible) — a small sample can't do that as well. It's also harder to spot <u>anomalies</u> if your sample size is too small.

2) The <u>bigger</u> the sample size the <u>better</u>, but scientists have to be <u>realistic</u> when choosing how big. For example, if you were studying how lifestyle affects people's weight it'd be great to study everyone in the UK (a huge sample), but it'd take ages and cost a bomb. It's more realistic to study a thousand people, with a mixture of ages, gender and race.

## *This is no high street survey — it's a designer investigation...*

Not only do you need to be able to plan your own investigations, you should also be able to look at someone else's plan and decide whether or not it needs improving. Those examiners aren't half demanding.

# Collecting Data

You've designed the perfect investigation — now it's time to get your hands mucky and collect some data.

## Your Data Should be Repeatable, Reproducible, Accurate and Precise

1) To check repeatability you need to repeat the readings and check that the results are similar. You need to repeat each reading at least three times.

2) To make sure your results are reproducible you can cross check them by taking a second set of readings with another instrument (or a different observer).

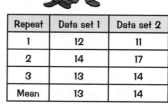

Brian's result was a curate.

3) Your data also needs to be ACCURATE. Really accurate results are those that are really close to the true answer. The accuracy of your results usually depends on your method — you need to make sure you're measuring the right thing and that you don't miss anything that should be included in the measurements. E.g. estimating the amount of gas released from a reaction by counting the bubbles isn't very accurate because you might miss some of the bubbles and they might have different volumes. It's more accurate to measure the volume of gas released using a gas syringe (see p.208).

| Repeat | Data set 1 | Data set 2 |
|--------|-----------|-----------|
| 1 | 12 | 11 |
| 2 | 14 | 17 |
| 3 | 13 | 14 |
| Mean | 13 | 14 |

Data set 1 is more precise than data set 2.

4) Your data also needs to be PRECISE. Precise results are ones where the data is all really close to the mean (average) of your repeated results (i.e. not spread out).

## Your Equipment has to be Right for the Job

1) The measuring equipment you use has to be sensitive enough to measure the changes you're looking for. For example, if you need to measure changes of 1 cm³ you need to use a measuring cylinder that can measure in 1 cm³ steps — it'd be no good trying with one that only measures in 10 cm³ steps.

2) The smallest change a measuring instrument can detect is called its RESOLUTION. E.g. some mass balances have a resolution of 1 g, some have a resolution of 0.1 g, and some are even more sensitive.

3) Also, equipment needs to be calibrated by measuring a known value. If there's a difference between the measured and known value, you can use this to correct the inaccuracy of the equipment.

## You Need to Look out for Errors and Anomalous Results

1) The results of your experiment will always vary a bit because of RANDOM ERRORS — unpredictable differences caused by things like human errors in measuring. E.g. the errors you make when reading from a measuring cylinder are random. You have to estimate or round the level when it's between two marks — so sometimes your figure will be a bit above the real one, and sometimes it will be a bit below.

2) You can reduce the effect of random errors by taking repeat readings and finding the mean. This will make your results more precise.

*If there's no systematic error, then doing repeats and calculating a mean can make your results more accurate.*

3) If a measurement is wrong by the same amount every time, it's called a SYSTEMATIC ERROR. For example, if you measured from the very end of your ruler instead of from the 0 cm mark every time, all your measurements would be a bit small. Repeating the experiment in the exact same way and calculating a mean won't correct a systematic error.

4) Just to make things more complicated, if a systematic error is caused by using equipment that isn't zeroed properly, it's called a ZERO ERROR. For example, if a mass balance always reads 1 gram before you put anything on it, all your measurements will be 1 gram too heavy.

5) You can compensate for some systematic errors if you know about them though, e.g. if your mass balance always reads 1 gram before you put anything on it you can subtract 1 gram from all your results.

6) Sometimes you get a result that doesn't fit in with the rest at all. This is called an ANOMALOUS RESULT. You should investigate it and try to work out what happened. If you can work out what happened (e.g. you measured something totally wrong) you can ignore it when processing your results.

## Watch what you say to that mass balance — it's very sensitive...

Weirdly, data can be really precise but not very accurate. For example, a fancy piece of lab equipment might give results that are really precise, but if it's not been calibrated properly those results won't be accurate.

# Processing and Presenting Data

Processing your data means doing some <u>calculations</u> with it to make it <u>more useful</u>. Once you've done that, you can present your results in a nice <u>chart</u> or <u>graph</u> to help you <u>spot any patterns</u> in your data.

## Data Needs to be Organised

Tables are dead useful for <u>organising data</u>. When you draw a table <u>use a ruler</u> and make sure <u>each column</u> has a <u>heading</u> (including the <u>units</u>).

## You Might Have to Process Your Data

1) When you've done repeats of an experiment you should always calculate the <u>mean</u> (a type of average). To do this <u>add together</u> all the data values and <u>divide</u> by the total number of values in the sample.

2) You might also need to calculate the <u>range</u> (how spread out the data is). To do this find the <u>largest</u> number and <u>subtract</u> the <u>smallest</u> number from it. ← *Ignore anomalous results when calculating these.*

**EXAMPLE:** The results of an experiment to find the volume of gas produced in an enzyme-controlled reaction are shown below. Calculate the mean volume and the range.

| Repeat 1 (cm³) | Repeat 2 (cm³) | Repeat 3 (cm³) | Mean (cm³) | Range (cm³) |
|---|---|---|---|---|
| 28 | 37 | 32 | (28 + 37 + 32) ÷ 3 = 32 | 37 − 28 = 9 |

3) You might also need to calculate the <u>median</u> or <u>mode</u> (two more types of average). To calculate the <u>median</u>, put all your data in <u>numerical order</u> — the median is the <u>middle value</u>. The number that appears <u>most often</u> in a data set is the <u>mode</u>.

*If you have an even number of values, the median is halfway between the middle two values.*

E.g. If you have the data set: 1 2 1 1 3 4 2
The <u>median</u> is: 1 1 1 <u>2</u> 2 3 4. The <u>mode</u> is <u>1</u> because 1 appears most often.

## Round to the Lowest Number of Significant Figures

The <u>first significant figure</u> of a number is the first digit that's <u>not zero</u>. The second and third significant figures come <u>straight after</u> (even if they're zeros). You should be aware of significant figures in calculations.

1) In <u>any</u> calculation, you should round the answer to the <u>lowest number of significant figures</u> (s.f.) given.

2) Remember to write down <u>how many</u> significant figures you've rounded to after your answer.

3) If your calculation has multiple steps, <u>only</u> round the <u>final</u> answer, or it won't be as accurate.

**EXAMPLE:** The mass of a solid is 0.24 g and its volume is 0.715 cm³. Calculate the density of the solid.

Density = 0.24 g ÷ 0.715 cm³ = 0.33566... = 0.34 g/cm³ (2 s.f.) — *Final answer should be rounded to 2 s.f.*
(2 s.f.)          (3 s.f.)

## If Your Data Comes in Categories, Present It in a Bar Chart

1) If the independent variable is <u>categoric</u> (comes in distinct categories, e.g. flower colour, blood group) you should use a <u>bar chart</u> to display the data.

2) You also use them if the independent variable is <u>discrete</u> (the data can be counted in chunks, where there's no in-between value, e.g. number of bacteria is discrete because you can't have half a bacterium).

3) There are some <u>golden rules</u> you need to follow for <u>drawing</u> bar charts:

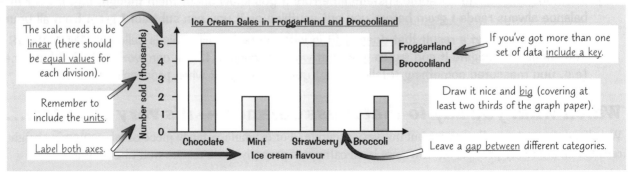

The scale needs to be <u>linear</u> (there should be <u>equal values</u> for each division).

Remember to include the <u>units</u>.

<u>Label both axes.</u>

If you've got more than one set of data <u>include a key</u>.

Draw it nice and <u>big</u> (covering at least two thirds of the graph paper).

Leave a <u>gap between</u> different categories.

Ice Cream Sales in Froggartland and Broccoliland
Number sold (thousands) / Ice cream flavour
Chocolate, Mint, Strawberry, Broccoli
□ Froggartland □ Broccoliland

## If Your Data is Continuous, Plot a Graph

If both variables are <u>continuous</u> (numerical data that can have any value within a range, e.g. length, volume, temperature) you should use a <u>graph</u> to display the data.

Here are the rules for plotting points on a graph:

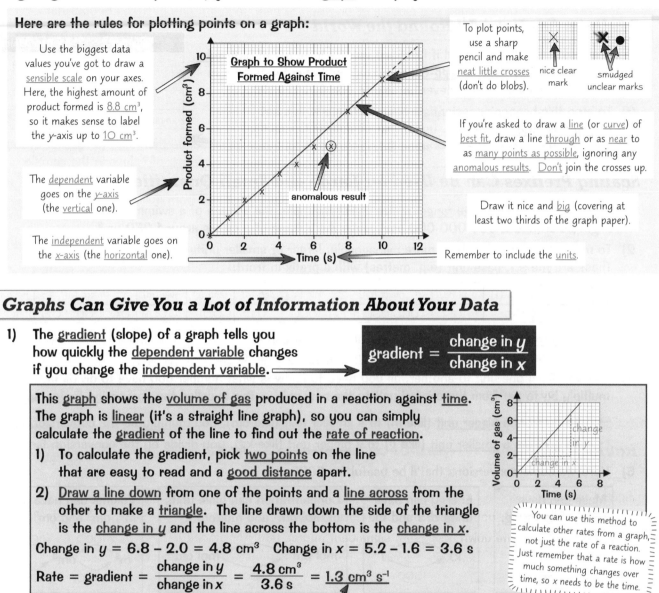

Use the biggest data values you've got to draw a <u>sensible scale</u> on your axes. Here, the highest amount of product formed is <u>8.8 cm³</u>, so it makes sense to label the *y*-axis up to 1O cm³.

The <u>dependent</u> variable goes on the *y*-axis (the <u>vertical</u> one).

The <u>independent</u> variable goes on the *x*-axis (the <u>horizontal</u> one).

To plot points, use a sharp pencil and make <u>neat little crosses</u> (don't do blobs). — nice clear mark — smudged unclear marks

If you're asked to draw a <u>line</u> (or <u>curve</u>) of <u>best fit</u>, draw a line <u>through</u> or as <u>near</u> to as <u>many points as possible</u>, ignoring any <u>anomalous results</u>. <u>Don't</u> join the crosses up.

Draw it nice and <u>big</u> (covering at least two thirds of the graph paper).

Remember to include the <u>units</u>.

Graph labels: Product formed (cm³) on y-axis, Time (s) on x-axis. **Graph to Show Product Formed Against Time**. anomalous result.

## Graphs Can Give You a Lot of Information About Your Data

1) The <u>gradient</u> (slope) of a graph tells you how quickly the <u>dependent variable</u> changes if you change the <u>independent variable</u>.

$$\text{gradient} = \frac{\text{change in } y}{\text{change in } x}$$

This <u>graph</u> shows the <u>volume of gas</u> produced in a reaction against <u>time</u>. The graph is <u>linear</u> (it's a straight line graph), so you can simply calculate the <u>gradient</u> of the line to find out the <u>rate of reaction</u>.

1) To calculate the gradient, pick <u>two points</u> on the line that are easy to read and a <u>good distance</u> apart.

2) <u>Draw a line down</u> from one of the points and a <u>line across</u> from the other to make a <u>triangle</u>. The line drawn down the side of the triangle is the <u>change in y</u> and the line across the bottom is the <u>change in x</u>.

Change in $y$ = 6.8 – 2.0 = 4.8 cm³    Change in $x$ = 5.2 – 1.6 = 3.6 s

$$\text{Rate} = \text{gradient} = \frac{\text{change in } y}{\text{change in } x} = \frac{4.8 \text{ cm}^3}{3.6 \text{ s}} = \underline{1.3 \text{ cm}^3 \text{ s}^{-1}}$$

The units of the gradient are (units of *y*)/(units of *x*). cm³ s⁻¹ can also be written as cm³/s.

Graph: Volume of gas (cm³) on y-axis, Time (s) on x-axis. change in y, change in x.

You can use this method to calculate other rates from a graph, not just the rate of a reaction. Just remember that a rate is how much something changes over time, so *x* needs to be the time.

2) To find the <u>gradient of a curve</u> at a <u>certain point</u>, draw a <u>tangent</u> to the curve at that point and then find the <u>gradient of the tangent</u>. See page 131 for details on how to do this.

3) The <u>intercept</u> of a graph is where the line of best fit crosses one of the <u>axes</u>. The <u>x-intercept</u> is where the line of best fit crosses the *x*-axis and the <u>y-intercept</u> is where it crosses the <u>y-axis</u>.

## Graphs Show the Relationship Between Two Variables

1) You can get <u>three</u> types of <u>correlation</u> (relationship) between variables:

2) Just because there's correlation, it doesn't mean the change in one variable is <u>causing</u> the change in the other — there might be <u>other factors</u> involved (see page 9).

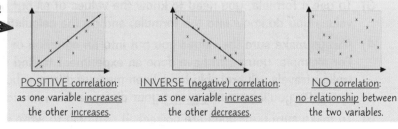

<u>POSITIVE correlation</u>: as one variable <u>increases</u> the other <u>increases</u>.

<u>INVERSE (negative) correlation</u>: as one variable <u>increases</u> the other <u>decreases</u>.

<u>NO correlation</u>: <u>no relationship</u> between the two variables.

## I love eating apples — I call it core elation...

Science is all about finding relationships between things. And I don't mean that chemists gather together in corners to discuss whether or not Devini and Sebastian might be a couple... though they probably do that too.

# Units and Equations

Graphs and maths skills are all very well, but the numbers don't mean much if you can't get the <u>units</u> right.

## S.I. Units Are Used All Round the World

1) It wouldn't be all that useful if I defined volume in terms of <u>bath tubs</u>, you defined it in terms of <u>egg-cups</u> and my pal Sarwat defined it in terms of <u>balloons</u> — we'd never be able to compare our data.

2) To stop this happening, scientists have come up with a set of <u>standard units</u>, called S.I. units, that all scientists use to measure their data. Here are some S.I. units you might see:

| Quantity | S.I. Base Unit |
|---|---|
| mass | kilogram, kg |
| length | metre, m |
| time | second, s |
| amount of substance | mole, mol |
| temperature | kelvin, K |

## Scaling Prefixes Can Be Used for Large and Small Quantities

1) Quantities come in a huge <u>range</u> of sizes. For example, the volume of a swimming pool might be around 2 000 000 000 cm³, while the volume of a cup is around 250 cm³.

2) To make the size of numbers more <u>manageable</u>, larger or smaller units are used. These are the <u>S.I. base unit</u> (e.g. metres) with a <u>prefix</u> in front:

| prefix | tera (T) | giga (G) | mega (M) | kilo (k) | deci (d) | centi (c) | milli (m) | micro (μ) | nano (n) |
|---|---|---|---|---|---|---|---|---|---|
| multiple of unit | $10^{12}$ | $10^9$ | 1 000 000 ($10^6$) | 1000 | 0.1 | 0.01 | 0.001 | 0.000001 ($10^{-6}$) | $10^{-9}$ |

3) These <u>prefixes</u> tell you <u>how much bigger</u> or <u>smaller</u> a unit is than the base unit. So one <u>kilometre</u> is <u>one thousand</u> metres.

*The conversion factor is the number of times the smaller unit goes into the larger unit.*

4) To <u>swap</u> from one unit to another, all you need to know is what number you have to divide or multiply by to get from the original unit to the new unit — this is called the <u>conversion factor</u>.

- To go from a <u>bigger unit</u> (like m) to a <u>smaller unit</u> (like cm), you <u>multiply</u> by the conversion factor.
- To go from a <u>smaller unit</u> (like g) to a <u>bigger unit</u> (like kg), you <u>divide</u> by the conversion factor.

5) Here are some conversions that'll be useful for GCSE science:

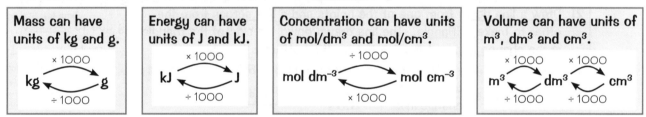

Mass can have units of kg and g.
kg ×1000→ g, g ÷1000→ kg

Energy can have units of J and kJ.
kJ ×1000→ J, J ÷1000→ kJ

Concentration can have units of mol/dm³ and mol/cm³.
mol dm⁻³ ÷1000→ mol cm⁻³, mol cm⁻³ ×1000→ mol dm⁻³

Volume can have units of m³, dm³ and cm³.
m³ ×1000→ dm³ ×1000→ cm³, cm³ ÷1000→ dm³ ÷1000→ m³

6) Numbers can also be written in <u>standard form</u>, e.g. $1 \times 10^2$ m = 100 m. There's more on this on p.14. Make sure you know how to work with standard form on <u>your calculator</u>.

## Always Check The Values in Equations and Formulas Have the Right Units

1) Equations show <u>relationships</u> between <u>variables</u>.

2) To <u>rearrange</u> an equation — whatever you do to <u>one side</u> of the equation also do to the <u>other</u>.

*wave speed = frequency × wavelength. You can <u>rearrange</u> this equation to find the <u>frequency</u> by <u>dividing each side</u> by wavelength to give: frequency = wave speed ÷ wavelength.*

3) To use a formula, you need to know the values of <u>all but one</u> of the variables. <u>Substitute</u> the values you do know into the formula, and do the calculation to work out the final variable.

4) Always make sure the values you put into an equation or formula have the <u>right units</u>. For example, you might have done an experiment to find the speed of a trolley. The distance the trolley travels will probably have been measured in cm, but the equation to find speed uses distance in m. So you'll have to <u>convert</u> your distance from cm to m before you put it into the equation.

5) To make sure your units are <u>correct</u>, it can help to write down the <u>units</u> on each line of your <u>calculation</u>.

## I wasn't sure I liked units, but now I'm converted...

It's easy to get in a muddle when converting between units, but there's a handy way to check you've done it right. If you're moving from a smaller unit to a larger unit (e.g. g to kg) the number should get smaller, and vice versa.

# Drawing Conclusions

Congratulations — you're nearly at the end of a gruelling investigation, time to draw conclusions.

## You Can Only Conclude What the Data Shows and NO MORE

1) Drawing conclusions might seem pretty straightforward — you just look at your data and say what pattern or relationship you see between the dependent and independent variables.

The table on the right shows the heights of pea plant seedlings grown for three weeks with different fertilisers.

| Fertiliser | Mean growth / mm |
|---|---|
| A | 13.5 |
| B | 19.5 |
| No fertiliser | 5.5 |

CONCLUSION:
Fertiliser B makes pea plant seedlings grow taller over a three week period than fertiliser A.

2) But you've got to be really careful that your conclusion matches the data you've got and doesn't go any further.

You can't conclude that fertiliser B makes any other type of plant grow taller than fertiliser A — the results could be totally different.

3) You also need to be able to use your results to justify your conclusion (i.e. back up your conclusion with some specific data).

Over the three week period, fertiliser B made the pea plants grow 6 mm more on average than fertiliser A.

4) When writing a conclusion you need to refer back to the original hypothesis and say whether the data supports it or not:

The hypothesis for this experiment might have been that adding fertiliser would increase the growth of plants and that different types of fertiliser would affect growth by different amounts. If so, the data supports the hypothesis.

## Correlation DOES NOT Mean Cause

If two things are correlated (i.e. there's a relationship between them) it doesn't necessarily mean a change in one variable is causing the change in the other — this is REALLY IMPORTANT — DON'T FORGET IT. There are three possible reasons for a correlation:

1) CHANCE: It might seem strange, but two things can show a correlation purely due to chance.

For example, one study might find a correlation between people's hair colour and how good they are at frisbee. But other scientists don't get a correlation when they investigate it — the results of the first study are just a fluke.

2) LINKED BY A 3RD VARIABLE: A lot of the time it may look as if a change in one variable is causing a change in the other, but it isn't — a third variable links the two things.

For example, there's a correlation between water temperature and shark attacks. This isn't because warmer water makes sharks crazy. Instead, they're linked by a third variable — the number of people swimming (more people swim when the water's hotter, and with more people in the water you get more shark attacks).

3) CAUSE: Sometimes a change in one variable does cause a change in the other. You can only conclude that a correlation is due to cause when you've controlled all the variables that could, just could, be affecting the result.

For example, there's a correlation between smoking and lung cancer. This is because chemicals in tobacco smoke cause lung cancer. This conclusion was only made once other variables (such as age and exposure to other things that cause cancer) had been controlled and shown not to affect people's risk of getting lung cancer.

## I conclude that this page is a bit dull...

...although, just because I find it dull doesn't mean that I can conclude it's dull (you might think it's the most interesting thing since that kid got his head stuck in the railings near school). In the exams you could be given a conclusion and asked whether some data supports it — so make sure you understand how far conclusions can go.

# Uncertainties and Evaluations

Hurrah! The end of another investigation. Well, now you have to work out all the things you did <u>wrong</u>.

## *Uncertainty is the Amount of Error Your Measurements Might Have*

1) When you <u>repeat</u> a measurement, you often get a <u>slightly different</u> figure each time you do it due to <u>random error</u>. This means that <u>each result</u> has some <u>uncertainty</u> to it.

2) The measurements you make will also have some uncertainty in them due to <u>limits</u> in the <u>resolution</u> of the equipment you use (see page 5).

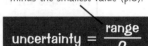
The range is the largest value minus the smallest value (p.6).

3) This all means that the <u>mean</u> of a set of results will also have some uncertainty to it. You can calculate the uncertainty of a <u>mean result</u> using the equation:

$$\text{uncertainty} = \frac{\text{range}}{2}$$

4) The <u>larger</u> the range, the <u>less precise</u> your results are and the <u>more uncertainty</u> there will be in your results. Uncertainties are shown using the '±' symbol.

**EXAMPLE:** The table below shows the results of a trolley experiment to determine the speed of the trolley as it moves along a horizontal surface. Calculate the uncertainty of the mean.

| Repeat | 1 | 2 | 3 | mean |
|---|---|---|---|---|
| Speed (m/s) | 2.02 | 1.98 | 2.00 | 2.00 |

1) First work out the range:
Range = 2.02 − 1.98
= 0.04 m/s

2) Use the range to find the uncertainty:
Uncertainty = range ÷ 2 = 0.04 ÷ 2 = 0.02 m/s     So, uncertainty of the mean = 2.00 ± 0.02 m/s

5) Measuring a <u>greater amount</u> of something helps to <u>reduce uncertainty</u>. For example, in a rate of reaction experiment, measuring the amount of product formed over a <u>longer period</u> compared to a shorter period will <u>reduce</u> the <u>percentage uncertainty</u> in your results.

## *Evaluations — Describe How it Could be Improved*

An evaluation is a <u>critical analysis</u> of the whole investigation.

I'd value this E somewhere in the region of 250-300k

1) You should comment on the <u>method</u> — was it <u>valid</u>? Did you control all the other variables to make it a <u>fair test</u>?

2) Comment on the <u>quality</u> of the <u>results</u> — was there <u>enough evidence</u> to reach a valid <u>conclusion</u>? Were the results <u>repeatable</u>, <u>reproducible</u>, <u>accurate</u> and <u>precise</u>?

3) Were there any <u>anomalous</u> results? If there were <u>none</u> then <u>say so</u>. If there were any, try to <u>explain</u> them — were they caused by <u>errors</u> in measurement? Were there any other <u>variables</u> that could have <u>affected</u> the results? You should comment on the level of <u>uncertainty</u> in your results too.

4) All this analysis will allow you to say how <u>confident</u> you are that your conclusion is <u>right</u>.

5) Then you can suggest any <u>changes</u> to the <u>method</u> that would <u>improve</u> the quality of the results, so that you could have <u>more confidence</u> in your conclusion. For example, you might suggest <u>changing</u> the way you controlled a variable, or <u>increasing</u> the number of <u>measurements</u> you took. Taking more measurements at <u>narrower intervals</u> could give you a <u>more accurate result</u>. For example:

<u>Enzymes</u> have an <u>optimum temperature</u> (a temperature at which they <u>work best</u>). Say you do an experiment to find an enzyme's optimum temperature and take measurements at 10 °C, 20 °C, 30 °C, 40 °C and 50 °C. The results of this experiment tell you the optimum is <u>40 °C</u>. You could then <u>repeat</u> the experiment, taking <u>more measurements around 40 °C</u> to a get a <u>more accurate</u> value for the optimum.

6) You could also make more <u>predictions</u> based on your conclusion, then <u>further experiments</u> could be carried out to test them.

When suggesting improvements to the investigation, always make sure that you say why you think this would make the results better.

## *Evaluation — next time, I'll make sure I don't burn the lab down...*

So there you have it — Working Scientifically. Make sure you know this stuff like the back of your hand. It's not just in the lab that you'll need to know how to work scientifically. You can be asked about it in the exams as well.

# Cells

When someone first peered down a microscope at a slice of cork and drew the boxes they saw, little did they know that they'd seen the <u>building blocks</u> of <u>every organism on the planet</u>...

## *Organisms Can be Eukaryotes or Prokaryotes*

1) <u>All living things</u> are made of <u>cells</u>.

2) Cells can be either <u>eukaryotic</u> or <u>prokaryotic</u>. Eukaryotic cells are <u>complex</u> and include all <u>animal</u> and <u>plant</u> cells. Prokaryotic cells are <u>smaller</u> and <u>simpler</u>, e.g. bacteria (see below).

3) <u>Eukaryotes</u> are organisms that are made up of <u>eukaryotic cells</u>.

4) A <u>prokaryote</u> is a <u>prokaryotic cell</u> (it's a single-celled organism).

## *Plant and Animal Cells Have Similarities and Differences*

The different parts of a cell are called <u>subcellular structures</u>.
Most <u>animal</u> cells have the following subcellular structures:

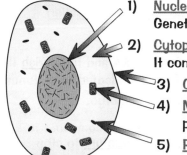

1) <u>Nucleus</u> — contains <u>genetic material</u> that controls the activities of the cell. Genetic material is arranged into <u>chromosomes</u> (see page 27).

2) <u>Cytoplasm</u> — gel-like substance where most of the <u>chemical reactions</u> happen. It contains <u>enzymes</u> (see page 15) that control these chemical reactions.

3) <u>Cell membrane</u> — holds the cell together and controls what goes <u>in</u> and <u>out</u>.

4) <u>Mitochondria</u> — these are where most of the reactions for <u>respiration</u> take place (see page 64). Respiration transfers <u>energy</u> that the cell needs to work.

5) <u>Ribosomes</u> — these are involved in <u>translation of genetic material</u> in the <u>synthesis of proteins</u>.

Plant cells usually have <u>all the bits</u> that <u>animal</u> cells have, plus a few <u>extra</u> things that animal cells <u>don't</u> have:

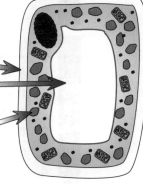

1) Rigid <u>cell wall</u> — made of <u>cellulose</u>. It <u>supports</u> the cell and strengthens it.

2) <u>Large vacuole</u> — contains <u>cell sap</u>, a weak solution of sugar and salts. It maintains the <u>internal pressure</u> to support the cell.

3) <u>Chloroplasts</u> — these are where <u>photosynthesis</u> occurs, which makes food for the plant (see page 47). They contain a <u>green</u> substance called <u>chlorophyll</u>.

## *Bacterial Cells Have No Nucleus*

<u>Bacterial cells</u> are a lot <u>smaller</u> than plant or animal cells and have these <u>subcellular structures</u>:

1) <u>Chromosomal DNA</u> (<u>one</u> long circular chromosome) — controls the cell's <u>activities</u> and <u>replication</u>. It <u>floats free</u> in the <u>cytoplasm</u> (not in a nucleus).

2) <u>Ribosomes</u>

3) <u>Cell membrane</u>

4) <u>Plasmid DNA</u> — <u>small loops</u> of <u>extra DNA</u> that aren't part of the chromosome. Plasmids contain genes for things like <u>drug resistance</u>, and can be <u>passed</u> between bacteria.

5) <u>Flagellum</u> (plural <u>flagella</u>) — a long, hair-like structure that <u>rotates</u> to make the bacterium <u>move</u>. It can be used to move the bacteria <u>away from</u> harmful substances like <u>toxins</u> and <u>towards</u> beneficial things like <u>nutrients or oxygen</u>.

---

## *Cell structures — become a property developer...*

On this page are typical cells with all the typical bits you need to know. But cells aren't all the same — they have different structures depending on the job they do. There's more about this on the next page.

Q1    Describe the function of these subcellular structures: a) nucleus, b) mitochondria, c) ribosomes. [3 marks]

# Specialised Cells

The previous page shows the structure of some <u>typical cells</u>. However, most cells are <u>specialised</u> for a particular function, so their <u>structure</u> can vary...

## Different Cells Have Different Functions

1) <u>Multicellular organisms</u> contain lots of different <u>types</u> of cells (i.e. cells with different <u>structures</u>).

2) Cells that have a structure which makes them <u>adapted</u> to their function are called <u>specialised cells</u>.

3) You need to know how <u>egg</u>, <u>sperm</u> and <u>ciliated epithelial cells</u> are <u>adapted</u> to their functions:

## Egg Cells and Sperm Cells Are Specialised for Reproduction

1) In <u>sexual reproduction</u>, the <u>nucleus</u> of an egg cell <u>fuses</u> with the nucleus of a <u>sperm cell</u> to create a <u>fertilised egg</u>, which then develops into an <u>embryo</u>. Both the nucleus of an egg cell and of a sperm cell only contain <u>half</u> the number of chromosomes that's in a <u>normal</u> body cell — so they are called 'haploid'.

*There's more about sexual reproduction on page 26.*

2) This is important as it means that when an egg and sperm nucleus <u>combine</u> at <u>fertilisation</u>, the resulting cell will have the <u>right number</u> of chromosomes.

**Egg cell**

Nucleus

The main functions of an <u>egg</u> are to carry the female DNA and to <u>nourish</u> the developing embryo in the early stages. This is how it's adapted to its function:

1) It contains <u>nutrients</u> in the <u>cytoplasm</u> to feed the embryo.

2) It has a <u>haploid nucleus</u>.

3) Straight after <u>fertilisation</u>, its <u>membrane</u> changes <u>structure</u> to stop any more sperm getting in. This makes sure the offspring end up with the <u>right amount</u> of DNA.

**Sperm cell**

The <u>function</u> of a sperm is to <u>transport</u> the <u>male's DNA</u> to the <u>female's egg</u>.

1) A sperm cell has a <u>long tail</u> so it can <u>swim</u> to the egg.

2) It has lots of <u>mitochondria</u> in the middle section to provide the <u>energy</u> (from respiration) needed to <u>swim</u> this distance.

3) It also has an <u>acrosome</u> at the front of the 'head', where it stores <u>enzymes</u> needed to <u>digest</u> its way through the <u>membrane</u> of the egg cell.

4) It also contains a <u>haploid nucleus</u>.

Tail      Middle section      Head

Nucleus

Acrosome

## Ciliated Epithelial Cells Are Specialised for Moving Materials

1) Epithelial cells <u>line the surfaces</u> of organs.

2) Some of them have <u>cilia</u> (hair-like structures) on the <u>top surface</u> of the cell.

3) The function of these <u>ciliated epithelial cells</u> is to <u>move substances</u> — the cilia beat to <u>move</u> substances in <u>one direction</u>, <u>along the surface</u> of the tissue.

4) For example, the <u>lining of the airways</u> contains <u>lots</u> of ciliated epithelial cells. These help to move <u>mucus</u> (and all of the particles from the air that it has trapped) up to the <u>throat</u> so it can be <u>swallowed</u> and <u>doesn't reach</u> the lungs.

Cilia

---

## Everyone knows eggs are specialised — fried, boiled, scrambled...

Nearly every cell in your body is specialised to carry out some kind of function, but the ones on this page are the examples you need to learn for your exams. Right, now have a go at this question to see what you remember.

Q1  a)  What is the function of sperm cells?                                                      [1 mark]
    b)  Explain two ways in which sperm cells are adapted for this function.          [4 marks]

# Microscopy

Without <u>microscopes</u> we would never have discovered cells. We can even use them to look <u>inside</u> cells.

## Cells are Studied Using Microscopes

1) Microscopes use lenses to <u>magnify</u> images (make them look bigger). They also increase the <u>resolution</u> of an image. <u>Resolution</u> means how well a microscope distinguishes between <u>two points</u> that are <u>close together</u>. A <u>higher resolution</u> means that the image can be seen <u>more clearly</u> and in <u>more detail</u>.

2) <u>Light microscopes</u> were invented in the 1590s. They work by passing <u>light</u> through the specimen. They let us see things like <u>nuclei</u> and <u>chloroplasts</u> and we can also use them to study <u>living cells</u>.

3) <u>Electron microscopes</u> were invented in the 1930s. They use <u>electrons</u> rather than <u>light</u>. Electron microscopes have a higher <u>magnification</u> and <u>resolution</u> than light microscopes, so they let us see much <u>smaller things</u> in <u>more detail</u> like the <u>internal structure</u> of mitochondria and chloroplasts. This has allowed us to have a much <u>greater understanding</u> of <u>how cells work</u> and the <u>role of subcellular structures</u> (although they can't be used to view living cells).

## This is How to View a Specimen Using a Light Microscope...  PRACTICAL

1) Your specimen needs to <u>let light through it</u> so you'll need to take a <u>thin slice</u> of it to start with.

2) Next, take a clean <u>slide</u> and use a <u>pipette</u> to put one drop of water in the middle of it — this will <u>secure</u> the specimen in place. Then use <u>tweezers</u> to place your specimen on the slide.

3) Add a drop of <u>stain</u> if your <u>specimen</u> is completely <u>transparent</u> or <u>colourless</u> — this makes the specimen <u>easier to see</u> (different stains highlight different structures within cells, e.g. methylene blue stains DNA).

4) Place a <u>cover slip</u> at one end of the specimen, holding it at an <u>angle</u> with a <u>mounted needle</u> and carefully <u>lower</u> it onto the slide. Press it down <u>gently</u> so that no <u>air bubbles</u> are trapped under it. Then <u>clip</u> the slide onto the <u>stage</u>.

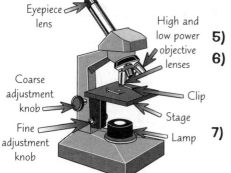

Eyepiece lens
High and low power objective lenses
Coarse adjustment knob
Clip
Stage
Fine adjustment knob
Lamp

5) Select the <u>lowest-powered objective lens</u>.

6) Use the <u>coarse adjustment knob</u> to move the stage <u>up</u> so that the slide is <u>just underneath</u> the objective lens. Then, <u>looking</u> down the <u>eyepiece</u>, move the stage <u>downwards</u> (so you don't accidently crash it into the lens) until the specimen is <u>nearly in focus</u>.

7) Then <u>adjust the focus</u> with the <u>fine adjustment knob</u>, until you get a <u>clear image</u>. Position a <u>clear ruler</u> on the stage and use it to measure the <u>diameter</u> of the circular area visible — your <u>field of view</u> (<u>FOV</u>).

8) If you need to see your specimen with <u>greater magnification</u>, swap to a <u>higher-powered objective lens</u>, <u>refocus</u> and <u>recalculate</u> your <u>FOV</u> accordingly (e.g. if your FOV was 5 mm then you swap to a lens that is 10 times more powerful, your FOV will now be 5 mm ÷ 10 = 0.5 mm).

*Measuring your field of view allows you to estimate the size of your specimen.*

## ...and this is How to Create a Scientific Drawing of a Specimen  PRACTICAL

1) Using a <u>sharp</u> pencil, draw <u>outlines</u> of the <u>main features</u> using <u>clear, unbroken lines</u>. Don't include any <u>colouring</u> or <u>shading</u>.

2) Make sure that your drawing takes up <u>at least half</u> of the space available and remember to keep all the parts <u>in proportion</u>.

3) <u>Label</u> the <u>important features</u> of your diagram with <u>straight lines</u> which <u>don't cross over</u> each other, and include the <u>magnification</u> used and a <u>scale</u>.

Plant Cell, × 400
nucleus
chloroplasts
cell wall
0.1 mm ✓   ✗

## Gather your microscopes, comrades — it's the bio resolution...

There's lots of important stuff here about how you use a light microscope to view specimens — so get learning.

Q1 A student prepares a slide with a sample of onion cells and places it on the stage of a light microscope. Describe the steps she should take to get a focused image of the cells. [4 marks]

PRACTICAL
# More Microscopy

Sometimes you need to do a bit of <u>maths</u> with microscope images. It's time to get your <u>numbers head on</u>...

What are you looking at?

## Magnification is How Many Times Bigger the Image is

1) If you know the <u>power</u> of the lenses used by a microscope to view an image, you can work out the <u>total magnification</u> of the image using this simple formula:

> total magnification = eyepiece lens magnification × objective lens magnification

2) For example, the <u>total magnification</u> of an image viewed with an <u>eyepiece lens</u> magnification of × 10 and an <u>objective lens</u> magnification of × 40 would be 10 × 40 = × 400.

3) If you don't know which lenses were used, you can still work out the magnification of an image as long as you can <u>measure the image</u> and know the <u>real size of the specimen</u>. This is the <u>formula</u> you need:

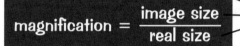
$$\text{magnification} = \frac{\text{image size}}{\text{real size}}$$

Both measurements should have the same units. If they don't, you'll need to convert them first (see below).

image size / (magnification × real size)

4) If you're working out the <u>image size</u> or the <u>real size</u> of the object, you can rearrange the equation using the <u>formula triangle</u>. <u>Cover up</u> the thing you're trying to find. The parts you can <u>still see</u> are the formula you need to use.

<u>Estimating</u> can help you to <u>check</u> that your answer is <u>correct</u>. To estimate an answer, <u>round</u> the numbers so you can do the maths in your <u>head</u>. E.g. say you know the real size of a specimen is <u>21.5 μm</u> and the image size is <u>9800 μm</u>. To get an estimate of the <u>magnification used</u>, round both numbers to <u>1 significant figure</u> (see p.7) and do <u>10000 ÷ 20 = × 500</u>.

## You Might Need to Work With Numbers in Standard Form and Convert Units

1) Because microscopes can see such <u>tiny objects</u>, sometimes it's useful to write figures in <u>standard form</u>.

2) This is where you change <u>very big</u> or <u>small</u> numbers with <u>lots of zeros</u> into something more manageable, e.g. 0.017 can be written $1.7 \times 10^{-2}$. To do this you just need to <u>move</u> the <u>decimal point</u> left or right.

3) The number of places the decimal point moves is then represented by a <u>power of 10</u> — this is <u>positive</u> if the decimal point's moved to the <u>left</u>, and <u>negative</u> if it's moved to the <u>right</u>.

4) You can also use <u>different units</u> to express very big or very small numbers. E.g. <u>0.0007 m</u> could be written as <u>0.7 mm</u>. The <u>table</u> shows you how to <u>convert between different units</u>. The right hand column of the table shows you how each unit can be expressed as a <u>metre</u> in <u>standard form</u>.

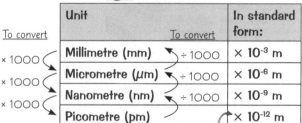

| | Unit | | In standard form: |
|---|---|---|---|
| To convert | | To convert | |
| × 1000 | Millimetre (mm) | ÷ 1000 | $\times 10^{-3}$ m |
| × 1000 | Micrometre (μm) | ÷ 1000 | $\times 10^{-6}$ m |
| × 1000 | Nanometre (nm) | ÷ 1000 | $\times 10^{-9}$ m |
| | Picometre (pm) | | $\times 10^{-12}$ m |

So 1 pm = 0.000000000001 m. (That's tiny!)

5) Here's an example of a <u>calculation</u> in standard form:

**EXAMPLE:** A specimen is $5 \times 10^{-6}$ m wide. Calculate the width of the image of the specimen under a magnification of × 100. Give your answer in standard form.

1) <u>Rearrange</u> the magnification formula.      image size = magnification × real size
2) Fill in the <u>values</u> you know.      image size = 100 × ($5 \times 10^{-6}$ m)
3) Write out the values <u>in full</u> (i.e. don't use standard form).      = 100 × 0.000005 m
4) Carry out the calculation and then <u>convert back</u> into standard form.      = 0.0005 m      = $5 \times 10^{-4}$ m

Note: 0.0005 m could also be written as 0.5 mm or 500 μm.

## Mi-cros-copy — when my twin gets annoyed...

If you've got a scientific calculator, you can put standard form numbers into your calculator using the 'EXP' or the '×10ˣ' button. For example, enter $2.67 \times 10^{15}$ by pressing 2.67 then 'EXP' or '10ˣ', then 15. Easy.

Q1    Calculate the length of a cell which has an image size of $7 \times 10^{-1}$ mm under a magnification of × 400. Write your answer in μm.      [3 marks]

# Enzymes

Chemical reactions are what make you work. And enzymes are what make them work.

## Enzymes Are Catalysts Produced by Living Things

1) Living things have thousands of different chemical reactions going on inside them all the time.

2) These reactions need to be carefully controlled — to get the right amounts of substances.

3) You can usually make a reaction happen more quickly by raising the temperature. This would speed up the useful reactions but also the unwanted ones too... not good.

4) So... living things produce enzymes which act as biological catalysts. Enzymes reduce the need for high temperatures and we only have enzymes to speed up the useful chemical reactions in the body.

> A catalyst is a substance which increases the speed of a reaction, without being changed or used up in the reaction.

## Enzymes Have Special Shapes So They Can Catalyse Reactions

1) Chemical reactions usually involve things either being split apart or joined together.

2) The substrate is the molecule changed in the reaction.

3) Every enzyme has an active site — the part where it joins on to its substrate to catalyse the reaction.

4) Enzymes usually only work with one substrate. They are said to have a high specificity for their substrate.

5) This is because, for the enzyme to work, the substrate has to fit into the active site. If the substrate's shape doesn't match the active site's shape, then the reaction won't be catalysed. This is called the 'lock and key' mechanism, because the substrate fits into the enzyme just like a key fits into a lock.

active site

products

enzyme    substrate    enzyme unchanged after reaction

## Temperature, pH and Substrate Concentration Affect the Rate of Reaction

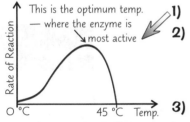

This is the optimum temp. — where the enzyme is most active

Rate of Reaction

0 °C     45 °C   Temp.

1) Changing the temperature changes the rate of an enzyme-catalysed reaction.

2) Like with any reaction, a higher temperature increases the rate at first. But if it gets too hot, some of the bonds holding the enzyme together break. This changes the shape of the enzyme's active site, so the substrate won't fit any more. The enzyme is said to be denatured.

3) All enzymes have an optimum temperature that they work best at.

4) The pH also affects enzymes. If it's too high or too low, the pH interferes with the bonds holding the enzyme together. This changes the shape of the active site and denatures the enzyme.

5) All enzymes have an optimum pH that they work best at. It's often neutral pH 7, but not always — e.g. pepsin is an enzyme used to break down proteins in the stomach. It works best at pH 2, which means it's well-suited to the acidic conditions there.

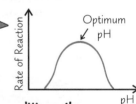

Rate of Reaction

Optimum pH

pH

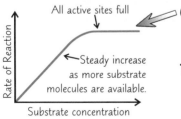

All active sites full

Rate of Reaction

Steady increase as more substrate molecules are available.

Substrate concentration

6) Substrate concentration also affects the rate of reaction — the higher the substrate concentration, the faster the reaction. This is because it's more likely that the enzyme will meet up and react with a substrate molecule.

7) This is only true up to a point though. After that, there are so many substrate molecules that the enzymes have about as much as they can cope with (all the active sites are full), and adding more makes no difference.

## If the lock and key mechanism fails, get in through a window...

Make sure you use the special terms like 'active site' and 'denatured' — the examiners will love it.

Q1     Explain why enzymes have an optimum pH.                    [2 marks]

# More on Enzymes

You'll soon know how to investigate the effect of pH on the rate of enzyme activity... I bet you're thrilled.

## You Can Investigate the Effect of pH on Enzyme Activity   PRACTICAL

The enzyme amylase catalyses the breakdown of starch to maltose. It's easy to detect starch using iodine solution — if starch is present, the iodine solution will change from browny-orange to blue-black. This is how you can investigate how pH affects amylase activity:

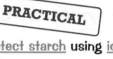
You could use an electric water bath, instead of a Bunsen and a beaker of water, to control the temperature.

1) Put a drop of iodine solution into every well of a spotting tile.

2) Place a Bunsen burner on a heat-proof mat, and a tripod and gauze over the Bunsen burner. Put a beaker of water on top of the tripod and heat the water until it is 35 °C (use a thermometer to measure the temperature). Try to keep the temperature of the water constant throughout the experiment.

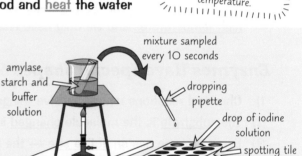
amylase, starch and buffer solution

mixture sampled every 10 seconds

dropping pipette

drop of iodine solution

spotting tile

3) Use a syringe to add 3 cm³ of amylase solution and 1 cm³ of a buffer solution with a pH of 5 to a boiling tube. Using test tube holders, put the boiling tube into the beaker of water and wait for five minutes.

4) Next, use a different syringe to add 3 cm³ of a starch solution to the boiling tube.

5) Immediately mix the contents of the boiling tube and start a stop clock.

6) Use continuous sampling to record how long it takes for the amylase to break down all of the starch. To do this, use a dropping pipette to take a fresh sample from the boiling tube every ten seconds and put a drop into a well. When the iodine solution remains browny-orange, starch is no longer present.

7) Repeat the whole experiment with buffer solutions of different pH values to see how pH affects the time taken for the starch to be broken down.

You could use a pH meter to accurately measure the pH of your solutions.

8) Remember to control any variables each time (e.g. concentration and volume of amylase solution) to make it a fair test.

## Here's How to Calculate the Rate of Reaction

1) It's often useful to calculate the rate of reaction after an experiment. Rate is a measure of how much something changes over time.

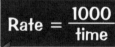
$$\text{Rate} = \frac{1000}{\text{time}}$$

2) For the experiment above, you can calculate the rate of reaction using this formula:
   E.g.

   At pH 6, the time taken for amylase to break down all of the starch in a solution was 50 seconds. So the rate of the reaction = 1000 ÷ 50 = 20 s⁻¹

   The units are in s⁻¹ since rate is given per unit time.

3) If an experiment measures how much something changes over time, you calculate the rate of reaction by dividing the amount that it has changed by the time taken.

EXAMPLE:
The enzyme catalase catalyses the breakdown of hydrogen peroxide into water and oxygen. During an investigation into the activity of catalase, 24 cm³ of oxygen was released in 50 seconds (s). Calculate the rate of the reaction. Write your answer in cm³ s⁻¹.

Amount of product formed = change = 24 cm³

Rate of reaction = change ÷ time = 24 cm³ ÷ 50 s = 0.48 cm³ s⁻¹

---

## If only enzymes could speed up revision...

You could easily adapt this experiment to investigate how factors other than pH affect the rate of amylase activity. For example, you could use a water bath set to different temperatures to investigate the effect of temperature.

Q1   An enzyme-controlled reaction was carried out at pH 4. After 60 seconds,
     33 cm³ of product had been released. Calculate the rate of reaction in cm³ s⁻¹.     [1 mark]

# Enzymes in Breakdown and Synthesis

Organisms can break big molecules down into smaller ones and build small molecules back up into bigger ones. It's pretty clever stuff, and all given a helping hand by our good friends, enzymes.

## Enzymes Break Down Big Molecules

1) Proteins, lipids and some carbohydrates are big molecules.

*Lipids are fats and oils.*

2) It's important that organisms are able to break them down into their smaller components so they can be used for growth and other life processes. For example:

- Many of the molecules in the food we eat are too big to pass through the walls of our digestive system, so digestive enzymes break them down into smaller, soluble molecules. These can pass easily through the walls of the digestive system, allowing them to be absorbed into the bloodstream. They can then pass into cells to be used by the body.
- Plants store energy in the form of starch (a carbohydrate). When plants need energy, enzymes break down the starch into smaller molecules (sugars). These can then be respired to transfer energy to be used by the cells (see p.64).

## Different Types of Enzymes Break Down Carbohydrates, Proteins and Lipids

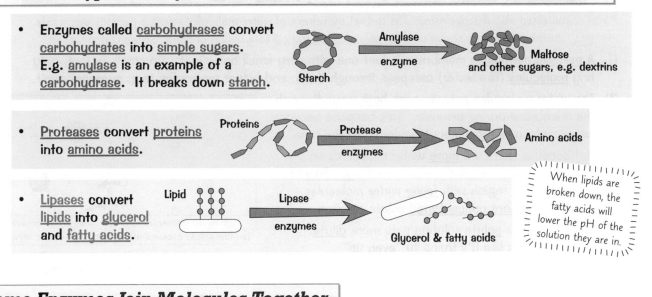

- Enzymes called carbohydrases convert carbohydrates into simple sugars. E.g. amylase is an example of a carbohydrase. It breaks down starch.

  Starch → Amylase enzyme → Maltose and other sugars, e.g. dextrins

- Proteases convert proteins into amino acids.

  Proteins → Protease enzymes → Amino acids

- Lipases convert lipids into glycerol and fatty acids.

  Lipid → Lipase enzymes → Glycerol & fatty acids

*When lipids are broken down, the fatty acids will lower the pH of the solution they are in.*

## Some Enzymes Join Molecules Together

Organisms need to be able to synthesise carbohydrates, proteins and lipids from their smaller components. Again, enzymes are used in this process.

- Carbohydrates can be synthesised by joining together simple sugars.

  Glycogen synthase is an enzyme that joins together lots of chains of glucose molecules to make glycogen (a molecule used to store energy in animals).

- Proteins are made by joining amino acids together. Enzymes catalyse the reactions needed to do this.

- Lots of enzymes are also involved in the synthesis of lipids from fatty acids and glycerol.

amino acid amino acid
amino acid amino acid amino acid

## What do you call an acid that's eaten all the pies...

Make sure you know all the smaller components that make up the bigger carbohydrates, proteins and lipids and understand that enzymes play a role in both the breakdown and synthesis of the bigger molecules.

Q1    Name the molecules that result from the breakdown of:  a) carbohydrates,  b) proteins.      [2 marks]

# Diffusion, Osmosis and Active Transport

Substances can move in and out of cells by <u>diffusion</u>, <u>osmosis</u> and <u>active transport</u>...

## *Diffusion — Don't be Put Off by the Fancy Word*

1) <u>Diffusion</u> is simple. It's just the <u>gradual movement</u> of particles from places where there are <u>lots</u> of them to places where there are <u>fewer</u> of them. That's all it is — just the <u>natural tendency</u> for stuff to <u>spread out</u>. Here's the fancy <u>definition</u>:

> <u>DIFFUSION</u> is the <u>net (overall) movement</u> of <u>particles</u> from an area of <u>higher concentration</u> to an area of <u>lower concentration</u>.

*If something moves from an area of higher concentration to an area of lower concentration it is said to have moved down a <u>concentration gradient</u>.*

2) Diffusion happens in both <u>liquids</u> and <u>gases</u> — that's because the particles in these substances are free to <u>move about</u> randomly.

3) Only very <u>small</u> molecules can <u>diffuse</u> through <u>cell membranes</u> — things like <u>glucose</u>, <u>amino acids</u>, <u>water</u> and <u>oxygen</u>. <u>Big</u> molecules like <u>starch</u> and <u>proteins</u> can't fit through the membrane.

## *Osmosis is a Special Case of Diffusion, That's All*

> <u>OSMOSIS</u> is the <u>net movement of water molecules</u> across a <u>partially permeable membrane</u> from a region of <u>higher water concentration</u> to a region of <u>lower water concentration</u>.

You could also describe osmosis as the net movement of water molecules across a partially permeable membrane from a region of <u>lower solute concentration</u> to a region of <u>higher solute concentration</u>.

1) A <u>partially permeable</u> membrane is just one with very small holes in it. So small, in fact, only tiny <u>molecules</u> (like water) can pass through them, and bigger molecules (e.g. <u>sucrose</u>) can't.

2) The water molecules actually pass <u>both ways</u> through the membrane during osmosis. This happens because water molecules <u>move about randomly</u> all the time.

3) But because there are <u>more</u> water molecules on one side than on the other, there's a steady <u>net flow</u> of water into the region with <u>fewer</u> water molecules, i.e. into the <u>more concentrated</u> solute solution.

4) This means the <u>solute</u> solution gets more <u>dilute</u>. The water acts like it's trying to "<u>even up</u>" the concentration either side of the membrane.

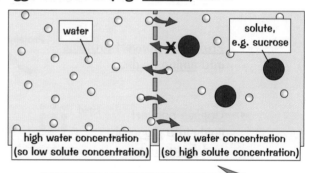

water

solute, e.g. sucrose

high water concentration (so low solute concentration)

low water concentration (so high solute concentration)

Net movement of water molecules

## *Active Transport Works Against a Concentration Gradient*

> <u>ACTIVE TRANSPORT</u> is the <u>movement of particles</u> across a membrane against a concentration gradient (i.e. from an area of <u>lower</u> to an area of <u>higher concentration</u>) <u>using energy</u> transferred during respiration.

1) Active transport is a bit <u>different from diffusion</u> because particles are moved <u>up a concentration gradient</u> rather than down, and the process requires <u>energy</u> (unlike diffusion, which is a passive process).

2) Here's an example of active transport at work in the <u>digestive system</u>:

> 1) When there's a <u>higher concentration</u> of nutrients in the gut than in the blood, the nutrients <u>diffuse naturally</u> into the blood.
>
> 2) <u>BUT</u> — sometimes there's a <u>lower concentration</u> of nutrients in the gut than in the blood.
>
> 3) Active transport allows nutrients to be taken into the blood, despite the fact that the <u>concentration gradient</u> is the wrong way. This is essential to stop us starving.

## *Revision by diffusion — you wish...*

Hopefully there'll have been a net movement of information from this page into your brain...

Q1    Give two differences between the processes of diffusion and active transport.    [2 marks]

# Investigating Osmosis

For all you non-believers — here's an <u>experiment</u> you can do to see <u>osmosis in action</u>.

## You Can Do an Experiment to Investigate Osmosis

This experiment involves putting <u>potato cylinders</u> into <u>different concentrations</u> of <u>sucrose solution</u> to see what effect different <u>water concentrations</u> have on them.

*The higher the concentration of the sucrose solution, the lower the water concentration*

### First You Do the Experiment...

1) Prepare <u>sucrose solutions</u> of different concentrations ranging from <u>pure water</u> to a <u>very concentrated sucrose solution</u>.

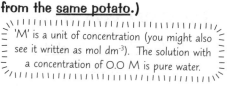

increasing sucrose concentration

0.0 M    0.2 M    0.4 M    0.6 M    0.8 M    1.0 M

2) Use a cork borer to cut a <u>potato</u> into the <u>same sized pieces</u> (The pieces need to be about <u>1 cm</u> in diameter and preferably from the <u>same potato</u>.)

3) Divide the cylinders into <u>groups of three</u> and use a <u>mass balance</u> to measure the <u>mass</u> of each <u>group</u>.

*'M' is a unit of concentration (you might also see it written as mol dm$^{-3}$). The solution with a concentration of 0.0 M is pure water.*

4) Place <u>one group</u> in each solution.

5) <u>Leave</u> the cylinders in the solution for <u>at least 40 minutes</u> (making sure that they all get the <u>same amount</u> of time).

6) <u>Remove</u> the cylinders and <u>pat dry gently</u> with a paper towel. This removes <u>excess water</u> from the surface of the cylinders, so you get a more <u>accurate</u> measurement of their <u>final masses</u>.

7) <u>Weigh</u> each <u>group</u> again and record your results.

8) The <u>only</u> thing that you should <u>change</u> in this experiment is the <u>sucrose solution concentration</u>. Everything else (e.g. the volume of solution, the size of the potato cylinders, the type of potatoes used, the amount of drying, etc.) must be kept the <u>same</u> or your results <u>won't be valid</u>.

### ...Then You Interpret the Results

1) Once you've got all your results, you need to <u>calculate</u> the <u>percentage change in mass</u> for each group of cylinders <u>before</u> and <u>after</u> their time in the sucrose.

*Calculating the percentage change allows you to compare the effect of sucrose concentration on cylinders that didn't have the same initial mass.*

**EXAMPLE:** A group of cylinders weighed 13.2 g at the start of the experiment. At the end they weighed 15.1 g. Calculate the percentage change in mass.

To find the <u>percentage change in mass</u>, use the following <u>formula</u>:

$$\text{percentage change} = \frac{\text{final mass} - \text{initial mass}}{\text{initial mass}} \times 100$$

$$\text{percentage change} = \frac{15.1 - 13.2}{13.2} \times 100 = 14.4\%$$

The positive result tells you the potato cylinders gained mass. If the answer was negative then the potato cylinders lost mass.

2) Then you can plot a <u>graph</u> and <u>analyse your results</u>:

At the points <u>above</u> the x-axis, the water concentration of the <u>sucrose solutions</u> is <u>higher</u> than in the <u>cylinders</u>. The cylinders <u>gain mass</u> as water is <u>drawn in</u> by osmosis.

Where there is <u>no change</u> in mass (where the curve <u>crosses the x-axis</u>) the fluid <u>inside</u> the cylinders and the <u>sucrose solution</u> are <u>isotonic</u> — they have the <u>same water concentration</u>.

At the points <u>below the x-axis</u>, the water concentration of the <u>sucrose solutions</u> is <u>lower</u> than in the <u>cylinders</u>. This causes the cylinders to <u>lose water</u> so their mass <u>decreases</u>.

*(graph: % change in mass vs Concentration of sucrose solution (M), y-axis marked 20, 10, 0, -10, -20; x-axis marked 0.2, 0.4, 0.6, 0.8, 1.0)*

## So that's how they make skinny fries...

This experiment used sucrose as a solute, but you could do the experiment with different solutes (e.g. salt).

Q1    A group of potato cubes were placed in a sucrose solution and left for one hour. The cubes weighed 13.3 g at the start of the experiment and 11.4 g at the end. Calculate the percentage change in mass.    [2 marks]

# Mitosis

In order to survive and grow, our cells have got to be able to <u>divide</u>. And that means our DNA as well...

## Chromosomes Contain Genetic Information

1) Most cells in your body have a <u>nucleus</u>. The nucleus contains your <u>genetic material</u> in the form of <u>chromosomes</u>. Chromosomes are <u>coiled up</u> lengths of <u>DNA molecules</u> (see p.27 for more on DNA).

2) <u>Body cells</u> normally have <u>two copies</u> of each <u>chromosome</u> — this makes them '<u>diploid</u>' cells. One chromosome comes from the organism's '<u>mother</u>', and one comes from its '<u>father</u>'.

3) When a cell divides by <u>mitosis</u> (see below) it makes two cells <u>identical</u> to the original cell — the nucleus of each new cell contains the <u>same number of chromosomes</u> as the original cell.

## The Cell Cycle Makes New Cells for Growth and Repair

1) <u>Body cells</u> in <u>multicellular</u> organisms <u>divide</u> to produce new cells during a process called the <u>cell cycle</u>. The stage of the cell cycle when the cell divides is called <u>mitosis</u>.

2) Multicellular organisms use <u>mitosis</u> to <u>grow</u> or to <u>replace cells</u> that have been <u>damaged</u>.

3) Some organisms use mitosis to <u>reproduce</u> — this is called <u>asexual reproduction</u>. E.g. strawberry plants form runners by mitosis, which become new plants.

4) You need to know about the main stages of the <u>cell cycle</u>:

Interphase

The Cell Cycle

Mitosis and Cytokinesis

**Interphase**

In a cell that's not dividing, the DNA is all spread out in <u>long strings</u>. Before it divides, the cell has to <u>grow</u> and to <u>increase</u> the amount of <u>subcellular structures</u> such as <u>mitochondria</u> and <u>ribosomes</u>. It then <u>duplicates</u> its <u>DNA</u> — so there's one copy for each new cell. The DNA is copied and forms <u>X-shaped</u> chromosomes. Each 'arm' of the chromosome is an <u>exact duplicate</u> of the other.

 The left arm has the same DNA as the right arm of the chromosome.

**Mitosis and Cytokinesis**

Once its contents and DNA have been copied, the cell is ready for <u>mitosis</u>. Mitosis is divided into <u>four stages</u>:

1) PROPHASE — The chromosomes <u>condense</u>, getting shorter and fatter. The <u>membrane</u> around the <u>nucleus breaks down</u> and the chromosomes <u>lie free</u> in the cytoplasm.

2) METAPHASE — The chromosomes <u>line up</u> at the centre of the cell.

3) ANAPHASE — <u>Cell fibres</u> pull the chromosomes apart. The <u>two arms</u> of each chromosome go to <u>opposite ends</u> of the cell.

4) TELOPHASE — Membranes form around each of the sets of chromosomes. These become the <u>nuclei</u> of the two new cells — the <u>nucleus has divided</u>.

Before telophase ends, the <u>cytoplasm</u> and <u>cell membrane</u> divide to form two separate cells — this process is called <u>cytokinesis</u>.

5) At the end of mitosis, the cell has produced <u>two new daughter cells</u>. Each daughter cell contains exactly the <u>same sets of chromosomes</u> in its nucleus as the other daughter cell — they're <u>genetically identical diploid cells</u>. They're also genetically identical to the <u>parent cell</u>.

6) You can <u>calculate</u> the <u>number of cells</u> there'll be after <u>multiple divisions</u> of a cell by mitosis. The formula you need is: <u>number of cells = $2^n$</u>, where '<u>n</u>' is the <u>number of divisions</u> by mitosis.

> E.g. if you start with 1 cell, after <u>5</u> divisions of mitosis there'll be $\underline{2^5} = 2 \times 2 \times 2 \times 2 \times 2 = \underline{32 \text{ cells}}$.

## A cell's favourite computer game — divide and conquer...

Mitosis can seem tricky at first. But don't worry — just go through it slowly, one step at a time.

Q1    Describe what happens during the interphase stage of the cell cycle.                    [2 marks]

# Cell Division and Growth

Growth — it happens to us all. You need to know the <u>processes</u> involved in both <u>animal</u> and <u>plant</u> growth. Then, just for you, there's a beauty of a <u>graph</u> at the bottom of the page. Enjoy.

## Growth Involves Cell Division, Differentiation and Elongation

1) <u>Growth</u> is an <u>increase</u> in <u>size</u> or <u>mass</u>. Plants and animals <u>grow</u> and <u>develop</u> due to these processes:

- <u>CELL DIFFERENTIATION</u> — the process by which a cell <u>changes</u> to become <u>specialised</u> for its <u>job</u>. Having specialised cells allows multicellular organisms to work more <u>efficiently</u>.
- <u>CELL DIVISION</u> — by <u>mitosis</u> (see previous page).

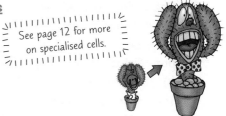
See page 12 for more on specialised cells.

Plants also grow by <u>CELL ELONGATION</u>. This is where a plant cell <u>expands</u>, making the cell <u>bigger</u> and so making the plant <u>grow</u>.

2) <u>All growth</u> in <u>animals</u> happens by <u>cell division</u>. Animals tend to grow while they're <u>young</u>, and then they reach <u>full growth</u> and <u>stop</u> growing. So when you're young, cells divide at a <u>fast rate</u> but once you're an adult, most cell division is for <u>repair</u> — the cells divide to <u>replace</u> old or damaged cells. This also means, in most animals, <u>cell differentiation</u> is <u>lost</u> at an <u>early stage</u>.

3) In <u>plants</u>, growth in <u>height</u> is mainly due to cell <u>elongation</u> — cell <u>division</u> usually just happens in the <u>tips</u> of the <u>roots</u> and <u>shoots</u> (in areas called meristems — see next page). But <u>plants</u> often grow <u>continuously</u> — even really old trees will keep putting out <u>new branches</u>. So, plants continue to <u>differentiate</u> to <u>develop new parts</u>, e.g. leaves, roots.

## Cancer is a Case of Uncontrolled Cell Division

1) The <u>rate</u> at which <u>cells divide</u> by <u>mitosis</u> is controlled by the chemical instructions (<u>genes</u>) in an organism's DNA.

2) If there's a <u>change</u> in one of the genes that controls cell division, the cell may start dividing <u>uncontrollably</u>.

3) This can result in a <u>mass of abnormal cells</u> called a <u>tumour</u>.

4) If the tumour <u>invades and destroys</u> surrounding tissue it is called <u>cancer</u>.

A random change in a gene is called a mutation — see page 30.

## Percentile Charts are Used to Monitor Growth

1) <u>Growth charts</u> are used to assess a <u>child's growth</u> over time, so that an <u>overall pattern in development</u> can be seen and any <u>problems highlighted</u> (e.g. obesity, malnutrition, dwarfism).

2) For example, a baby's growth is regularly <u>monitored</u> after birth to make sure it's growing <u>normally</u>. Three measurements are taken — <u>length</u>, <u>mass</u> and <u>head circumference</u>.

3) These results are plotted on <u>growth charts</u>, like this one. ⟹

4) The chart shows a number of '<u>percentiles</u>'. E.g. the <u>50th percentile</u> shows the mass that <u>50%</u> of babies will have reached at a certain age.

5) Babies <u>vary</u> in size, but doctors are likely to investigate if a baby's size is above the <u>top</u> percentile line or below the <u>bottom</u> percentile line, their size increases or decreases by <u>two or more</u> percentile lines over time, or if there's an <u>inconsistent pattern</u> (e.g. a small baby with a very large head).

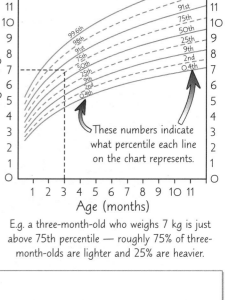
These numbers indicate what percentile each line on the chart represents.

E.g. a three-month-old who weighs 7 kg is just above 75th percentile — roughly 75% of three-month-olds are lighter and 25% are heavier.

## I'm growing rather sick of this section...

Growth is pretty important. Obviously. Without it, you wouldn't be able to reach anything on the top shelf.

Q1  a) Name a process that's used for growth in plants but not in animals. [1 mark]
    b) Describe how a plant grows by the process you named in part a). [1 mark]

# Stem Cells

Your body is made up of all sorts of weird and wonderful cells. This page tells you where they all came from...

## Stem Cells can Differentiate into Different Types of Cells

1) As you saw on the previous page, cells differentiate to become specialised cells.

2) Undifferentiated cells are called stem cells.

3) Depending on what instructions they're given, stem cells can divide by mitosis to become new cells, which then differentiate.

4) Stem cells are found in early human embryos. These embryonic stem cells have the potential to divide and produce any kind of cell at all. This makes sense — all the different types of cell found in a human have to come from those few cells in the early embryo.

5) This means stem cells are really important for the growth and development of organisms.

6) Adults also have stem cells, but they're only found in certain places, like bone marrow. These aren't as versatile as embryonic stem cells — they can't produce any cell type at all, only certain ones. In animals, adult stem cells are used to replace damaged cells, e.g. to make new skin or blood cells.

undifferentiated stem cell

differentiated ciliated epithelial cell (see p.12)

## Meristems Contain Plant Stem Cells

1) In plants, the only cells that divide by mitosis are found in plant tissues called meristems.

2) Meristem tissue is found in the areas of a plant that are growing, e.g. the tips of the roots and shoots.

3) Meristems produce unspecialised cells that are able to divide and form any cell type in the plant — they act like embryonic stem cells. But unlike human stem cells, these cells can divide and differentiate to generate any type of cell for as long as the plant lives.

4) The unspecialised cells go on to form specialised tissues like xylem and phloem (see p.49).

A merry stem.

## Stem Cells Can be Used in Medicine

1) Doctors already use adult stem cells to cure some diseases. E.g. sickle cell anaemia can sometimes be cured with a bone marrow transplant (containing adult stem cells which produce new blood cells).

2) Scientists have experimented with extracting stem cells from very early human embryos and growing them. Under certain conditions the stem cells can be stimulated to differentiate into specialised cells.

3) It might be possible to use stem cells to create specialised cells to replace those which have been damaged by disease or injury, e.g. new cardiac muscle cells could be transplanted into someone with heart disease. This potential for new cures is the reason for the huge scientific interest in stem cells.

4) Before this can happen, a lot of research needs to be done. There are many potential risks which scientists need to learn more about. For example:

- Tumour development — stem cells divide very quickly. If scientists are unable to control the rate at which the transplanted cells divide inside a patient, a tumour may develop (see previous page).

- Disease transmission — viruses live inside cells. If donor stem cells are infected with a virus and this isn't picked up, the virus could be passed on to the recipient and so make them sicker.

- Rejection — if the transplanted cells aren't grown using the patient's own stem cells, the patient's body may recognise the cells as foreign and trigger an immune response to try to get rid of them. The patient can take drugs to suppress this response, but this makes them susceptible to diseases.

5) Research using embryonic stem cells raises ethical issues. E.g. some people argue that human embryos shouldn't be used for experiments because each one is a potential human life. But others think that the aim of curing patients who are suffering should be more important than the potential life of the embryos.

## Cheery cells, those merry-stems...

Turns out stem cells are pretty nifty. Now, let's see if you're specialised to answer this question...

Q1    If the tip is cut off a plant shoot, the tip can be used to grow a whole new plant. Explain why.    [3 marks]

# The Nervous System

The nervous system is what lets you react to what goes on around you, so you'd find life tough without it.

## The CNS Coordinates a Response

1) The nervous system is made up of neurones (nerve cells) which go to all parts of the body.

2) The body has lots of sensory receptors — groups of cells that can detect a change in your environment (a stimulus). Different receptors detect different stimuli. For example, receptors in your eyes detect light, while receptors in your skin detect touch (pressure) and temperature change.

3) When a stimulus is detected by receptors, the information is converted to a nervous (electrical) impulse and sent along sensory neurones to the CNS (the brain and spinal cord).

4) The CNS coordinates the response (in other words, it decides what to do about the stimulus and tells something to do it). Impulses travel through the CNS along relay neurones.

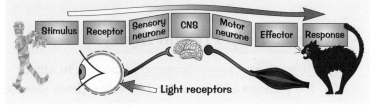

5) The CNS sends information to an effector (muscle or gland) along a motor neurone. The effector then responds accordingly — e.g. a muscle may contract or a gland may secrete a hormone.

6) The time it takes you to respond to a stimulus is called your reaction time.

## Neurones Transmit Information Rapidly as Electrical Impulses

1) All neurones have a cell body with a nucleus (plus cytoplasm and other subcellular structures).

2) The cell body has extensions that connect to other neurones — dendrites and dendrons carry nerve impulses towards the cell body, and axons carry nerve impulses away from the cell body.

3) Some axons are surrounded by a myelin sheath. This acts as an electrical insulator, speeding up the electrical impulse.

4) Neurones can be very long, which also speeds up the impulse (connecting with another neurone slows the impulse down, so one long neurone is much quicker than lots of short ones joined together).

5) You need to know the structure and function of sensory, motor and relay neurones.

### SENSORY NEURONE
- One long dendron carries nerve impulses from receptor cells to the cell body, which is located in the middle of the neurone.
- One short axon carries nerve impulses from the cell body to the CNS.

### MOTOR NEURONE
- Many short dendrites carry nerve impulses from the CNS to the cell body.
- One long axon carries nerve impulses from the cell body to effector cells.

The diagram shows a myelinated motor neurone but you can get unmyelinated ones too. Sensory and relay neurones can also be myelinated.

### RELAY NEURONE
- Many short dendrites carry nerve impulses from sensory neurones to the cell body.
- An axon carries nerve impulses from the cell body to motor neurones.

## Don't let the thought of exams play on your nerves...

Make sure you understand how the different parts of the nervous system work together to coordinate a response.

Q1    Describe the structure and function of a sensory neurone.                    [3 marks]

# Synapses and Reflexes

Information is passed between neurones really quickly, especially when there's a reflex involved...

## Synapses Connect Neurones

1) The connection between two neurones is called a synapse.
2) The nerve signal is transferred by chemicals called neurotransmitters, which diffuse (move) across the gap.
3) The neurotransmitters then set off a new electrical signal in the next neurone.
4) The transmission of a nervous impulse is very fast, but it is slowed down a bit at the synapse because the diffusion of neurotransmitters across the gap takes time.

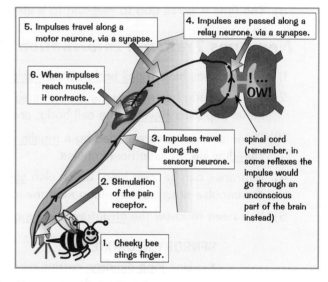

## Reflexes Help Prevent Injury

1) Reflexes are automatic, rapid responses to stimuli — they can reduce the chances of being injured.
2) The passage of information in a reflex (from receptor to effector) is called a reflex arc.
3) The neurones in reflex arcs go through the spinal cord or through an unconscious part of the brain.
4) When a stimulus (e.g. a bee sting) is detected by receptors, impulses are sent along a sensory neurone to a relay neurone in the CNS.
5) When the impulses reach a synapse between the sensory neurone and the relay neurone, they trigger neurotransmitters to be released (see above). These cause impulses to be sent along the relay neurone.
6) When the impulses reach a synapse between the relay neurone and a motor neurone, the same thing happens. Neurotransmitters are released and cause impulses to be sent along the motor neurone.
7) The impulses then travel along the motor neurone to the effector (in this example it's a muscle, but it could be a gland).
8) The muscle then contracts and moves your hand away from the bee.
9) Because you don't have to spend time thinking about the response, it's quicker than normal responses.

## A Reflex Helps to Protect the Eye

1) Very bright light can damage the eye — so you have a reflex to protect it.
2) Light receptors in the eye detect very bright light and send a message along a sensory neurone to the brain.
3) The message then travels along a relay neurone to a motor neurone, which tells circular muscles in the iris (the coloured part of the eye) to contract, making the pupil smaller.

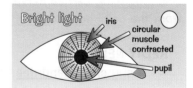

---

## Don't get all twitchy — just learn it...

Reflexes bypass conscious parts of your brain completely when a super quick response is essential — your body just gets on with things. If you had to stop and think first, you'd end up a lot more sore (or worse).

Q1     A chef touches a hot tray. A reflex reaction causes him to immediately move his hand away.
        Describe the pathway of the reflex arc from receptors to effector.        [5 marks]

# Revision Questions for Sections 1 and 2

I hope you remember that Section 1 stuff now — here's your chance to check you've learnt it and Section 2.

- Try these questions and <u>tick off each one</u> when you <u>get it right</u>.
- When you've done <u>all the questions</u> under a heading and are <u>completely happy</u>, tick it off.

## Cells and Specialised Cells (p.11-12) ☑

1) What is the function of the cell membrane?
2) Give three structures found in plant cells but not in animal cells.
3) Name two structures that are found in both prokaryotic cells and eukaryotic cells.
4) What does the term 'haploid' mean?
5) What are cilia?
6) What is the purpose of the ciliated epithelial cells that line the airways?

## Microscopy (p.13-14) ☑

7) Give an advantage of electron microscopes over light microscopes.
8) Why is it necessary to use thin samples of tissue when viewing cells using a light microscope?
9) Describe how you would convert a measurement from mm to $\mu$m.
10) Which unit can be expressed in standard form as $\times 10^{-12}$ m?

## Enzymes (p.15-17) ☑

11) What part of an enzyme makes it specific to a particular substrate?
12) Explain how temperature affects enzyme activity.
13) Describe how you could investigate the effect of pH on the rate of amylase activity.

## Diffusion, Osmosis and Active Transport (p.18-19) ☑

14) Define the following terms:  a) diffusion,  b) osmosis,  c) active transport.
15) If a potato cylinder is placed in a solution with a very high sucrose concentration, what will happen to the mass of the potato cylinder over time?  Explain why.

## Mitosis, Growth and Stem Cells (p.20-22) ☑

16) What is the cell cycle?
17) Give three uses of mitosis in organisms.
18) Name the four stages of mitosis.  Describe what happens in each one.
19) What major illness can result from uncontrolled cell division?
20) Describe how a percentile chart is used to monitor growth.
21) What is a stem cell?
22) What are meristems?  Where are they found?
23) Give one benefit and one risk associated with using stem cells in medicine.

## The Nervous System (p.23-24) ☐

24) Draw and label a motor neurone.
25) What is a synapse?
26) Describe the role of neurotransmitters in the transmission of nervous impulses.
27) Why are reflexes faster than normal responses?

# Sexual Reproduction and Meiosis

Ever wondered why you look <u>like</u> your <u>family members</u>, but <u>not exactly the same</u>? Well today's your lucky day.

## *Sexual Reproduction Produces Genetically Different Cells*

1) <u>Sexual reproduction</u> is where genetic information from <u>two</u> organisms (a <u>father</u> and a <u>mother</u>) is combined to produce offspring which are <u>genetically different</u> to either parent.

2) In <u>sexual reproduction</u>, the father and mother produce <u>gametes</u> (reproductive cells). In animals these are <u>sperm</u> and <u>egg cells</u>.

3) Gametes only contain <u>half the number</u> of <u>chromosomes</u> of normal cells — they are <u>haploid</u>. <u>Normal cells</u> (with the full number of chromosomes) are <u>diploid</u> (see p.20).

4) At <u>fertilisation</u>, a male gamete <u>fuses</u> with a female gamete to produce a <u>fertilised egg</u>, also known as a <u>zygote</u>. The zygote ends up with the <u>full set</u> of chromosomes (so it is diploid).

5) The zygote then undergoes <u>cell division</u> (by mitosis — see p.20) and develops into an <u>embryo</u>.

6) The embryo <u>inherits characteristics</u> from <u>both parents</u>, as it has received a <u>mixture of chromosomes</u> (and therefore <u>genes</u>) from its mum and its dad.

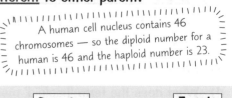

A human cell nucleus contains 46 chromosomes — so the diploid number for a human is 46 and the haploid number is 23.

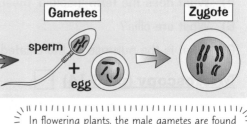

In flowering plants, the male gametes are found in the pollen and the female gametes are found in the ovaries at the bottom of the stigma.

## *Gametes are Produced by Meiosis*

Meiosis is a type of <u>cell division</u>. It's different to mitosis because it <u>doesn't produce identical cells</u>. In humans, meiosis <u>only</u> happens in the <u>reproductive organs</u> (ovaries and testes).

**Division 1**

1) Before the cell starts to divide, it <u>duplicates</u> its <u>DNA</u> (so there's enough for each new cell). One arm of each X-shaped chromosome is an <u>exact copy</u> of the other arm.

2) In the <u>first division</u> in meiosis (there are two divisions) the chromosomes <u>line up</u> in pairs in the centre of the cell. One chromosome in each pair came from the organism's mother and one came from its father.

3) The <u>pairs</u> are then <u>pulled apart</u>, so each new cell only has one copy of each chromosome. <u>Some</u> of the father's chromosomes and <u>some</u> of the mother's chromosomes go into each new cell.

4) Each new cell will have a <u>mixture</u> of the mother's and father's chromosomes. Mixing up the genes like this is <u>really important</u> — it creates <u>genetic variation</u> in the offspring.

**Division 2**

5) In the <u>second division</u> the chromosomes <u>line up</u> again in the centre of the cell. It's a lot like mitosis. The <u>arms</u> of the chromosomes are <u>pulled apart</u>.

6) You get <u>four haploid daughter cells</u> — these are the <u>gametes</u>. Each <u>gamete</u> only has a <u>single set</u> of chromosomes. The gametes are all <u>genetically different</u>.

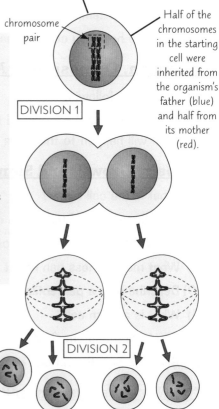

This cell has duplicated each chromosome — each arm of the X-shape is identical.

chromosome pair

Half of the chromosomes in the starting cell were inherited from the organism's father (blue) and half from its mother (red).

DIVISION 1

DIVISION 2

## *Now that I have your undivided attention...*

Remember — in humans, meiosis only occurs in the reproductive organs.

Q1    The haploid gamete of a plant species has 12 chromosomes. Two of these gametes fuse to make a zygote. How many chromosomes will there be in the zygote?    [1 mark]

Q2    How does meiosis introduce genetic variation?    [2 marks]

# DNA

Reproduction is all about <u>passing on your DNA</u> to the next generation. This molecule carries all the <u>instructions</u> for your characteristics — so it's a big part of what makes you <u>you</u>.

## DNA is a Polymer

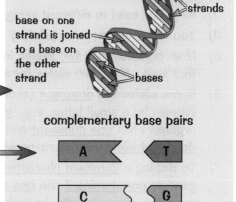

Part of a DNA double helix

strands

base on one strand is joined to a base on the other strand

bases

complementary base pairs

| A | T |
| C | G |

1) DNA strands are <u>polymers</u>. This means they're made up of lots of <u>repeating units</u> joined together.

2) Each 'unit' contains one of <u>four</u> different <u>bases</u>. The bases are: <u>A</u> (adenine), <u>T</u> (thymine), <u>C</u> (cytosine) and <u>G</u> (guanine).

3) A DNA molecule has <u>two strands coiled together</u> in the shape of a <u>double helix</u> (a double stranded spiral).

4) Each base <u>links</u> to a base on the opposite strand in the helix.

5) A <u>always pairs up</u> with T, and C <u>always pairs up</u> with G. This is called <u>complementary base pairing</u>.

6) The complementary base pairs are joined together by <u>weak hydrogen bonds</u>.

## DNA is Stored as Chromosomes and Contains Genes

1) <u>Chromosomes</u> are <u>long</u>, <u>coiled up</u> molecules of <u>DNA</u>. They're found in the <u>nucleus</u> of <u>eukaryotic cells</u>.

2) A <u>gene</u> is a <u>section</u> of DNA on a chromosome that codes for a <u>particular protein</u>. The <u>sequence</u> of bases in the gene determines <u>what</u> protein is produced.

3) <u>All</u> of an organism's DNA makes up its <u>genome</u>.

## You Need to Know How to Extract DNA From Fruit Cells

Don't believe that cells contain DNA? Well here's a practical you can do to get it out...

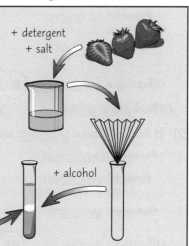

+ detergent + salt

+ alcohol

1) Mash some <u>strawberries</u> and then put them in a beaker containing a solution of <u>detergent</u> and <u>salt</u>. Mix well.
   - The <u>detergent</u> will <u>break down</u> the <u>cell membranes</u> to release the DNA.
   - The <u>salt</u> will make the <u>DNA stick together</u>.

2) <u>Filter</u> the mixture to get the <u>froth</u> and <u>big</u>, <u>insoluble</u> bits of cell out.

3) Gently add some <u>ice-cold alcohol</u> to the filtered mixture.

4) The DNA will start to come <u>out of solution</u> as it's <u>not soluble</u> in <u>cold alcohol</u>. It will appear as a <u>stringy white precipitate</u> (a solid) that can be carefully fished out with a <u>glass rod</u>.

## My band has a great rhythm section — it has paired basses...

Hope you enjoyed extracting all that DNA and learning about its structure. Sadly, though, you won't be getting a Nobel Prize for your efforts — you're too late. Crick, Watson and Wilkins were awarded the Nobel Prize for their work in determining the structure of DNA in 1962. Typical. I'm always late for everything...

Q1 Which DNA bases pair up according to complementary base pairing? [2 marks]

Q2 Why is it useful to use salt when extracting DNA from fruit cells? [1 mark]

# Genetic Diagrams

You can use genetic diagrams to predict how different characteristics will be inherited.

## Alleles Are Different Versions of the Same Gene

1) What genes you inherit control what characteristics you develop.

2) Different genes control different characteristics. Some characteristics are controlled by a single gene. However most characteristics are controlled by several genes interacting.

3) All genes exist in different versions called alleles (which are represented by letters in genetic diagrams).

4) You have two versions (alleles) of every gene in your body — one on each chromosome in a pair.

5) If an organism has two alleles for a particular gene that are the same, then it's homozygous for that trait. If its two alleles for a particular gene are different, then it's heterozygous.

6) Some alleles are dominant (shown with a capital letter, e.g. 'C') and some are recessive (shown by a small letter, e.g. 'c'). Dominant alleles overrule recessive alleles, so if an organism has one dominant and one recessive allele for a gene (e.g. 'Cc'), then the dominant allele will determine what characteristic is present.

7) To display a dominant characteristic, an organism can have either two dominant alleles for a particular gene or one dominant and one recessive allele for that gene. But for an organism to display a recessive characteristic, both its alleles must be recessive.

8) Your genotype is the combination of alleles you have. Your alleles determine what characteristics you have — your phenotype. So different combinations of alleles give rise to different phenotypes.

## Genetic Diagrams Can Show the Inheritance of a Single Characteristic

1) The inheritance of a single characteristic is called monohybrid inheritance. You can use a monohybrid cross to show how recessive and dominant traits for a single characteristic are inherited.

2) For example, let's say an allele that causes hamsters to have superpowers is recessive ("b"), and that normal (boring) hamsters don't have superpowers due to a dominant allele ("B"). Here's how you could use a monohybrid cross to show the probability of either the dominant or recessive trait being inherited:

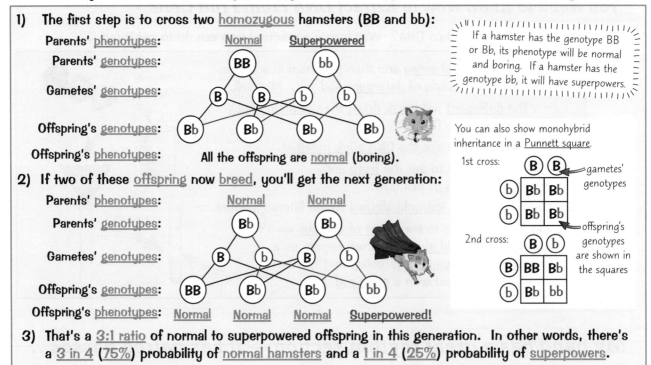

1) The first step is to cross two homozygous hamsters (BB and bb):

| Parents' phenotypes: | Normal | Superpowered |
| Parents' genotypes: | BB | bb |

*If a hamster has the genotype BB or Bb, its phenotype will be normal and boring. If a hamster has the genotype bb, it will have superpowers.*

Gametes' genotypes: B B b b

Offspring's genotypes: Bb Bb Bb Bb

Offspring's phenotypes: All the offspring are normal (boring).

You can also show monohybrid inheritance in a Punnett square.

1st cross: gametes' genotypes

2) If two of these offspring now breed, you'll get the next generation:

| Parents' phenotypes: | Normal | Normal |
| Parents' genotypes: | Bb | Bb |

Gametes' genotypes: B b B b

Offspring's genotypes: BB Bb Bb bb

Offspring's phenotypes: Normal Normal Normal Superpowered!

offspring's genotypes are shown in the squares

2nd cross:

3) That's a 3:1 ratio of normal to superpowered offspring in this generation. In other words, there's a 3 in 4 (75%) probability of normal hamsters and a 1 in 4 (25%) probability of superpowers.

## Your meanotype determines how nice you are to your sibling...

Remember, genetic diagrams only tell you probabilities. They don't say what will definitely happen.

Q1    Define genotype and phenotype.                                                [2 marks]

# More Genetic Diagrams

Here's <u>another</u> page of funny diagrams with squares, circles and lines going everywhere. And it's not the last...

## A Genetic Diagram Can Show How Sex is Determined in Humans

1) There are <u>23 matched pairs</u> of chromosomes in every human body cell. The <u>23rd pair</u> is labelled <u>XX</u> or <u>XY</u>. They're the two chromosomes that decide whether you turn out <u>male</u> or <u>female</u>.

2) Males have an <u>X</u> and a <u>Y</u> chromosome (<u>XY</u>). The <u>Y</u> chromosome causes <u>male</u> characteristics.

3) Females have <u>two X chromosomes</u> (<u>XX</u>). The <u>XX combination</u> allows <u>female characteristics</u> to develop.

4) Because of this, there's an <u>equal chance</u> of having either a <u>boy</u> or a <u>girl</u>. Here's a <u>genetic diagram</u> to prove it:

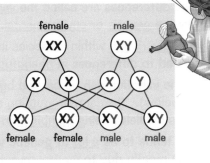

> 1) Even though we're talking about inheriting <u>chromosomes</u> here and not <u>single genes</u>, the <u>genetic diagram</u> still works the same way.
>
> 2) When you plug all the letters into the diagram, it shows that there are <u>two XX</u> results and <u>two XY</u> results, so there's the <u>same probability</u> of getting a boy or a girl.
>
> 3) Don't forget that this <u>50 : 50 ratio</u> is <u>only a probability</u>. If you had four kids they could all be boys.

5) All <u>eggs</u> have one <u>X chromosome</u>, but a <u>sperm</u> can have either an <u>X chromosome</u> or a <u>Y chromosome</u>. So <u>sex determination</u> in humans depends on whether the <u>sperm</u> that <u>fertilises</u> an egg carries an <u>X</u> or a <u>Y</u>.

## Family Pedigrees Can Also Show Monohybrid Inheritance

Knowing how inheritance works helps you to interpret a <u>family pedigree</u> (a family tree of genetic disorders). Here's a worked example using <u>cystic fibrosis</u> — a genetic disorder of the cell membranes.

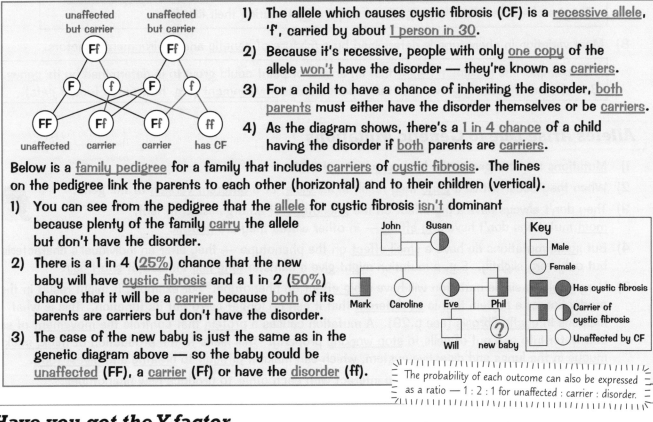

1) The allele which causes cystic fibrosis (CF) is a <u>recessive allele</u>, 'f', carried by about <u>1 person in 30</u>.

2) Because it's recessive, people with only <u>one copy</u> of the allele <u>won't</u> have the disorder — they're known as <u>carriers</u>.

3) For a child to have a chance of inheriting the disorder, <u>both parents</u> must either have the disorder themselves or be <u>carriers</u>.

4) As the diagram shows, there's a <u>1 in 4 chance</u> of a child having the disorder if <u>both</u> parents are <u>carriers</u>.

Below is a <u>family pedigree</u> for a family that includes <u>carriers</u> of <u>cystic fibrosis</u>. The lines on the pedigree link the parents to each other (horizontal) and to their children (vertical).

1) You can see from the pedigree that the <u>allele</u> for cystic fibrosis <u>isn't</u> dominant because plenty of the family <u>carry</u> the allele but don't have the disorder.

2) There is a 1 in 4 (<u>25%</u>) chance that the new baby will have <u>cystic fibrosis</u> and a 1 in 2 (<u>50%</u>) chance that it will be a <u>carrier</u> because <u>both</u> of its parents are carriers but don't have the disorder.

3) The case of the new baby is just the same as in the genetic diagram above — so the baby could be <u>unaffected</u> (**FF**), a <u>carrier</u> (**Ff**) or have the <u>disorder</u> (**ff**).

The probability of each outcome can also be expressed as a ratio — 1 : 2 : 1 for unaffected : carrier : disorder.

## Have you got the Y-factor...

I bet you're sick of genetic diagrams by now. Still, that family pedigree makes a nice change. Umm... sort of.

Q1    Use the family pedigree above for the following question. Mark and his wife (who is not shown in the diagram) have a baby with cystic fibrosis. What are the possible genotypes of Mark's wife?    [1 mark]

# Variation

There's been a lot of talk about genes in this here uhh... genetics... section — but when it comes to variation in organisms, the environment is also really important. So make sure you don't forget about it.

## Organisms of the Same Species Have Differences

1) Different species look... well... different — my dog definitely doesn't look like a daisy.

2) But even organisms of the same species will usually look at least slightly different — e.g. all dogs are the same species, but a Dalmatian looks quite different to a Pug.

3) These differences are called the variation within a species. It can be genetic or environmental.

4) Genetic variation within a species is caused by organisms having different alleles (versions of genes) which can lead to differences in phenotype (the characteristics an organism displays).

5) Genetic variation can be caused by new alleles arising through mutations (see below). Sexual reproduction also causes genetic variation since it results in alleles being combined in lots of different ways in offspring.

> Sexual reproduction means no two members of a species are genetically identical (apart from identical twins).

6) There tends to be a lot of genetic variation within a population of a species. This is mostly due to neutral mutations (see below).

7) Variation within a species can also be caused by the environment (the conditions in which organisms live). For example:

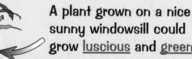

| A plant grown on a nice sunny windowsill could grow luscious and green. | The same plant grown in darkness would grow tall and spindly and its leaves would turn yellow. |

These environmental variations in phenotype are also known as acquired characteristics. They're characteristics that organisms acquire (get) during their lifetimes.

8) Most variation in phenotype is determined by a mixture of genetic and environmental factors.

> For example, the maximum height that an animal or plant could grow to is determined by its genes. But whether it actually grows that tall depends on its environment (e.g. how much food it gets).

## Alleles Arise Due to Genetic Mutations

> There's more DNA bases on page 27.

1) Mutations are changes to the base sequence of DNA.

2) When they occur within a gene they result in an allele, or a different version of the gene.

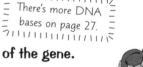

3) They don't always have a big effect on the phenotype of an organism. In fact, most mutations don't have any effect — in other words they are neutral.

4) But some mutations do have a small effect on the phenotype — they alter an individual's characteristics, but only very slightly. E.g. a mutation might give a hamster long hair instead of short hair.

5) Very rarely, a single mutation will have a big effect on phenotype. For example, it might result in the production of a protein that is so different that it can no longer carry out its function. This is what happens in cystic fibrosis (see p.29). A mutation causes a protein that controls the movement of salt and water into and out of cells to stop working properly. This leads to the production of thick, sticky mucus in the lungs and digestive system, which can make it difficult to breathe and digest food.

6) New combinations of alleles may also interact with each other to produce new phenotypes.

---

## Environmental variation — pretty much sums up British weather...

So, all the variation that you see around you is a complicated mixture of environmental and genetic influences. In fact, it's often really tricky to decide which factor is more influential, your genes or the environment.

Q1  Why does sexual reproduction result in genetic variation in a population? [1 mark]

# The Human Genome Project

The Human Genome Project is one of the most exciting things to have happened in science in recent years. Some people even called it "more exciting than the first moon landing"...

## Researchers Managed to Map Over 20 000 Human Genes

1) Thousands of scientists from all over the world collaborated (worked together) on the Human Genome Project. The big idea was to find every single human gene.

2) The project officially started in 1990 and a complete map of the human genome, including the locations of around 20 500 genes, was completed in 2003.

3) Now that the genes have all been found, scientists are trying to figure out what they all do.

4) So far, the project has helped to identify about 1800 genes related to disease, which has huge potential benefits for medicine (see below).

## There are Lots of Medical Applications for the Project's Research

### Prediction and prevention of diseases

Many common diseases like cancers and heart disease are caused by the interaction of different genes, as well as lifestyle factors. If doctors knew what genes predisposed people to what diseases, we could all get individually tailored advice on the best diet and lifestyle to avoid our likely problems. Doctors could also check us regularly to ensure early treatment if we do develop the diseases we're susceptible to.

### Testing and treatment for inherited disorders

1) Inherited disorders (e.g. cystic fibrosis) are caused by the presence of one or more faulty alleles in a person's genome.

2) Thanks to the Human Genome Project, scientists are now able to identify the genes and alleles that are suspected of causing an inherited disorder much more quickly than they could do in the past.

3) Once an allele that causes an inherited disorder has been identified, people can be tested for it and it may be possible to develop better treatments or even (eventually) a cure for the disease.

### New and better medicines

1) Genome research has highlighted some common genetic variations between people. Some variations affect how our individual bodies will react to certain diseases and to the possible treatments for them.

2) Scientists can use this knowledge to design new drugs that are specifically tailored to people with a particular genetic variation. They can also determine how well an existing drug will work for an individual. Tests can already identify whether or not someone with breast cancer will respond to a particular drug, and what dosage is most appropriate for certain drugs in different patients.

3) More generally, knowing how a disease affects us on a molecular level should make it possible to design more effective treatments with fewer side-effects.

## But There Could Also be Drawbacks

1) Increased stress — if someone knew from an early age that they're susceptible to a nasty brain disease, they could panic every time they get a headache (even if they never get the disease).

2) Gene-ism — people with genetic problems could come under pressure not to have children.

3) Discrimination by employers and insurers — life insurance could become impossible to get (or blummin' expensive at least) if you have any genetic likelihood of serious disease. And employers may discriminate against people who are genetically likely to get a disease.

## DNA lipstick is part of my genetic make-up...

The Human Genome Project has resulted in some pretty useful discoveries, but there's still loads of work to do.

Q1 How could information from the Human Genome Project be used to help prevent individuals from developing certain diseases? [2 marks]

# Natural Selection and Evidence for Evolution

Evolution is the <u>slow and continuous change</u> of organisms from one generation to the next.
<u>Charles Darwin</u> came up with the theory of <u>natural selection</u> to explain how <u>evolution</u> occurs.

## *Natural Selection Means "Survival of the Fittest"*

1) Individuals in a population show <u>genetic variation</u> because of differences in their <u>alleles</u> (see page 30). New alleles arise through <u>mutations</u>.

> Alleles are versions of genes — see page 28.

2) Things like <u>predation</u>, <u>competition</u> for resources (e.g. food, water, mates, etc.) and <u>disease</u> act as <u>selection pressures</u>. This means they affect an organism's chance of <u>surviving</u> and <u>reproducing</u>.

3) Those individuals with <u>characteristics</u> that make them <u>better adapted</u> to the selection pressures in their environment have a <u>better chance of survival</u> and so are more likely to <u>breed</u> successfully.

4) This means the <u>alleles</u> that are responsible for the useful characteristics are more likely to be <u>passed on</u> to the <u>next generation</u>.

5) However, some individuals will be <u>less well adapted</u> to the selection pressures in their environment and may be less able to compete. These individuals are <u>less likely</u> to survive and reproduce.

6) The <u>beneficial characteristics</u> become more <u>common</u> in the population over time.

> A species that can't compete is likely to go extinct.

## *Bacteria Provide Evidence for Evolution*

1) Like all organisms, bacteria sometimes develop <u>random mutations</u> in their DNA. These can create <u>new alleles</u>, which can <u>change</u> the bacteria's <u>characteristics</u> — e.g. a bacterium could become <u>less affected</u> by a particular <u>antibiotic</u> (a drug designed to kill bacteria or prevent them from reproducing).

2) For the bacterium, the ability to <u>resist</u> this antibiotic is a big <u>advantage</u>. In a host who's being treated to get rid of the infection, a resistant bacterium is <u>better able to survive</u> than a non-resistant bacterium — and so it lives for longer and <u>reproduces</u> many more times.

3) This leads to the allele for antibiotic resistance being <u>passed on</u> to lots of offspring — it's just <u>natural selection</u>. This is how it spreads and becomes <u>more common</u> in a population of bacteria over time.

> It's easy to see evolution happening in bacteria because they reproduce so rapidly.

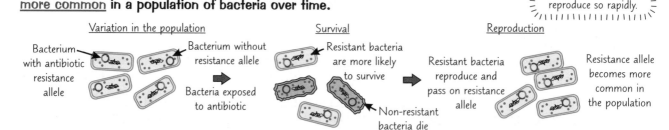

Variation in the population

Bacterium with antibiotic resistance allele    Bacterium without resistance allele    Bacteria exposed to antibiotic

Survival

Resistant bacteria are more likely to survive    Non-resistant bacteria die

Reproduction

Resistant bacteria reproduce and pass on resistance allele    Resistance allele becomes more common in the population

4) Antibiotic resistance provides <u>evidence</u> for evolution because it makes the bacteria <u>better adapted</u> to an <u>environment</u> in which <u>antibiotics</u> (a <u>selection pressure</u>) are <u>present</u>. And as a result, antibiotic resistance becomes <u>more common</u> in the population over time. The emergence of <u>other</u> resistant organisms (e.g. <u>rats</u> resistant to the poison <u>warfarin</u>) <u>also</u> provides evidence for evolution.

## *Fossils Provide More Evidence for Evolution*

1) A fossil is <u>any trace</u> of an animal or plant that lived <u>a long time ago</u> (e.g. over a thousand years). They are most commonly found in <u>rocks</u>. Generally, the <u>deeper</u> the rock, the <u>older</u> the fossil.

2) By arranging fossils in <u>chronological</u> (date) order, <u>gradual changes</u> in organisms can be observed. This provides <u>evidence</u> for evolution, because it shows how species have <u>changed</u> and <u>developed</u> over billions of years. Fossils that provide evidence for <u>human evolution</u> are covered on the next page.

## *Natural Selection — sounds like vegan chocolates...*

DNA and genes hadn't been discovered when Darwin was doing his work, so he didn't know exactly how characteristics were passed on — these details were added to the theory much later on.

Q1    How do fossils provide evidence that organisms evolved from simpler life forms?    [1 mark]

# Fossil Evidence for Human Evolution

There's a lot of fossil evidence that suggests that humans evolved from a common ancestor with other apes.

## Fossils Give Us Clues About What Human Ancestors Were Like...

1) Evidence from fossils suggests that humans and chimpanzees evolved from a common ancestor that existed around 6 million years ago.

2) Human beings and their ancestors are known as hominids. Fossils of several different hominid species have been found.

3) These fossils have characteristics that are between apes and humans — by looking at hominid fossils you can see how humans have evolved over time.

## 'Ardi' is a Fossil Hominid 4.4 Million Years Old

Ardi is a fossil of the species *Ardipithecus ramidus*. She was found in Ethiopia and is 4.4 million years old. Ardi's features are a mixture of those found in humans and in apes:

1) The structure of her feet suggests she climbed trees — she had an ape-like big toe to grasp branches.

2) She also had long arms and short legs (more like an ape than a human) and her brain size was about the same as a chimpanzee's.

3) But the structure of her legs suggests that she walked upright like a human. The structure of her hand bones also suggests she didn't use her hands to help her walk (like apes do).

> Brain size is found by working out 'cranial capacity' — the space taken up by the brain in the skull.

## 'Lucy' is a Fossil Hominid 3.2 Million Years Old

Lucy is a fossil of the species *Australopithecus afarensis*. She was found in Ethiopia and is 3.2 million years old. Lucy also has a mixture of human and ape features, but she is more human-like than Ardi.

1) Lucy had arched feet, more adapted to walking than climbing, and no ape-like big toe.

2) The size of her arms and legs was between what you would expect to find in apes and humans.

3) Her brain was slightly larger than Ardi's but still similar in size to a chimp's brain.

4) The structure of Lucy's leg bones and feet suggest she walked upright, but more efficiently than Ardi.

## Leakey and His Team Found Fossil Hominids 1.6 Million Years Old

In 1984 scientist Richard Leakey organised an expedition to Kenya to look for hominid fossils. He and his team discovered many important fossils of different *Australopithecus* and *Homo* species.

1) One of their finds was Turkana Boy — a 1.6 million year old fossil skeleton of the species *Homo erectus*. He has a mixture of human and ape-like features, but is more human-like than Lucy.

2) His short arms and long legs are much more like a human than an ape, and his brain size was much larger than Lucy's — similar to human brain size.

3) The structure of his legs and feet suggest he was even better adapted to walking upright than Lucy.

# Fossil Evidence for Human Evolution

## Fossils Can be Put on a Timeline to Show Human Evolution

So you know that the Ardipithecus and Australopithecus species were more ape-like, compared to the Homo species, which are human-like. They can all be put on a time line, showing how humans have evolved:

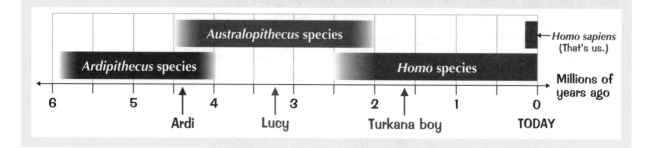

## Stone Tools Also Provide Evidence For Human Evolution

The different Homo species continued to evolve. You can tell this because they started using stone tools and these gradually became more complex (so their brains must have been getting larger):

| Homo species | Tool use |
|---|---|
| Homo habilis (2.5-1.5 million years ago) | Made simple stone tools called pebble tools by hitting rocks together to make sharp flakes. These could be used to scrape meat from bones or crack bones open. |
| Homo erectus (2-0.3 million years ago) | Sculpted rocks into shapes to produce more complex tools like simple hand-axes. These could be used to hunt, dig, chop and scrape meat from bones. |
| Homo neanderthalis (300 000-25 000 years ago) | More complex tools. Evidence of flint tools, pointed tools and wooden spears. |
| Homo sapiens (200 000 years ago-present) | Flint tools widely used. Pointed tools including arrowheads, fish hooks, buttons and needles appeared around 50 000 years ago. |

When an ancient stone tool or hominid fossil (see previous page) is found, there are several different ways scientists can work out how old it is. These include:

*Dating tools and fossils isn't always very accurate, e.g. rock layers can move over time.*

1) Looking at the structural features of the tool or fossil. For example, simpler tools are likely to be older than more complex tools.

2) Using stratigraphy — the study of rock layers. Older rock layers are normally found below younger layers, so tools or fossils in deeper layers are usually older.

3) Stone tools are often found with carbon-containing material, e.g. a wooden handle. Carbon-14 dating can be used to date this material.

## Dating fossils — I might have better luck with them...

So the evidence for evolution is right under our feet. Literally... But you've got to know what you're looking for. 'Ardi', 'Lucy' and the fossils discovered by Richard Leakey are all key findings in the study of human evolution. Make sure you learn the key features of these fossils, including their ages, for your exam.

Q1     An archaeologist discovered a fossil-rich site for hominid skeletons.
She discovered what appeared to be pieces of pointed stone tools among the bones.
a) What does the shape of the stone tools suggest about the fossils present at the site?    [1 mark]
b) State one method that the scientist could use to find the age of the stone tools.    [1 mark]

# Classification

It seems to be a basic human urge to want to <u>classify</u> things — that's the case in biology anyway...

## Classification is Organising Living Organisms into Groups

1) Traditionally, organisms were <u>classified</u> according to similarities and differences in their <u>observable</u> <u>characteristics</u>, i.e. things you can see (like how many legs something has). As <u>technology</u> <u>improved</u>, this included things you can see with a <u>microscope</u>, e.g. <u>cell structure</u>.

2) These characteristics were used to classify organisms in the <u>five</u> <u>kingdom classification system</u>. In this system, living things are first divided into <u>five groups</u> called <u>kingdoms</u>. These are:

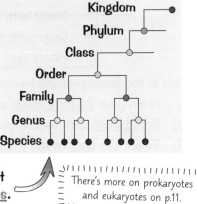

- <u>Animals</u> — fish, mammals, reptiles, etc.
- <u>Plants</u> — grasses, trees, etc.
- <u>Fungi</u> — mushrooms and toadstools, yeasts, all that mouldy stuff on your loaf of bread (yuck).
- <u>Prokaryotes</u> — all <u>single-celled</u> organisms <u>without</u> a nucleus.
- <u>Protists</u> — <u>eukaryotic single-celled</u> organisms, e.g. algae.

3) The <u>kingdoms</u> are then subdivided into smaller and smaller groups that have common features — <u>phylum</u>, <u>class</u>, <u>order</u>, <u>family</u>, <u>genus</u>, <u>species</u>.

*There's more on prokaryotes and eukaryotes on p.11.*

## Classification Systems Change Over Time

1) The <u>five kingdom</u> classification system is still used, but it's now a bit <u>out of date</u>.

2) Over time, <u>technology</u> has developed further and our understanding of things like <u>biochemical processes</u> and <u>genetics</u> has increased. For example, we are now able to determine the <u>sequence of DNA bases</u> in different organisms' <u>genes</u> and <u>compare them</u> — the more <u>similar</u> the sequence of a gene, the more <u>closely related</u> the organisms.

3) This led to a bit of a rethink about the way organisms are <u>classified</u> and to the proposal of the <u>three domain system</u> of classification by a scientist called Carl Woese.

*There's more on DNA on page 27.*

4) Using <u>genetic analysis</u>, Woese found that some members of the <u>Prokaryote kingdom</u> were not as closely related as first thought. He proposed that this kingdom should be split into two groups called <u>Archaea</u> and <u>Bacteria</u>.

5) In fact, Woese suggested that all organisms should first be divided into <u>three large groups</u> called <u>domains</u>. Archaea and Bacteria are <u>two</u> of these domains. The third domain is <u>Eukarya</u>.

1) ARCHAEA — Organisms in this domain <u>look similar</u> to <u>bacteria</u> but are actually quite <u>different</u> — as differences in their <u>genetic sequences</u> show. They were first found in <u>extreme places</u> such as hot springs and salt lakes.

2) BACTERIA — This domain contains <u>true bacteria</u> like *E. coli* and *Staphylococcus*.

3) EUKARYA — This domain includes a <u>broad range</u> of organisms including <u>fungi</u>, <u>plants</u>, <u>animals</u> and <u>protists</u>.

6) The three domains are then <u>subdivided</u> into <u>smaller groups</u> used in the <u>five kingdom system</u> (beginning with kingdom and finishing with species).

## Why did the Bacterium break up with the Archaean?

...they didn't have much in common. Biologists have the best jokes. It's strange to think that Archaea and Bacteria, which look really similar, are actually more different than we are to a mushroom.

Q1 Give one example of how advances in technology allowed scientists to distinguish between Archaea and Bacteria.

[1 mark]

# Selective Breeding

'Selective breeding' sounds like it has the potential to be a tricky topic, but it's actually dead simple.
You take the best plants or animals and breed them together to get the best possible offspring. That's it.

## Selective Breeding is Very Simple

Selective breeding is when humans artificially select the plants or animals that are
going to breed so that the genes for particular characteristics remain in the population.
Organisms are selectively bred to develop features that are useful or attractive,
for example:

lovely

- Animals that produce more meat or milk.
- Crops with disease resistance.
- Dogs with a good, gentle temperament.
- Plants that produce bigger fruit.

This is the basic process involved in selective breeding:

1) From your existing stock select the ones which have the characteristics you're after.

2) Breed them with each other.

3) Select the best of the offspring, and breed them together.

4) Continue this process over several generations, and the desirable trait gets
stronger and stronger. Eventually, all the offspring will have the characteristic.

*Selective breeding is also known as 'artificial selection'.*

Selective breeding is nothing new — people have been doing it for thousands of years. It's how we ended
up with edible crops from wild plants and how we got domesticated animals like cows and dogs.

## Selective Breeding is Useful...

Selective breeding is important in agriculture. For example:

Genetic variation means some cattle will have better characteristics for producing meat than
others (e.g. a larger size). To improve meat yields, a farmer could select cows and bulls with
these characteristics and breed them together. After doing this, and selecting the best of
the offspring for several generations, the farmer would get cows with a very high meat yield.

It's also used in medical research. For example:

In several studies investigating the reasons behind alcoholism, rats have been bred
with either a strong preference for alcohol or a weak preference for alcohol. This
has allowed researchers to compare the differences between the two different types
of rats, including differences in their behaviour and in the way that their brains work.

## ...but Also Has Disadvantages

1) The main problem with selective breeding is that it reduces the gene pool — the number of different
alleles (forms of a gene) in a population. This is because the "best" animals or plants are
always used for breeding — and they are all closely related. This is known as inbreeding.

2) Inbreeding can cause health problems because there's more chance of the organisms inheriting harmful
genetic defects when the gene pool is limited. Some dog breeds are susceptible to certain defects
because of inbreeding, e.g. pugs often have breathing problems. This leads to ethical considerations —
particularly if animals are deliberately bred to have negative characteristics for medical research.

3) There can also be serious problems if a new disease appears. There's not much variation in the
population, so there's less chance of resistance alleles being present. All the stock are closely related to
each other, so if one is going to be killed by a new disease, the others are also likely to succumb to it.

## I use the same genes all the time too — they flatter my hips...

Different breeds of dog came from selective breeding. For example, somebody thought 'I really like this small,
yappy wolf — I'll breed it with this other one'. After thousands of generations, we got poodles.

Q1    Give three potential problems selective breeding can cause.                    [3 marks]

# Genetic Engineering

Genetic engineering involves modifying an organism's genome (its DNA) to introduce desirable characteristics. This involves the use of enzymes and vectors (carriers).

## Enzymes Can Be Used To Cut Up DNA or Join DNA Pieces Together

1) Restriction enzymes recognise specific sequences of DNA and cut the DNA at these points — the pieces of DNA are left with sticky ends where they have been cut.
2) Ligase enzymes are used to join two pieces of DNA together at their sticky ends.
3) Two different bits of DNA stuck together are known as recombinant DNA.

## Vectors Can Be Used To Insert DNA Into Other Organisms

A vector is something that's used to transfer DNA into a cell. There are two sorts — plasmids and viruses:

- Plasmids are small, circular molecules of DNA that can be transferred between bacteria.
- Viruses insert DNA into the organisms they infect.

Here's how genetic engineering works:

1) The DNA you want to insert (e.g. the gene for human insulin) is cut out with a restriction enzyme. The vector DNA is then cut open using the same restriction enzyme.

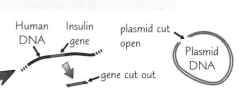

2) The vector DNA and the DNA you're inserting are left with sticky ends. They are mixed together with ligase enzymes.
3) The ligases join the pieces of DNA together to make recombinant DNA.

4) The recombinant DNA (i.e. the vector containing new DNA) is inserted into other cells, e.g. bacteria.
5) These cells can now use the gene you inserted to make the protein you want. E.g. bacteria containing the gene for human insulin can be grown in huge numbers in a fermenter to produce insulin for people with diabetes.

## Genetic Engineering is Useful in Agriculture and Medicine

1) For example, in agriculture, crops can be genetically modified to be resistant to herbicides (chemicals that kill plants). Making crops herbicide-resistant means farmers can spray their crops to kill weeds, without affecting the crop itself. This can also increase crop yield.

2) In medicine, as well as genetically engineering bacteria to produce human insulin, researchers have managed to transfer human genes that produce useful proteins into sheep and cows. E.g. human antibodies used in therapy for illnesses like arthritis, some types of cancer and multiple sclerosis. These proteins can then be extracted from the animal, e.g. from their milk. Animals that have organs suitable for organ transplantation into humans might also be produced in the future.

3) However, there are concerns about the genetic engineering of animals. It can be hard to predict what effect modifying its genome will have on the organism — many genetically modified embryos don't survive and some genetically modified animals suffer from health problems later in life.

4) There are also concerns about growing genetically modified crops. One is that transplanted genes may get out into the environment. E.g. a herbicide resistance gene may be picked up by weeds, creating a new 'superweed' variety. Another concern is that genetically modified crops could adversely affect food chains — or even human health.

## If only there was a gene to make revision easier...

Genetically modified (GM) organisms have a lot of potential to be very useful. But we don't yet know what all the consequences of using them might be — so it's good to be familiar with the arguments for and against them.

Q1 Explain one benefit of being able to genetically engineer herbicide-resistant crops. [2 marks]

# Revision Questions for Sections 3 and 4

A double whammy here — just make sure you can answer the Section 3 bits before moving on to Section 4.

- Try these questions and tick off each one when you get it right.
- When you've done all the questions under a heading and are completely happy, tick it off.

## Reproduction, Meiosis and DNA (p.26-27) ☑

1) Name the gametes in humans. ☑
2) What happens to the DNA in a cell before the first division in meiosis? ☑
3) What word is used to describe all of an organism's DNA? ☑
4) What is meant by the term 'double helix'? ☑
5) When extracting DNA from a fruit, what is the purpose of mixing the fruit with detergent? ☑
6) What effect does ice-cold alcohol have on a solution containing free DNA molecules? ☑

## Genetic Diagrams (p.28-29) ☑

7) What does it mean if an organism is  a)  homozygous for a gene?  b)  heterozygous for a gene? ☑
8) What is monohybrid inheritance? ☑
9) What's the probability that a baby will be born with the **XX** combination of sex chromosomes? ☑
10) How are carriers shown on a family pedigree? ☑

## Variation and The Human Genome Project (p.30-31) ☑

11) What causes genetic variation in a species? ☑
12) What is an acquired characteristic? ☑
13) Write down three applications of the knowledge gained from the Human Genome Project. ☑
14) Describe three potential drawbacks of being able to read a person's genome. ☑

## Natural Selection and Evolution (p.32-34) ☑

15) Describe how organisms evolve by the process of natural selection. ☑
16) How do antibiotic-resistant bacteria provide evidence for evolution? ☑
17) What are hominids? ☑
18) Which fossil is older — "Ardi" or "Lucy"? ☑
19) Who was Richard Leakey?  What important discoveries did he make in relation to human evolution? ☑
20) What is stratigraphy?  How might it be used to date stone tools? ☑

## Classification (p.35) ☑

21) Describe how organisms were classified using the five kingdom classification system. ☑
22) What classification system was proposed by Carl Woese and what led him to propose it? ☑

## Selective Breeding and Genetic Engineering (p.36-37) ☑

23) What is artificial selection? ☑
24) How can selective breeding be used to improve yields in the meat industry? ☑
25) Describe one way in which selective breeding can be useful outside of agriculture. ☑
26) What is a gene pool? ☑
27) Why does selective breeding reduce gene pools? ☑
28) What are restriction enzymes used for in genetic engineering? ☑
29) What is a vector? ☑
30) What are the concerns over creating genetically modified organisms? ☑

# Health and Disease

If you're hoping I'll ease you gently into this new section, no such luck. Straight on to the baddies of biology.

## You Need to Know How 'Health' is Defined

1) It might surprise you to know that being healthy is about more than just not being sick.

2) The World Health Organisation (the WHO) defines health as "a state of complete physical, mental and social well-being, and not merely the absence of disease or infirmity".

3) This means that even if someone is very physically fit, they still might be unhealthy if, e.g. they have mental health issues or are socially isolated.

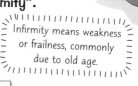
Infirmity means weakness or frailness, commonly due to old age.

## Diseases Can be Communicable or Non-Communicable

1) A disease is a condition where part of an organism doesn't function properly. There are two sorts of disease — communicable and non-communicable.

2) Communicable diseases are diseases that can be spread between individuals. See the table below.

3) Non-communicable diseases can't be transmitted between individuals. They include things like cancer and heart disease. There's more on these on page 44.

4) If you are affected by one disease, it could make you more susceptible to others — your body may become weakened by the disease, so it's less able to fight off others.

Being susceptible to a disease, means that you have an increased chance of getting it.

## Communicable Diseases are Caused by Pathogens

Pathogens are organisms such as viruses, bacteria, fungi and protists (see p. 35) that cause communicable diseases. Here are some examples of communicable diseases that you need to know about for your exam:

| Disease | Pathogen | Symptoms/ Effects | How it spreads | How to reduce/prevent transmission |
|---|---|---|---|---|
| Cholera | A bacterium called *Vibrio cholerae*. | Diarrhoea. | Via contaminated water sources. | Making sure that people have access to clean water supplies. |
| Tuberculosis | A bacterium called *Mycobacterium tuberculosis*. | Coughing and lung damage. | Through the air when infected individuals cough. | Infected people should avoid crowded public spaces, practise good hygiene and sleep alone. Their homes should also be well-ventilated. |
| Malaria | A protist. | Damage to red blood cells and, in severe cases, to the liver. | Mosquitoes act as animal vectors (carriers) — they pass on the protist to humans but don't get the disease themselves. | Use of mosquito nets and insect repellent to prevent mosquitoes carrying the pathogen from biting people. |
| Chalara ash dieback | A fungus that infects ash trees. | Leaf loss and bark lesions (wounds). | Carried through the air by the wind. (It also spreads when diseased ash trees are moved between areas.) | Removing young, infected ash trees and replanting with different species. Restricting the import or movement of ash trees. |

## Coughs and sneezes spread diseases...

Yuck, lots of nasties out there that can cause disease. Plants need to be worried too, as you can see.

Q1     Describe how *Vibrio cholerae* is spread and what can be done to prevent its spread.     [2 marks]

# STIs

I hope you're not too squeamish... this page is about two of the
diseases that can be spread between people during sex.

## STIs are Sexually Transmitted Infections

1) STIs are infections that are spread through sexual contact, including sexual intercourse.
2) You need to learn about the STIs HIV and *Chlamydia* for your exam,
   including ways of reducing or preventing their spread.

## HIV is a Sexually Transmitted Virus

1) Viruses aren't cells. They're not much more than a protein coat around a strand of genetic material.
2) This means that they have to infect living cells (called host cells) in order to reproduce.
   Specific types of viruses will only infect specific cells.
3) HIV is the Human Immunodeficiency Virus.
4) It infects and kills white blood cells, which are really important in the
   immune response (the body's response to pathogens — see p.41).
5) HIV infection eventually leads to AIDS
   (Acquired Immune Deficiency Syndrome).
6) This is when the infected person's immune system deteriorates
   and eventually fails — because of this, the person becomes very
   vulnerable to opportunistic infections by other pathogens.

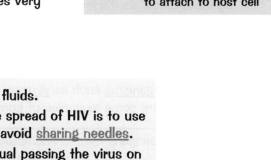

HIV

protein coat

genetic material

outer envelope, with proteins
to attach to host cell

### HIV is Spread via Infected Bodily Fluids

1) These bodily fluids include blood, semen and vaginal fluids.
2) This means that one of the main ways to prevent the spread of HIV is to use
   a condom when having sex. Drug users should also avoid sharing needles.
3) Medication can reduce the risk of an infected individual passing the virus on
   to others during sex (or of a mother passing the virus to her baby during
   pregnancy) so screening and proper treatment are also important.

## Chlamydia is a Sexually Transmitted Bacterial Infection

1) *Chlamydia* is a kind of bacterium, but it behaves in a similar way to
   a virus because it can only reproduce inside host cells.
2) Although it doesn't always cause symptoms, it can result in infertility in men and women.

### There are Ways to Reduce the Spread of Chlamydia

The spread of *Chlamydia* can be reduced by:
* wearing a condom when having sex,
* screening individuals so they can be treated for the infection,
* avoiding sexual contact.

Some STIs, including *Chlamydia*,
are spread by genital contact,
not just sexual intercourse.

## STIs are no joke...

Condoms are a cheap and effective way of reducing the spread of both of HIV and *Chlamydia*,
as well as many other STIs. They can also be used to prevent pregnancy (see page 55). Neat.

Q1   What is meant by the term 'STI'?                                                    [1 mark]

Q2   Give two ways of reducing the spread of HIV.                                        [2 marks]

# Fighting Disease

The human body has some pretty neat features when it comes to <u>fighting disease</u>.

## *Physical and Chemical Barriers Stop Pathogens Entering the Body*

The <u>human body</u> has <u>physical</u> and <u>chemical</u> defences against pathogen entry. Here are a few examples:

### Physical barriers

1) The skin acts as a <u>barrier</u> to pathogens, and, if it gets <u>damaged</u>, <u>blood clots</u> quickly <u>seal cuts</u> and keep microorganisms <u>out</u>.

2) <u>Hairs</u> and <u>mucus</u> in your nose <u>trap</u> particles that could contain <u>pathogens</u>.

3) <u>Cells</u> in your <u>trachea</u> and <u>bronchi</u> (airways in the lungs) also produce <u>mucus</u>, which traps pathogens. <u>Other cells</u> that line the trachea and bronchi have <u>cilia</u>. These are <u>hair-like structures</u> which waft the mucus up to the <u>back of the throat</u> where it can be <u>swallowed</u>.

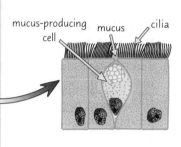

mucus-producing cell   mucus   cilia

### Chemical barriers

1) The <u>stomach</u> produces <u>hydrochloric acid</u>. This <u>kills</u> most pathogens that are swallowed.

2) The <u>eyes</u> produce a chemical called <u>lysozyme</u> (in tears) which <u>kills bacteria</u> on the <u>surface</u> of the eye.

*These physical and chemical barriers are non-specific — they work against many different types of pathogens.*

## *Your Immune System Can Attack Pathogens*

1) If pathogens do make it into your body, your <u>immune system</u> kicks in to <u>destroy</u> them.

2) The most important part of your immune system is the <u>white blood cells</u>. They travel around in your <u>blood</u> and crawl into every part of you, patrolling for <u>pathogens</u>.

3) <u>B-lymphocytes</u> are a type of white blood cell that are involved in the <u>specific immune response</u> — this is the immune response to a <u>specific pathogen</u>. Here's how it works:

1) Every pathogen has <u>unique molecules</u> (e.g. proteins) on its surface called <u>antigens</u>.

2) When your B-lymphocytes come across an antigen on a <u>pathogen</u>, they start to produce <u>proteins</u> called <u>antibodies</u>. Antibodies <u>bind</u> (lock on) to the new invading <u>pathogen</u>, so it can be <u>found</u> and <u>destroyed</u> by other white blood cells. The antibodies produced are <u>specific</u> to that pathogen — they won't lock on to any <u>other</u> pathogens.

3) The <u>antibodies</u> are then produced <u>rapidly</u> and flow all round the body to find all similar <u>pathogens</u>.

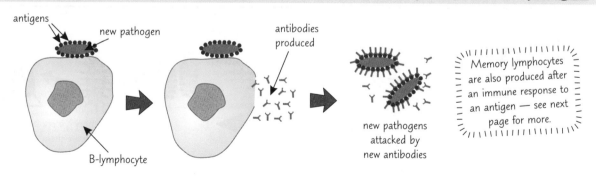

antigens   new pathogen   antibodies produced   new pathogens attacked by new antibodies   B-lymphocyte

*Memory lymphocytes are also produced after an immune response to an antigen — see next page for more.*

## *Fight disease — blow your nose with boxing gloves...*

If you have a low level of white blood cells, you'll be more susceptible to infections. HIV attacks white blood cells and weakens the immune system, making it easier for other pathogens to invade.

Q1   Describe how the trachea and bronchi are adapted to defend against the entry of pathogens.   [3 marks]

Q2   What are B-lymphocytes?   [1 mark]

# Memory Lymphocytes and Immunisation

Forgive and forget, they always say. Fortunately for us, though, our immune system tends to hold grudges...

## Memory Lymphocytes Give Immunity To Later Infection

1) When a pathogen enters the body for the first time the response is slow because there aren't many B-lymphocytes that can make the antibody needed to lock on to the antigen.

2) Eventually the body will produce enough of the right antibody to overcome the infection. Meanwhile the infected person will show symptoms of the disease.

3) As well as antibodies, memory lymphocytes are also produced in response to a foreign antigen. Memory lymphocytes remain in the body for a long time, and 'remember' a specific antigen.

4) The person is now immune — their immune system has the ability to respond quickly to a second infection.

5) If the same pathogen enters the body again, there are more cells that will recognise it and produce antibodies against it. This secondary immune response is faster and stronger.

6) The secondary response often gets rid of the pathogen before you begin to show any symptoms.

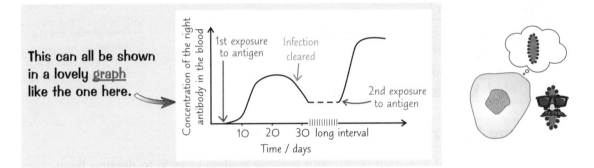

This can all be shown in a lovely graph like the one here.

## Immunisation Stops You Getting Infections

1) To avoid getting ill, you can be immunised against some diseases, e.g. measles.

2) Immunisation usually involves injecting dead or inactive pathogens into the body. These are antigenic (they carry antigens), so even though they're harmless your body makes antibodies to help destroy them.

3) The antigens also trigger memory lymphocytes to be made.

4) So, if live pathogens of the same type get into the body, there will already be memory lymphocytes that can cause a fast secondary immune response. This means that you're less likely to get the disease. Cool.

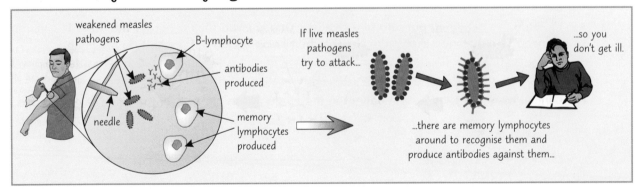

## Take that, you evil antigen...

Immunisation's great. It's helped to save millions of lives all around the world — and all because of those nifty antibodies and memory cells. Make sure you know how it works, including the role of memory lymphocytes.

Q1    Why is the secondary immune response to a pathogen much faster than the first response?        [2 marks]

Section 5 — Health, Disease and the Development of Medicines

# Antibiotics and Other Medicines

New medicines are constantly being developed. This nifty little page tells you all about how that happens.

## Antibiotics Are Used to Treat Bacterial Infections

1) Antibiotics work by inhibiting processes in bacterial cells, but not in the host organism. For example, some antibiotics inhibit the building of bacterial cell walls — this prevents the bacteria from dividing, and eventually kills them, but has no effect on cells in the human host (which don't have cell walls).

2) Different antibiotics kill different types of bacteria, so it's important to be treated with the right one.

3) But antibiotics don't destroy viruses (e.g. flu or cold viruses). Viruses reproduce using your body cells, which makes it very difficult to develop drugs that destroy just the virus without killing the body's cells.

## There Are Several Stages in the Development of New Drugs

1) First a drug has to be discovered. This can happen in lots of different ways — for example:

> Penicillin is an antibiotic. It was discovered by Alexander Fleming when he was clearing out Petri dishes containing bacteria. He noticed that one of the dishes had mould on it and that the area around the mould was free of bacteria. The mould was producing penicillin, which was killing the bacteria.

2) Nowadays, most scientists use their knowledge of how a disease works to try and identify molecules that could be used as drugs to fight the disease.

3) Once a new potential drug has been discovered, it needs to be developed. This involves preclinical and clinical testing.

### Preclinical testing:

1) In preclinical testing, drugs are first tested on human cells and tissues in the lab. However, you can't use human cells and tissues to test drugs that affect whole or multiple body systems, e.g. a drug for blood pressure must be tested on a whole animal.

2) The next step is to test the drug on live animals. This is to test that the drug works (produces the effect you're looking for), to find out how toxic (harmful) it is and to find the best dosage.

### Clinical testing:

1) If the drug passes the tests on animals then it's tested on human volunteers in a clinical trial.

2) First, the drug is tested on healthy volunteers to make sure that it doesn't have any harmful side effects when the body is working normally.

3) If the results of the tests on healthy volunteers are good, the drugs can be tested on people suffering from the illness. The optimum dose is found — this is the dose of drug that is the most effective and has the fewest side effects.

4) Patients are randomly put into two groups. One is given the new drug, the other is given a placebo (a substance that looks like the drug being tested but doesn't do anything, e.g. a sugar pill). This is to allow for the placebo effect (when the patient expects the treatment to work and so feels better, even though the treatment isn't doing anything).

5) Clinical trials are blind — the patient in the study doesn't know whether they're getting the drug or the placebo. In fact, they're often double-blind — neither the patient nor the doctor knows until all the results have been gathered. This is so the doctors monitoring the patients and analysing the results aren't subconsciously influenced by their knowledge.

4) When a drug has finally passed all of these tests, it still needs to be approved by a medical agency before it can be used to treat patients. All of this means that drugs are as effective and safe as possible.

## The placebo effect doesn't work with revision...

Testing, retesting and then...yep, more testing. You'd know all about that anyway, it's just like being in school...

Q1    Explain how a double-blind trial would be carried out.                    [2 marks]

# Non-Communicable Diseases

Non-communicable diseases aren't caused by pathogens. Instead, there are risk factors associated with them.

## Lifestyle Factors May Increase the Risk of a Non-Communicable Disease

1) Risk factors are things that are linked to an increase in the likelihood that a person will develop a certain disease during their lifetime. They don't guarantee that someone will get the disease.

2) Risk factors can be unavoidable, e.g. a person's age or gender may make them more likely to get a disease. But some are lifestyle factors that people can change. For example:

> Smoking is a major risk factor associated with cardiovascular disease — any disease associated with the heart or blood vessels, e.g. a heart attack or stroke (see p.46). This is because:
> - Nicotine in cigarette smoke increases heart rate, which increases blood pressure.
> - High blood pressure damages artery walls, which contributes to the build up of fatty deposits in the arteries. These deposits restrict blood flow and increase the risk of a heart attack or stroke.
> - Smoking increases the risk of blood clots forming in arteries, which can restrict or block blood flow, leading to a heart attack or stroke.

3) Other lifestyle factors are associated with different diseases. E.g.
   - a diet with too many or too few nutrients can lead to malnutrition (and diseases associated with malnutrition, e.g. scurvy — a vitamin C deficiency disease.)

   *Malnutrition doesn't just mean not getting enough nutrients. Getting too many nutrients is also a form of malnutrition, and it can lead to obesity.*

   - not getting enough exercise and having a diet high in fat and sugar are risk factors for obesity.
   - drinking too much alcohol is a major risk factor for the development of liver disease, e.g. cirrhosis (scarring of the liver). This is because alcohol is broken down by enzymes in the liver and some of the products are toxic. Drinking too much over a long period of time can cause permanent liver damage.

## Non-Communicable Diseases Have Many Risk Factors

1) As well as smoking, there are lots of other risk factors associated with cardiovascular disease, including: drinking too much alcohol, lack of exercise, and a diet high in saturated fat.

2) In fact, many non-communicable diseases are caused by several different risk factors interacting with each other, rather than one factor alone, including cancer, liver and lung diseases and obesity. Obesity is also a risk factor for other non-communicable diseases, e.g. type 2 diabetes (see p.57) and cardiovascular disease.

## Non-Communicable Diseases Can Have Wide-Ranging Effects

1) Non-communicable diseases can have knock-on effects for local areas. For example, in areas where there are high levels of obesity, smoking or excess alcohol consumption, there's likely to be a high occurrence of certain non-communicable diseases, e.g. cardiovascular or liver disease. This can put pressure on the resources (money, beds, staff, etc.) of local hospitals.

2) Non-communicable diseases are also costly at a national level because the National Health Service provides the resources for the treatment of patients all over the UK. And sometimes, people suffering from a non-communicable disease may not be able to work. A reduction in the number of people able to work can affect a country's economy.

3) As well as being costly, non-communicable diseases are very common, e.g. cardiovascular disease is the number one cause of death worldwide. In developing countries, malnutrition is also a big problem because people are not able to access enough food. The high cost and occurrence of these diseases can hold back the development of a country — so they have an effect at a global level.

---

## Best put down that cake and go for a run...

You may be given data about risk factors in the exam — see p.9 for how you can draw conclusions using data.

Q1    Give one example of a lifestyle factor that increases the risk of cardiovascular disease.    [1 mark]

# Measures of Obesity

People come in all sorts of <u>shapes</u> and <u>sizes</u>, so you can't just say that anyone <u>over a particular weight</u> is <u>obese</u>. You have to use <u>indices</u> and <u>ratios</u> to figure this out instead — which is what this page is all about.

## A Body Mass Index Indicates If You're Under- or Overweight

1) The <u>Body Mass Index</u> (<u>BMI</u>) is used as a guide to help decide whether someone is <u>underweight</u>, <u>normal</u>, <u>overweight</u> or <u>obese</u>. It's calculated from their <u>height</u> and <u>weight</u>:

$$BMI = \frac{\text{weight (kg)}}{(\text{height (m)})^2}$$

| Body Mass Index | Weight Description |
|---|---|
| below 18.5 | underweight |
| 18.5 - 24.9 | normal |
| 25 - 29.9 | overweight |
| 30 - 40 | moderately obese |
| above 40 | severely obese |

2) Once you have a <u>value</u> for a person's BMI, you can refer to a <u>table</u> that shows how the different values are <u>classified</u>.

**EXAMPLE:** Calculate the BMI of a person who weighs 63.0 kg and is 1.70 m tall. Is this person overweight?

$$BMI = \frac{\text{weight (kg)}}{(\text{height (m)})^2} = 63.0 \text{ kg} \div 1.70 \text{ m}^2 = 21.8 \text{ kg m}^{-2}$$

This person is not overweight — their BMI lies between 18.5 and 24.9. (the normal weight range).

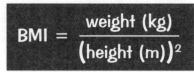

Martin prefers to use a "Body Splash Index".

3) If you eat a <u>high fat</u>, <u>high sugar diet</u> and you <u>don't do</u> enough <u>exercise</u>, you're likely to <u>take in</u> more energy than you <u>use</u>. The <u>excess</u> energy is <u>stored</u> as <u>fat</u>, so you're more likely to have a <u>high BMI</u> and be obese.

4) BMI <u>isn't</u> always a <u>reliable</u> measure of obesity. For example, athletes have lots of <u>muscle</u>, which <u>weighs more</u> than fat, so they can come out with a <u>high BMI</u> even though they're <u>not overweight</u>.

## A Waist-to-Hip Ratio Can Also Be Used

1) By measuring the <u>circumference</u> of a person's <u>waist</u> and <u>hips</u>, you can use the following formula to figure out their <u>waist-to-hip ratio</u>.

$$\text{waist-to-hip ratio} = \frac{\text{waist circumference}}{\text{hip circumference}}$$

(e.g. in cm)
(e.g. in cm)

The <u>circumference</u> of a person's waist or hips is the distance the whole way around their body at that point.

2) The <u>higher</u> your waist-to-hip ratio, the <u>more weight</u> you're likely to be carrying around your middle.

3) A ratio <u>above 1.0</u> for <u>males</u> and <u>above 0.85</u> for <u>females</u> indicates you're carrying <u>too much weight</u> around your middle — this is known as <u>abdominal obesity</u>. It puts you at a <u>greater risk</u> of developing obesity-related health problems, such as type 2 diabetes (see p.57).

**EXAMPLE:** A woman has a waist measurement of 29 cm and a hip measurement of 36 cm. Find her waist-to-hip ratio.

$$\text{waist-to-hip ratio} = \frac{\text{waist circumference (cm)}}{\text{hip circumference (cm)}} = 29 \div 36 = 0.81$$

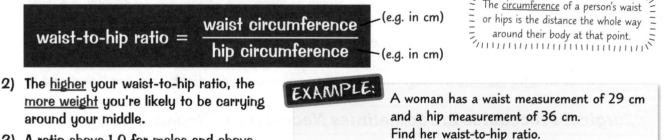

## Shakira was really onto something then...

...it's true. Hips don't lie. Seriously though, obesity is a major health issue. BMI and waist-to-hip ratios might not be perfect but they do provide a good guide for helping people know when it's time to lose weight.

Q1 Before beginning a new diet and exercise routine, a person weighs 76.0 kg and has a height of 1.58 m. Three weeks later their weight has dropped to 73.0 kg.
   a) Calculate the person's BMI at the beginning and the end of the three week period. [2 marks]
   b) Use the table at the top of the page to determine the weight description of the person before and after the three week period. [2 marks]

# Treatments for Cardiovascular Disease

Cardiovascular disease is a big, big problem in the UK. The good news is there are lots of ways to treat it.

## Cardiovascular Disease Affects Your Heart and Blood Vessels

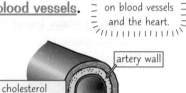

See pages 62-63 for more on blood vessels and the heart.

Cardiovascular disease (CVD) is any disease associated with your heart and blood vessels.

1) Arteries are blood vessels that carry blood away from the heart.

2) Cholesterol is a fatty substance that the body needs to make things like cell membranes. But too much cholesterol in the blood can cause fatty deposits to build up in arteries, restricting blood flow.

artery wall

cholesterol builds up to form a plaque

3) Deposits occur in areas where the artery wall has been damaged, e.g. by high blood pressure.

4) The fatty deposits can also trigger blood clots to form, which can block blood flow completely. If this happens in an artery supplying the heart muscle, the heart muscle will be deprived of oxygen. This causes a heart attack. A blockage in the brain deprives the brain of oxygen and can cause a stroke.

## Lifestyle Changes Can be Used to Treat CVD

1) Making changes to your lifestyle can reduce your risk of developing CVD. If you already have CVD, these changes can form part of the treatment, helping to reduce the risk of a further heart attack or stroke.

2) People with (or at risk of) CVD may be encouraged to eat a healthy, balanced diet, which is low in saturated fat (as saturated fat can increase blood cholesterol level). They may also be encouraged to exercise regularly, lose weight if necessary and stop smoking.

3) Lifestyle changes are often recommended first because they don't really have any downsides.

## Some Drugs Can Reduce the Risk of a Heart Attack or Stroke

Lifestyle changes aren't always enough to treat CVD. Sometimes medicines are needed too. Some people may need to take these medicines for the rest of their lives.

1) Statins reduce the amount of cholesterol in the bloodstream. This slows down the rate at which fatty deposits form — reducing the risk of heart attacks and strokes. However, they can sometimes cause negative side effects, e.g. aching muscles. Some of these side effects can be serious, e.g. liver damage.

2) Anticoagulants (e.g. warfarin) are drugs which make blood clots less likely to form. However, this can cause excessive bleeding if the person is hurt in an accident.

3) Antihypertensives reduce blood pressure. This helps to prevent damage to blood vessels and so reduces the risk of fatty deposits forming. However, they can cause side effects, e.g. headaches and fainting.

## Surgical Procedures are Sometimes Necessary to Repair Damage

1) Stents are tubes that are inserted inside arteries. They keep them open, making sure blood can pass through to the heart muscles, lowering the risk of a heart attack. But over time, the artery can narrow again as stents can irritate the artery and make scar tissue grow. The patient also has to take drugs to stop blood clotting on the stent.

2) If part of a blood vessel is blocked, a piece of healthy vessel taken from elsewhere can be used to bypass the blocked section. This is known as coronary bypass surgery.

3) The whole heart can be replaced with a donor heart. However, the new heart does not always start pumping properly and drugs have to be taken to stop the body rejecting it. These drugs can have side effects, e.g. making you more vulnerable to infections.

Any heart surgery is a major procedure and there is risk of bleeding, clots and infection.

---

## *Look after yerselves me hearties...*

Make sure you're aware of the drawbacks of each treatment for cardiovascular disease, as well as the advantages.

Q1      Why might surgery be considered to be a last resort when treating cardiovascular disease?      [2 marks]

# Photosynthesis

You don't know <u>photosynthesis</u> 'til you know its <u>equation</u>. It's in a nice <u>green box</u> so you can't possibly miss it.

## Plants are Able to Make Their Own Food by Photosynthesis

1) During photosynthesis, <u>photosynthetic organisms</u>, such as <u>green plants</u> and <u>algae</u>, use <u>energy</u> from the Sun to make <u>glucose</u>.

2) Some of the glucose is used to make <u>larger</u>, <u>complex molecules</u> that the plants or algae need to <u>grow</u>. These make up the organism's <u>biomass</u> — the mass of <u>living material</u>.

3) The <u>energy stored</u> in the organisms' <u>biomass</u> then works its way through the <u>food chain</u> as animals <u>eat</u> them and each other. So photosynthetic organisms are the main producers of food for <u>nearly all life on Earth</u>.

4) Photosynthesis happens inside <u>chloroplasts</u> — they contain <u>chlorophyll</u> which <u>absorbs light</u>. Energy is <u>transferred</u> to the <u>chloroplasts</u> by <u>light</u>. This is the <u>equation</u> for photosynthesis:

$$\text{carbon dioxide} + \text{water} \xrightarrow[\text{chlorophyll}]{\text{LIGHT}} \text{glucose} + \text{oxygen}$$
$$6CO_2 + 6H_2O \longrightarrow C_6H_{12}O_6 + 6O_2$$

5) Photosynthesis is an <u>endothermic</u> reaction — <u>energy</u> is <u>taken in</u> during the reaction.

6) The rate of photosynthesis is affected by the <u>light intensity</u>, the <u>concentration of CO$_2$</u> and the <u>temperature</u>. Any of these three factors can become the <u>limiting factor</u>. This just means that it's stopping photosynthesis from happening any <u>faster</u>. There's more about limiting factors on page 48.

## You Can Investigate the Effect of Light Intensity on the Rate of Photosynthesis

<u>Canadian pondweed</u> (an aquatic plant) can be used to measure the effect of <u>light intensity</u> on the <u>rate of photosynthesis</u>. The rate at which the pondweed produces <u>oxygen</u> corresponds to the rate at which it's photosynthesising — the <u>faster</u> the rate of oxygen production, the <u>faster</u> the rate of photosynthesis. Here's how the experiment works:

**PRACTICAL**

1) The <u>apparatus</u> is <u>set up</u> according to the <u>diagram</u>. The gas syringe should be empty to start with. <u>Sodium hydrogencarbonate</u> may be added to the water to make sure the plant has enough <u>carbon dioxide</u> (sodium hydrogencarbonate releases CO$_2$ in solution).

*You can also do this experiment with algal balls, instead of pondweed. These are little balls of jelly which contain algae.*

gas syringe

light source

Canadian pondweed

small O$_2$ bubbles

water (+ sodium hydrogencarbonate)

ruler to vary distance from plant

2) A source of <u>white light</u> is placed at a <u>specific distance</u> from the pondweed.

3) The pondweed is left to photosynthesise for a <u>set amount of time</u>.

4) As it photosynthesises, the oxygen released will collect in the <u>gas syringe</u>. This allows you to <u>accurately measure</u> the <u>volume</u> of oxygen produced.

*This experiment can be modified to test the effect of temperature or carbon dioxide concentration too — just remember to only change one variable at a time.*

5) The whole experiment is repeated with the <u>light source</u> at <u>different distances</u> from the pondweed. The <u>rate of oxygen production</u> at each distance can then be calculated (volume produced ÷ time taken).

6) For this experiment, any <u>variables</u> that could affect the results should be <u>controlled</u>, e.g. the <u>temperature</u> (which can be controlled by putting the conical flask in a <u>water bath</u>) and the <u>carbon dioxide concentration</u> (which can be controlled by adding a <u>set amount</u> of sodium hydrogencarbonate to a <u>set volume</u> of water).

## I'm working on sunshine — woah oh...

You could also measure how much oxygen's produced by counting the bubbles — fun, but it's not as accurate.

Q1    Explain how photosynthesis contributes to a plant's biomass.          [2 marks]

Q2    State three limiting factors of photosynthesis.          [3 marks]

# Limiting Factors in Photosynthesis

Remember, light intensity, $CO_2$ concentration and temperature are all underlined _limiting factors_ in photosynthesis.

## Three Important Graphs for Rate of Photosynthesis

### Not Enough LIGHT Slows Down the Rate of Photosynthesis

1) Light transfers the _energy_ needed for photosynthesis.

2) At first, as the _light level_ is raised, the rate of photosynthesis _increases steadily_ (the rate is _directly proportional_ to light intensity). But this is only true up to a _certain point_.

3) Beyond that, it _won't_ make any difference — it'll be either the _temperature_ or the $CO_2$ _level_ which is the limiting factor.

4) In the lab you can investigate light intensity by _moving_ a _lamp_ closer to or further away from your plant (see previous page).

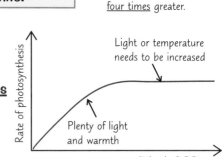

_rate is no longer increasing, so the graph flattens out_

_$CO_2$ or temp needs to be increased_

_rate increases with light intensity_

Rate of photosynthesis

Light intensity

5) But if you just plot the rate of photosynthesis against "distance of lamp from the plant", you get a _weird-shaped graph_. To get a graph like the one above you either need to _measure_ the light intensity at the plant using a _light meter_ or do a bit of nifty maths with your results. Here's why:

The distance from the lamp and light intensity are _inversely proportional_ to each other — this means as the _distance increases_, the _light intensity decreases_. However, light intensity decreases in proportion to the _square_ of the distance. This is called the _inverse square law_ and is written like this:

$\propto$ is the 'proportional to' symbol.

$$\text{light intensity} \propto \frac{1}{\text{distance (d)}^2}$$

6) The inverse square law means that if you _halve_ the _distance_, the _light intensity_ will be _four times greater_. And if you _double_ the distance, the light intensity will be _four times smaller_. (_Trebling_ the distance would make it _six times smaller_.) You can use $1/d^2$ as a measure of light intensity:

E.g. at 20 cm, light intensity = $1/20^2$ = 1/400 = 0.0025 arbitrary units.
At 10 cm, light intensity = $1/10^2$ = 1/100 = 0.0100 arbitrary units.

Halving the distance has made the light intensity _four times_ greater.

### Too Little CARBON DIOXIDE Also Slows it Down

1) $CO_2$ is one of the _raw materials_ needed for photosynthesis.

2) As with light intensity, increasing the $CO_2$ concentration _increases_ the rate of photosynthesis up to a point. After this the graph _flattens out_, showing that $CO_2$ is no longer the _limiting factor_.

3) As long as _light_ and $CO_2$ are in plentiful supply then the factor limiting photosynthesis must be _temperature_.

Rate of photosynthesis

_Light or temperature needs to be increased_

_Plenty of light and warmth_

% level of $CO_2$

### The TEMPERATURE has to be Just Right

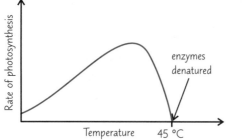

Rate of photosynthesis

enzymes denatured

Temperature   45 °C

1) Usually, if the temperature is the _limiting factor_ it's because it's _too low_ — the _enzymes_ needed for photosynthesis work more _slowly_ at low temperatures.

2) But if the plant gets _too hot_, the enzymes it needs for photosynthesis and its other reactions will be _denatured_ (see page 15).

3) This happens at about _45 °C_ (pretty hot for outdoors, but _greenhouses_ can get that hot if you're not careful).

## _Don't blame it on the sunshine, don't blame it on the $CO_2$..._

...don't blame it on the temperature, blame it on the plant. Nothing like a song to help you revise.

Q1   Describe the relationship between increasing light intensity and the rate of photosynthesis.   [2 marks]

# Transport in Plants

Plants need to get stuff from <u>A to B</u>. Flowering plants have <u>two types</u> of <u>transport vessel</u> — <u>xylem</u> and <u>phloem</u>. Both types of vessel go to <u>every part</u> of the plant, but they are totally <u>separate</u>.

## Root Hairs Take In Minerals and Water

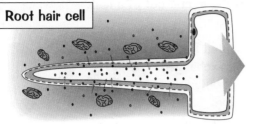

Root hair cell

1) The cells on the surface of plant roots grow into "<u>hairs</u>", which stick out into the soil.
2) Each branch of a root will be covered in <u>millions</u> of these microscopic hairs.
3) This gives the plant a <u>large surface area</u> for absorbing <u>water</u> and <u>mineral ions</u> from the soil.
4) The concentration of mineral ions is usually <u>higher</u> in the <u>root hair cells</u> than in the <u>soil</u> around them, so mineral ions are absorbed by <u>active transport</u> (see page 18). Water is absorbed by <u>osmosis</u>.

## Phloem Tubes Transport Food

1) Phloem tubes are made of columns of <u>elongated</u> living cells with small <u>pores</u> in the <u>end walls</u> to allow stuff to flow through.
2) They transport <u>food substances</u> (mainly <u>sucrose</u>) made in the leaves to the rest of the plant for <u>immediate use</u> (e.g. in growing regions) or for <u>storage</u>.
3) This process is called <u>translocation</u> and it requires <u>energy</u> from respiration (see page 64). The transport goes in <u>both directions</u>.

Food (mainly dissolved sucrose)

Water and minerals

## Xylem Tubes Take Water UP

1) Xylem tubes are made of <u>dead cells</u> joined end to end with <u>no</u> end walls between them and a hole down the middle. They're strengthened with a material called <u>lignin</u>.
2) They carry <u>water</u> and <u>mineral ions</u> from the <u>roots</u> to the <u>stem</u> and <u>leaves</u>.
3) The movement of water <u>from</u> the <u>roots</u>, <u>through</u> the <u>xylem</u> and <u>out</u> of the <u>leaves</u> is called the <u>transpiration stream</u> (see below).

## Transpiration is the Loss of Water from the Plant

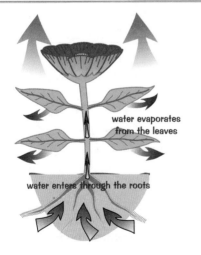

water evaporates from the leaves

water enters through the roots

1) Transpiration is caused by the <u>evaporation</u> and <u>diffusion</u> (see p.18) of water from a plant's surface. Most transpiration happens at the <u>leaves</u>.
2) The loss of water creates a slight <u>shortage</u> of water in the leaf, and so more water is drawn up from the rest of the plant through the <u>xylem vessels</u> to replace it.
3) This in turn means more water is drawn up from the <u>roots</u>, and so there's a constant <u>transpiration stream</u> of water through the plant.
4) The transpiration stream carries <u>mineral ions</u> that are dissolved in the water along with it.

---

### Don't let revision stress you out — just go with the phloem...

Phloem transports substances in <u>both</u> directions, but xylem only transports things upwards — xy to the sky.

Q1     Explain how water moves through a plant in the transpiration stream.                [3 marks]

# Stomata and Transpiration

Sorry, more on <u>transpiration</u>. But first, you need to learn about <u>stomata</u>...

## Stomata are Needed for Gas Exchange

Stomata are <u>tiny pores</u> on the surface of a plant. They're mostly found on the lower surface of <u>leaves</u>. Stomata allow $CO_2$ and <u>oxygen</u> to <u>diffuse</u> directly in and out of a leaf. They also allow <u>water vapour</u> to escape during <u>transpiration</u>.

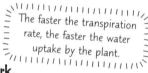
It's one stoma, but two or more stomata.

Transpiration is really just a <u>side-effect</u> of the way leaves are adapted for <u>photosynthesis</u>. They have to have <u>stomata</u> so that gases can be exchanged easily. Because there's more water <u>inside</u> the plant than in the <u>air outside</u>, the water escapes from the leaves through the stomata by diffusion.

guard cells
stoma

guard cells turgid — stoma <u>open</u>
guard cells flaccid — stoma <u>closed</u>

Stomata are surrounded by <u>guard cells</u>, which <u>change shape</u> to control the size of the pore — when the guard cells are <u>turgid</u> (swollen with water) the stomata are <u>open</u> and when the guard cells are <u>flaccid</u> (low on water and limp) the stomata are <u>closed</u>.

## Transpiration Rate is Affected by Environmental Factors

The faster the transpiration rate, the faster the water uptake by the plant.

1) <u>LIGHT INTENSITY</u> — the <u>brighter</u> the light, the <u>greater</u> the transpiration rate. <u>Stomata</u> begin to <u>close</u> as it gets darker. Photosynthesis can't happen in the dark, so they don't need to be open to let $CO_2$ in. When the stomata are closed, very little water can escape.

2) <u>TEMPERATURE</u> — the <u>warmer</u> it is, the <u>faster</u> transpiration happens. When it's warm the water particles have <u>more energy</u> to evaporate and diffuse out of the stomata.

3) <u>AIR FLOW</u> — the <u>better</u> the air flow around a leaf, e.g. stronger wind, the <u>greater</u> the transpiration rate. If air flow around a leaf is <u>poor</u>, the water vapour just <u>surrounds the leaf</u> and doesn't move away. This means there's a <u>high concentration</u> of water particles outside the leaf as well as inside it, so <u>diffusion</u> doesn't happen as quickly. If there's <u>good</u> air flow, the water vapour is <u>swept away</u>, maintaining a <u>low concentration</u> of water in the air outside the leaf. Diffusion then happens quickly, from an area of higher concentration to an area of lower concentration.

## You Can Estimate Transpiration Rate

You can use a special piece of apparatus called a <u>potometer</u> to <u>estimate transpiration rate</u>. It actually <u>measures water uptake</u> by a plant, but it's <u>assumed</u> that water uptake by the plant is <u>directly related</u> to water loss from the leaves (transpiration). Here's what you do:

1) Set up the apparatus as in the diagram, and then record the <u>starting position</u> of the air bubble.

2) Start a stopwatch and record the <u>distance moved</u> by the bubble per unit time, e.g. per hour. Calculating the <u>speed</u> of <u>air bubble movement</u> gives an <u>estimate</u> of the <u>transpiration rate</u>.

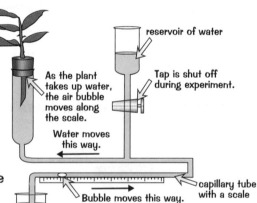
reservoir of water
As the plant takes up water, the air bubble moves along the scale.
Water moves this way.
Tap is shut off during experiment.
Bubble moves this way.
capillary tube with a scale
Beaker of water.

**EXAMPLE:** A potometer was used to estimate the transpiration rate of a plant cutting. The bubble moved 25 mm in 10 minutes. Estimate the transpiration rate.

To estimate the <u>rate of transpiration</u>, divide the <u>distance</u> the bubble moved by the <u>time taken</u>.

$$\frac{\text{distance moved}}{\text{time taken}} = \frac{25 \text{ mm}}{10 \text{ min}} = 2.5 \text{ mm min}^{-1}$$

You can use a potometer to estimate how <u>light intensity</u>, <u>temperature</u> or <u>air flow</u> around the plant affect the transpiration rate. Just remember to <u>only change one variable at a time</u> and control the rest.

## I say stomaaaarta, you say stomaaaayta...

Sunny, warm and windy — the perfect conditions for transpiration and for hanging out your washing.

Q1  Explain how low light intensity affects the rate of water uptake by a plant.      [3 marks]

# Revision Questions for Sections 5 and 6

Well there you go. Some nasty stuff on <u>diseases</u>, followed by some lovely(ish) stuff on <u>plants</u>.

- Try these questions and <u>tick off each one</u> when you <u>get it right</u>.
- When you've done <u>all the questions</u> under a heading and are <u>completely happy</u>, tick it off.

## Health, Disease and STIs (p.39-40) ☑

1) Explain why being healthy doesn't just mean not being sick. ☑
2) What is a 'non-communicable' disease? ☑
3) How can the transmission of malaria be prevented? ☑
4) How can the spread of *Chlamydia* be reduced? ☑
5) Why does HIV eventually lead to AIDS? ☑

## Fighting Disease (p.41-42) ☐

6) Give two types of chemical defence that prevent pathogens from infecting humans. ☑
7) What is an antigen? ☑
8) What does a B-lymphocyte do when it recognises a pathogen? ☑
9) How do vaccines prepare the immune system against infection by a particular pathogen? ☑

## Antibiotics and Other Medicines (p.43) ☐

10) Which type of pathogen can antibiotics be used to kill? ☑
11) What is the placebo effect? ☑

## Non-Communicable Diseases (p.44-46) ☐

12) Describe how smoking can increase the risk of a heart attack or stroke. ☑
13) Give a risk factor related to lifestyle for the development of liver disease. ☑
14) Write the equation for finding the body mass index of an individual. ☑
15) Give three examples of lifestyle changes that can help to prevent cardiovascular disease. ☑

## Photosynthesis (p.47-48) ☑

16) In what part of a cell does photosynthesis take place? ☑
17) Apart from water vapour, what gas is needed for photosynthesis? ☑
18) Name the two products of photosynthesis. ☑
19) Why is photosynthesis described as an endothermic reaction? ☑
20) Describe how you could investigate the effect of light intensity on the rate of photosynthesis. ☑
21) Describe the relationship between light intensity and distance from a light source. ☑
22) What effect would a low carbon dioxide concentration have on the rate of photosynthesis? ☑
23) What effect would a temperature above 45 °C usually have on the rate of photosynthesis? Why? ☑

## Transport in Plants and Transpiration (p.49-50) ☑

24) How are root hair cells adapted to their function? ☑
25) By what process do phloem tubes transport sucrose around a plant? ☑
26) Describe the structure of xylem vessels. ☑
27) a) What are stomata?
    b) What is the role of stomata in transpiration? ☑
28) Give three factors that affect the rate of transpiration. ☑
29) Describe how you'd use a potometer to estimate the rate of transpiration. ☑

# Hormones

Way back in Section 2 you learnt how information is passed around the body via neurones. Well the body also uses hormones as a way to communicate, which is what this page is all about. Enjoy.

## Hormones Are Chemical Messengers Sent in the Blood

1) Hormones are chemicals released directly into the blood. They are carried in the blood to other parts of the body, but only affect particular cells in particular organs (called target organs). Hormones control things in organs and cells that need constant adjustment.

2) Hormones are produced in (and secreted by) various glands, called endocrine glands. These glands make up your endocrine system.

3) These are the endocrine glands you need to know:

### THE PITUITARY GLAND

The pituitary gland produces many hormones that regulate body conditions. It is sometimes called the 'master gland' because these hormones act on other glands, directing them to release hormones that bring about change.

### OVARIES — females only

Produce oestrogen, which is involved in the menstrual cycle (see page 54).

### TESTES — males only

Produce testosterone, which controls puberty and sperm production in males.

### THYROID GLAND

This produces thyroxine, which is involved in regulating things like the rate of metabolism, heart rate and temperature (see next page).

### ADRENAL GLANDS

These produce adrenaline, which is used to prepare the body for a 'fight or flight' response (see next page).

### THE PANCREAS

This produces insulin, which is used to regulate the blood glucose level (see page 56).

## Hormones and Neurones Have Differences

NEURONES:
Very FAST action.
Act for a very SHORT TIME.
Act on a very PRECISE AREA.

HORMONES:
SLOWER action.
Act for a LONG TIME.
Act in a more GENERAL way.

So if you're not sure whether a response is nervous or hormonal, have a think...

1) If the response is really quick, it's probably nervous. Some information needs to be passed to effectors really quickly (e.g. pain signals, or information from your eyes telling you about the lion heading your way), so it's no good using hormones to carry the message — they're too slow.

2) But if a response lasts for a long time, it's probably hormonal. For example, when you get a shock, the hormone adrenaline is released into the body (causing the 'fight or flight' response, where your body is hyped up ready for action). You can tell it's a hormonal response (even though it kicks in pretty quickly) because you feel a bit wobbly for a while afterwards.

## Nerves, hormones — no wonder revision makes me tense...

Hormones control various organs and cells in the body, though they tend to control things that aren't immediately life-threatening (so things like sexual development, blood glucose level, water content, etc.).

Q1     Name the endocrine glands that only males have.                    [1 mark]

# Adrenaline and Thyroxine

On the previous page you learnt what hormones are.  Now it's time to look at a couple of examples...

## Adrenaline Prepares you for 'Fight or Flight'

1) Adrenaline is a hormone released by the adrenal glands (which are located just above the kidneys — see previous page).

2) Adrenaline prepares the body for 'fight or flight' — in other words, standing your ground in the face of a threat (e.g. a predator) or bravely running away.  It does this by activating processes that increase the supply of oxygen and glucose to cells.  For example:

- Adrenaline binds to specific receptors in the heart.  This causes the heart muscle to contract more frequently and with more force, so heart rate and blood pressure increase.
- This increases blood flow to the muscles, so the cells receive more oxygen and glucose for increased respiration.
- Adrenaline also binds to receptors in the liver.  This causes the liver to break down its glycogen stores (see p.56) to release glucose.
- This increases the blood glucose level, so there's more glucose in the blood to be transported to the cells.

3) When your brain detects a stressful situation, it sends nervous impulses to the adrenal glands, which respond by secreting adrenaline.  This gets the body ready for action.

## Hormone Release can be Affected by Negative Feedback

Your body can control the levels of hormones (and other substances) in the blood using negative feedback systems.  When the body detects that the level of a substance has gone above or below the normal level, it triggers a response to bring the level back to normal again.  Here's an example of just that:

### Thyroxine Regulates Metabolism

1) Thyroxine is a hormone released by the thyroid gland.

2) It plays an important role in regulating metabolic rate — the speed at which chemical reactions in the body occur.

> An underactive thyroid gland can cause weight gain.  Less thyroxine is produced, so your metabolic rate drops.  This means that less of the glucose you take in gets broken down in respiration, so more is stored as fat.

3) A negative feedback system keeps the amount of thyroxine in the blood at the right level:

- When the blood thyroxine level is lower than normal, the hypothalamus (a structure in the brain) is stimulated to release thyrotropin releasing hormone (TRH).
- TRH stimulates the pituitary gland to release thyroid stimulating hormone (TSH).
- TSH stimulates the thyroid gland to release thyroxine, so the blood thyroxine level rises back towards normal.
- When the blood thyroxine level becomes higher than normal, the release of TRH from the hypothalamus is inhibited, which reduces the production of TSH, so the blood thyroxine level falls.

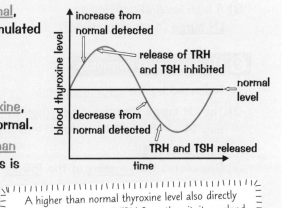

> A higher than normal thyroxine level also directly inhibits the secretion of TSH from the pituitary gland.

## Negative feedback sucks, especially from your science teacher...

You can think about negative feedback working like a thermostat — if the temperature gets too low, the thermostat will turn the heating on, then if the temperature gets too high, it'll turn the heating off again.

Q1    Name the gland that releases thyroxine.                                                                [1 mark]

Q2    Describe how release of TRH from the hypothalamus affects the blood thyroxine level.        [2 marks]

# The Menstrual Cycle

You need to know all about the <u>hormones</u> that control the <u>menstrual cycle</u> — lucky you...

## The Menstrual Cycle Has Four Stages

The menstrual cycle is the <u>monthly sequence of events</u> in which the female body releases an <u>egg</u> and prepares the <u>uterus</u> (womb) in case the egg is <u>fertilised</u>. This is what happens at <u>each stage</u>:

<u>Stage 1</u> <u>Day 1 is when menstruation starts.</u>
The lining of the uterus breaks down and is released.

*The fancy name for the lining of the uterus is the 'endometrium'.*

<u>Stage 2</u> <u>The uterus lining is repaired</u>, from day 4 to day 14, until it becomes a thick spongy layer full of blood vessels ready for a fertilised egg to implant there.

<u>Stage 3</u> <u>An egg develops and is released</u> from the ovary (<u>ovulation</u>) at about day 14.

<u>Stage 4</u> <u>The lining is then maintained</u> for about 14 days, until day 28. If no fertilised egg has landed on the uterus wall by day 28, the spongy lining starts to break down again and the whole cycle starts over.

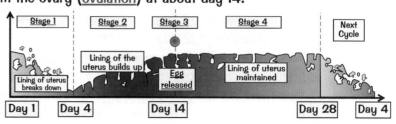

## The Menstrual Cycle is Controlled by Four Hormones

**① FSH (follicle-stimulating hormone)**

1) Released by the pituitary gland.
2) Causes a follicle (an egg and its surrounding cells) to mature in one of the ovaries.
3) Stimulates oestrogen production.

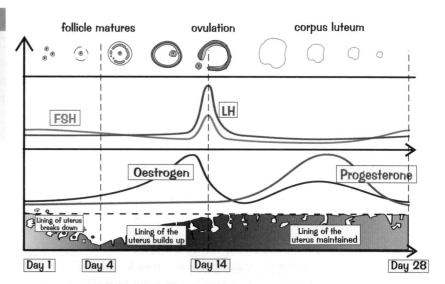

**② Oestrogen**

1) Released by the <u>ovaries</u>.
2) Causes the lining of the uterus to <u>thicken</u> and <u>grow</u>.
3) A high level stimulates an <u>LH surge</u> (a rapid increase).

**③ LH (luteinising hormone)**

1) Released by the <u>pituitary gland</u>.
2) The LH surge stimulates <u>ovulation</u> at day 14 — the follicle ruptures and the <u>egg is released</u>.
3) Stimulates the <u>remains</u> of the <u>follicle</u> to develop into a structure called a <u>corpus luteum</u> — which secretes <u>progesterone</u>.

**④ Progesterone**

1) Released by the <u>corpus luteum</u> after ovulation.
2) <u>Maintains</u> the lining of the uterus.
3) <u>Inhibits</u> the release of <u>FSH</u> and <u>LH</u>.
4) When the level of progesterone <u>falls</u>, and there's a low oestrogen level, the uterus lining <u>breaks down</u>.
5) A <u>low</u> progesterone level allows <u>FSH</u> to <u>increase</u>... and then the whole cycle starts again.

If a fertilised egg implants in the uterus (i.e. the woman becomes <u>pregnant</u>) then the level of <u>progesterone</u> will <u>stay high</u> to maintain the lining of the uterus during pregnancy.

## What do you call a fish with no eye — FSH...

OK, this stuff is pretty tricky. Try scribbling down everything on the page until you can get it all without peeking.

Q1     Explain the role of LH in the menstrual cycle.                                    [3 marks]

# Controlling Fertility

Hormones can be used artificially to help infertile women have babies and to help fertile women not have babies.

## Hormones can be Used to Treat Infertility

If a person is infertile, it means they can't reproduce naturally. There are methods an infertile couple can use to become pregnant, many of which involve hormones. You need to learn these two examples:

### Clomifene therapy

Some women are infertile because they don't ovulate or they don't ovulate regularly. These women can take a drug called clomifene. This works by causing more FSH and LH to be released by the body, which stimulate egg maturation and ovulation — see previous page. By knowing when the woman will be ovulating, the couple can have intercourse during this time period to improve the chance of becoming pregnant.

### IVF ("in vitro fertilisation")

IVF involves collecting eggs from the woman's ovaries and fertilising them in a lab using the man's sperm. These are then grown into embryos. Once the embryos are tiny balls of cells, one or two of them are transferred to the woman's uterus to improve the chance of pregnancy. FSH and LH are given before egg collection to stimulate egg production (so more than one egg can be collected).

IVF is an example of Assisted Reproductive Technology (ART) — a fertility treatment that involves eggs being handled (and usually fertilised) outside of the body.

## Contraceptives are Used to Prevent Pregnancy

1) Hormones can also be used as contraceptives. For example, oestrogen can be used to prevent the release of an egg. This may seem kind of strange (since naturally oestrogen helps stimulate the release of eggs). But if oestrogen is taken every day to keep the level of it permanently high, it inhibits the production of FSH, and after a while egg development and production stop and stay stopped.

2) Progesterone can also be used to reduce fertility. It works in several different ways — one of which is by stimulating the production of thick cervical mucus, which prevents any sperm getting through the entrance to the uterus (the cervix) and reaching an egg.

3) Some hormonal contraceptives contain both oestrogen and progesterone — for example, the combined pill (which is an oral contraceptive) and the contraceptive patch (which is worn on the skin).

4) The mini-pill (another oral contraceptive) and the contraceptive injection both contain progesterone only.

5) Pregnancy can also be prevented by barrier methods of contraception — these put a barrier between the sperm and egg so they don't meet. Examples include condoms (both male and female) and diaphragms (flexible, dome-shaped devices that fit over the opening of the uterus and are inserted before sex).

*Diaphragms must be used with a spermicide — a chemical that kills sperm.*

## Hormonal and Barrier Contraceptive Methods Have Pros and Cons

1) Generally, when used correctly, hormonal methods are more effective at preventing pregnancy than barrier methods. Also, hormonal methods mean the couple don't have to stop and think about contraception each time they have intercourse (as they would if they relied on barrier methods).

2) However, hormonal methods can have unpleasant side-effects, such as headaches, acne and mood changes. Also, hormonal methods don't protect against sexually transmitted infections — condoms are the only form of contraception that do this.

*I've got this barrier thing sorted...*

## IVF... FSH... LH... ART — I feel like I'm at the opticians...

Make sure you understand how and why hormones are used in fertility treatments and contraceptive methods.

Q1    Describe how hormones are used in IVF.    [3 marks]

# Homeostasis — Control of Blood Glucose

Homeostasis means <u>maintaining</u> the right <u>conditions</u> inside your body, so that everything <u>works properly</u>.  Ace.

## Homeostasis is Maintaining a Constant Internal Environment

1) Conditions in your body need to be kept <u>steady</u> — this is really important because your cells need the <u>right conditions</u> in order to <u>function properly</u>, including the right conditions for <u>enzyme action</u> (see p.15). It can be <u>dangerous</u> for your <u>health</u> if conditions <u>vary too much</u> from normal levels.

2) To maintain a constant internal environment, your body needs to respond to both <u>internal</u> and <u>external</u> changes, whilst balancing <u>inputs</u> (stuff going into your body) with <u>outputs</u> (stuff leaving).

3) <u>Examples</u> of homeostasis in action include:

- <u>Blood glucose</u> regulation — you need to make sure the amount of glucose in your blood doesn't get too high or too low (see below).
- <u>Osmoregulation</u> (regulating <u>water</u> content) — you need to keep a balance between the water you gain (in drink, food, and from respiration) and the water you pee, sweat and breathe out.
- <u>Thermoregulation</u> (regulating <u>body temperature</u>) — you need to reduce your body temperature when you're hot, but increase it when the environment is cold.

4) <u>Negative feedback systems</u> (see p.53) help to keep conditions in your body steady.  This means that if a condition <u>changes</u> away from the normal level, a <u>response</u> is triggered that <u>counteracts</u> the change. E.g. a <u>rise</u> in blood glucose level causes a <u>response</u> that <u>lowers</u> blood glucose level (and vice versa).

## Insulin and Glucagon Control Blood Glucose Concentration

1) Eating foods containing <u>carbohydrate</u> puts <u>glucose</u> into the <u>blood</u> from the <u>small intestine</u>.

2) The normal <u>metabolism</u> of cells <u>removes glucose</u> from the blood.

3) Vigorous <u>exercise</u> removes <u>much more</u> glucose from the blood.

4) <u>Excess</u> glucose can be stored as <u>glycogen</u> in the <u>liver</u> and in the <u>muscles</u>.

5) When these stores are <u>full</u> then the excess glucose is stored as <u>lipid</u> (fat) in the tissues.

6) <u>Changes</u> in blood glucose are monitored and controlled by the <u>pancreas</u>, using the hormones <u>insulin</u> and <u>glucagon</u>, as shown:

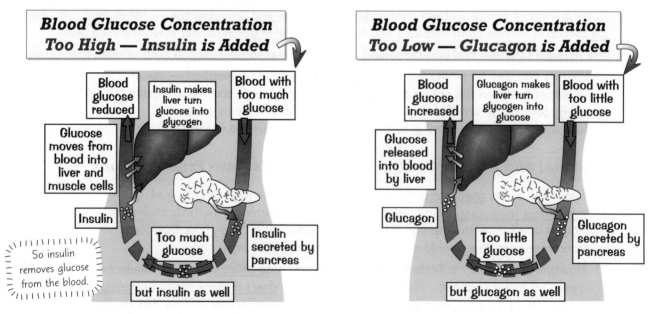

## Learn about homeostasis — and keep your cool...

Homeostasis is really important for keeping processes in your body ticking over nicely.  Make sure you learn the definition of homeostasis and can explain how blood glucose concentration is regulated by insulin and glucagon.

Q1  Explain how blood glucose concentration is returned to normal when it has become too high.  [3 marks]

# Diabetes

Diabetes is an example of when homeostasis doesn't work. Make sure you fully understand how insulin affects blood glucose concentration (on the previous page) before you try getting your head around diabetes.

## Type 1 Diabetes — Caused by a Lack of Insulin

1) Type 1 diabetes is a condition where the pancreas produces little or no insulin. The result is that a person's blood glucose can rise to a level that can kill them.

*Remember, insulin reduces blood glucose level.*

2) A person with type 1 diabetes will need to be treated with insulin therapy — this usually involves injecting insulin into the blood. This is often done at mealtimes to make sure that the glucose is removed from the blood quickly once the food has been digested. This stops the level of glucose in the blood from getting too high and is a very effective treatment. Insulin is usually injected into subcutaneous tissue (fatty tissue just under the skin). The amount of insulin that needs to be injected depends on the person's diet and how active they are.

*Injecting too much insulin could result in a dangerously low blood glucose level.*

3) As well as insulin therapy, people with type 1 diabetes also need to think about:

- Limiting the intake of foods rich in simple carbohydrates, i.e. sugars (which cause the blood glucose level to rise rapidly).
- Taking regular exercise — this helps to remove excess glucose from the blood.

## Type 2 Diabetes — a Person is Resistant to Insulin

1) Type 2 diabetes is a condition where the pancreas doesn't produce enough insulin or when a person becomes resistant to insulin (their body's cells don't respond properly to the hormone). In both of these cases, blood glucose level rises.

2) There is a correlation (see p.9) between obesity and type 2 diabetes — this means that obese people have an increased risk of developing type 2 diabetes. People are classified as obese if they have a body mass index (BMI) of over 30. BMI is worked out using this formula:

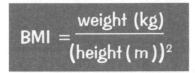

$$BMI = \frac{weight\ (kg)}{(height\ (m))^2}$$

*See page 45 for more on calculating BMI and waist-to-hip ratios.*

3) Where the body stores excess fat is also important — storing a lot of fat around the abdomen (tummy area) is associated with an increased risk of developing type 2 diabetes. Calculating a person's waist-to-hip ratio gives an indication of how fat is stored. This is the formula you need:

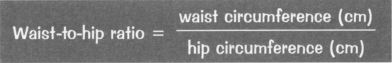

$$Waist\text{-}to\text{-}hip\ ratio = \frac{waist\ circumference\ (cm)}{hip\ circumference\ (cm)}$$

A ratio above 1.0 for men and above 0.85 for women is associated with an increased risk of type 2 diabetes because it indicates that a lot of fat is being stored around the abdomen.

4) Type 2 diabetes can be controlled by eating a healthy diet, getting regular exercise and losing weight if needed. Some people with type 2 diabetes also have medication or insulin injections.

## And people used to think the pancreas was just a cushion... (true)

Don't forget that there are two types of diabetes. Make sure you know how each one is caused and what the different treatments are. Remember as well that obesity is a big risk factor for developing type 2 diabetes.

Q1    Describe the cause of type 1 diabetes.     [1 mark]

Q2    Give two measures of obesity that can help to assess a person's risk of developing type 2 diabetes.     [2 marks]

# Revision Questions for Section 7

Congratulations, you've made it to the end of Section 7 — now for some questions to make sure you've been paying attention...

*   Try these questions and tick off each one when you get it right.
*   When you've done all the questions under a heading and are completely happy, tick it off.

## Hormones (p.52-53) ☑

1) What is a hormone?
2) How do hormones travel to target organs?
3) What is an endocrine gland?
4) Name the gland where each of the following hormones is produced:
   a) oestrogen,
   b) testosterone,
   c) insulin.
   d) adrenaline.
5) Explain how adrenaline prepares the body for the 'fight or flight' response.
6) Describe how a negative feedback system works in the body.
7) Which hormone, released by the thyroid gland, controls metabolic rate?

## The Menstrual Cycle and Fertility (p.54-55) ☐

8) Draw a timeline of the 28 day menstrual cycle.
   Label the four stages of the cycle and label when the egg is released.
9) Describe two effects of FSH on the body.
10) Describe two effects of oestrogen on the body.
11) Which hormone is secreted by a corpus luteum?
12) What is clomifene therapy? Who might use it?
13) Briefly describe how IVF is carried out.
14) Explain how progesterone can be used in contraception to prevent pregnancy.
15) Write down two pros and two cons of hormonal contraceptives.

## Homeostasis (p.56-57) ☐

16) What is homeostasis?
17) Why is homeostasis important?
18) Describe the roles of insulin and glucagon in controlling a person's blood glucose concentration.
19) Explain how type 1 and type 2 diabetes can be treated.

# Exchange of Materials

Like all organisms, animals need to <u>exchange</u> things with their environment — but being <u>multicellular</u> makes things a little bit complicated...

## Organisms Exchange Substances with their Environment

1) All organisms must <u>take in</u> substances that they <u>need</u> from the environment and <u>get rid</u> of any <u>waste products</u>. For example:

- Cells need <u>oxygen</u> for <u>aerobic respiration</u> (see p. 64), which produces <u>carbon dioxide</u> as a waste product. These two <u>gases</u> move between <u>cells</u> and the <u>environment</u> by <u>diffusion</u> (see next page).
- <u>Water</u> is taken up by cells by <u>osmosis</u>. In animals, dissolved <u>food molecules</u> (the products of digestion, e.g. glucose, amino acids) and <u>mineral ions</u> diffuse along with it.

  There's more on diffusion and osmosis on page 18.

- <u>Urea</u> (a waste product produced by animals from proteins) diffuses from <u>cells</u> to the <u>blood plasma</u> for removal from the body by the kidneys.

2) How <u>easy</u> it is for an organism to exchange substances with its environment depends on the organism's <u>surface area to volume ratio</u> (<u>SA : V</u>).

## You Can Compare Surface Area to Volume Ratios

A ratio shows <u>how big</u> one value is <u>compared</u> to another. The <u>larger</u> an organism is, the <u>smaller</u> its surface area is compared to its volume. You can show this by calculating <u>surface area to volume ratios</u>:

1) A hippo can be represented by a 2 cm × 4 cm × 4 cm block.

   The <u>area</u> of a surface is found by the equation: LENGTH × WIDTH
   So the hippo's <u>total surface area</u> is:
   $$(4 \times 4) \times 2 \text{ (top and bottom surfaces of block)}$$
   $$+ (4 \times 2) \times 4 \text{ (four sides of the block)}$$
   $$= 64 \text{ cm}^2.$$

   4 cm
   4 cm
   2 cm

   The <u>volume</u> of a block is found by the equation:
   LENGTH × WIDTH × HEIGHT
   So the hippo's <u>volume</u> is $4 \times 4 \times 2 = 32 \text{ cm}^3$.

   The surface area to volume ratio of the hippo can be written as <u>64 : 32</u>.
   To get the ratio in the form <u>n : 1</u>, <u>divide both sides</u> of the ratio by the <u>volume</u>.
   So the surface area to volume ratio of the hippo is <u>2 : 1</u>.

2) A mouse can be represented by a 1 cm × 1 cm × 1 cm block.
   Its <u>surface area</u> is $(1 \times 1) \times 6 = 6 \text{ cm}^2$.
   Its <u>volume</u> is $1 \times 1 \times 1 = 1 \text{ cm}^3$.
   So the surface area to volume ratio of the mouse is <u>6 : 1</u>.

   1 cm
   1 cm
   1 cm

   The cube mouse's surface area is <u>six</u> times its volume, but the cube hippo's surface area is only <u>twice</u> its volume. So the <u>mouse</u> has a <u>larger</u> surface area compared to its volume.

## Not that I'm endorsing putting animals in boxes...

Have a go at this question to make sure you understand how to calculate surface area to volume ratios.

Q1    A bacterial cell can be represented by a 1 μm × 1 μm × 4 μm block.
Calculate the cell's surface area to volume ratio.
Give your ratio in its simplest whole number form.        [3 marks]

# Specialised Exchange Surfaces — the Alveoli

The alveoli are an exchange surface found in the lungs of mammals. They're well-adapted for the efficient exchange of two important gases — oxygen and carbon dioxide.

## Multicellular Organisms Need Exchange Surfaces

1) In single-celled organisms, gases and dissolved substances can diffuse directly into (or out of) the cell across the cell membrane — it's because they have a large surface area compared to their volume, so enough substances can be exchanged across the membrane to supply the volume of the cell.

2) Multicellular organisms (such as animals) have a smaller surface area compared to their volume.

3) This makes it difficult to exchange enough substances to supply their entire volume across their outside surface alone. So they need some sort of exchange surface for efficient diffusion and a mass transport system to move substances between the exchange surface and the rest of the body.

4) The exchange surfaces have to allow enough of the necessary substances to pass through, so they are adapted to maximise effectiveness. You need to know about the adaptations of the alveoli (see below) for your exam.

## Gas Exchange in Mammals Happens in the Alveoli

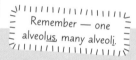

Remember — one alveolus, many alveoli.

1) The job of the lungs is to transfer oxygen ($O_2$) to the blood and to remove waste carbon dioxide ($CO_2$) from it.

2) To do this, the lungs contain millions of little air sacs called alveoli where gas exchange takes place.

3) Blood arriving at the alveoli has just returned to the lungs from the rest of the body, so it contains lots of $CO_2$ and not much $O_2$. This maximises the concentration gradient for the diffusion of both gases.

   ('Concentration gradient' means 'difference in concentration'. Substances diffuse faster if there's a big difference in concentration between the area they are diffusing from and the area they are diffusing to.)

4) $O_2$ diffuses out of the air in the alveoli (where the concentration of $O_2$ is high) and into the blood (where the concentration of $O_2$ is low).

5) $CO_2$ diffuses in the opposite direction to be breathed out.

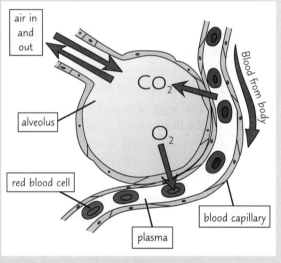

air in and out

$CO_2$

$O_2$

alveolus

red blood cell

Blood from body

blood capillary

plasma

## The Alveoli are Adapted for Efficient Gas Exchange

The alveoli are specialised to maximise the diffusion of $O_2$ and $CO_2$. They have:
- A moist lining for dissolving gases.
- A good blood supply to maintain the concentration gradients of $O_2$ and $CO_2$.
- Very thin walls — minimising the distance that gases have to move.
- An enormous surface area (about 75 m² in humans).

$O_2$ and $CO_2$ diffuse across the membranes of the cells that make up the walls of the capillary and alveolus. These membranes are partially permeable — see page 18.

## Al Veoli — the Italian gas man...

Without gas exchange surfaces like the alveoli, multicellular organisms wouldn't be able to absorb oxygen quickly enough to supply all of their cells. Have a go at this question and see what you've learnt.

Q1    Give one way in which the alveoli are adapted for gas exchange.                    [1 mark]

# Circulatory System — Blood

<u>Blood</u> is a <u>tissue</u>. One of its jobs is to act as a huge <u>transport</u> system. There are four main things in blood...

## Red Blood Cells Carry Oxygen

1) The job of red blood cells (also called <u>erythrocytes</u>) is to carry <u>oxygen</u> from the lungs to all the cells in the body.

2) They have a <u>biconcave disc</u> shape (in other words, they look a bit like a jam doughnut that's being pressed in at the top and bottom) to give a <u>large surface area</u> for absorbing <u>oxygen</u>.

3) They <u>don't</u> have a nucleus — this allows more <u>room</u> to carry oxygen.

4) They contain a red pigment called <u>haemoglobin</u>, which contains iron.

5) In the <u>lungs</u>, haemoglobin binds to <u>oxygen</u> to become <u>oxyhaemoglobin</u>. In body tissues, the reverse happens — oxyhaemoglobin splits up into haemoglobin and oxygen, to <u>release oxygen</u> to the <u>cells</u>.

The more red blood cells you've got, the more oxygen can get to your cells. At high altitudes there's less oxygen in the air — so people who live there produce more red blood cells to compensate.

## White Blood Cells Defend Against Infection

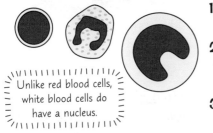

Unlike red blood cells, white blood cells do have a nucleus.

1) <u>Phagocytes</u> are white blood cells that can change shape to <u>engulf</u> (gobble up) unwelcome <u>microorganisms</u> — this is called <u>phagocytosis</u>.

2) <u>Lymphocytes</u> are white blood cells that produce <u>antibodies</u> against microorganisms (see p.41). Some also produce <u>antitoxins</u> to neutralise any toxins produced by the microorganisms.

3) When you have an <u>infection</u>, your white blood cells <u>multiply</u> to fight it off — so a <u>blood test</u> will show a <u>high</u> white blood cell count.

## Platelets Help Blood Clot

1) These are <u>small fragments</u> of <u>cells</u>. They have <u>no nucleus</u>.

2) They help the blood to <u>clot</u> at a wound — to stop all your <u>blood pouring out</u> and to stop <u>microorganisms</u> getting in. (So platelets kinda float about waiting for accidents to happen.)

3) <u>Lack</u> of platelets can cause excessive bleeding and bruising.

## Plasma is the Liquid That Carries Everything in Blood

This is a pale straw-coloured liquid which <u>carries just about everything</u>:

1) <u>Red</u> and <u>white blood cells</u> and <u>platelets</u>.

2) Nutrients like <u>glucose</u> and <u>amino acids</u>. These are the soluble products of digestion which are absorbed from the gut and taken to the cells of the body.

3) <u>Carbon dioxide</u> from the organs to the lungs.

4) <u>Urea</u> from the liver to the kidneys.

5) <u>Hormones</u>.

6) <u>Proteins</u>.

7) <u>Antibodies</u> and <u>antitoxins</u> produced by the white blood cells.

## Platelets — ideal for small dinners...

When you're ill the doctor often takes a blood sample for analysis. Blood tests can be used to diagnose loads of things — not just disorders of the blood. This is because the blood transports so many chemicals produced by so many organs... and it's easier to take blood than, say, a piece of muscle.

Q1 Describe the purpose of platelets in blood. [1 mark]

Q2 Outline three ways in which red blood cells are adapted to carry oxygen. [3 marks]

# Circulatory System — Blood Vessels

Want to know more about the circulatory system... Good. Because here's another page.

## Blood Vessels are Designed for Their Function

There are three different types of blood vessel:

1) ARTERIES — these carry the blood <u>away</u> from the heart.
2) CAPILLARIES — these are involved in the <u>exchange of materials</u> at the tissues.
3) VEINS — these carry the blood <u>to</u> the heart.

## Arteries Carry Blood Under Pressure

1) The heart pumps the blood out at <u>high pressure</u> so the artery walls are <u>strong</u> and <u>elastic</u>.

2) The walls are <u>thick</u> compared to the size of the hole down the middle (the "<u>lumen</u>" — silly name!).

3) They contain thick layers of <u>muscle</u> to make them <u>strong</u>, and <u>elastic fibres</u> to allow them to stretch and <u>spring back</u>.

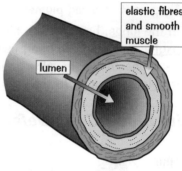

elastic fibres and smooth muscle

lumen

## Capillaries are Really Small

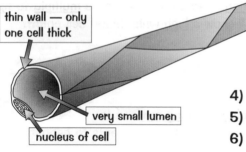

thin wall — only one cell thick

very small lumen

nucleus of cell

1) Arteries branch into <u>capillaries</u>.

2) Capillaries are really <u>tiny</u> — too small to see.

3) They are very <u>narrow</u>, so they can squeeze into the gaps between cells. This means they can carry the blood <u>really close</u> to <u>every cell</u> in the body to <u>exchange substances</u> with them.

4) They have <u>permeable walls</u>, so substances can <u>diffuse in</u> and <u>out</u>.

5) They supply <u>food</u> and <u>oxygen</u>, and take away <u>waste</u> like $CO_2$.

6) Their walls are usually <u>only one cell thick</u>. This <u>increases</u> the rate of diffusion by <u>decreasing</u> the <u>distance</u> over which it occurs.

## Veins Take Blood Back to the Heart

1) Capillaries eventually <u>join up</u> to form <u>veins</u>.

2) The blood is at <u>lower pressure</u> in the veins so the walls don't need to be as <u>thick</u> as artery walls.

3) They have a <u>bigger lumen</u> than arteries to help the blood <u>flow</u> despite the lower pressure.

4) They also have <u>valves</u> to help keep the blood flowing in the <u>right direction</u>.

large lumen

elastic fibres and smooth muscle

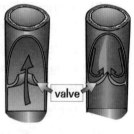

valve

## Learn this page — don't struggle in vein...

Here's an interesting fact for you — your body contains about 60 000 miles of blood vessels. That's about six times the distance from London to Sydney in Australia. Of course, capillaries are really tiny, which is how they can be such a big length — they can only be seen with a microscope.

Q1    Explain how veins are adapted to carry blood back to the heart.    [2 marks]

Q2    Explain the advantage of capillary walls being only one cell thick.    [1 mark]

# Circulatory System — The Heart

The heart basically just <u>pushes</u> the blood around — it's kind of a bully...

## Mammals Have a Double Circulatory System

1) This means that the heart pumps blood around the body in <u>two circuits</u>. In the first circuit, the heart pumps <u>deoxygenated blood</u> to the <u>lungs</u> to <u>take in oxygen</u>. Oxygenated blood then returns to the heart. In the <u>second circuit</u>, the heart pumps <u>oxygenated blood</u> around all the <u>other organs</u> of the body to deliver oxygen to the body cells. Deoxygenated blood then returns to the heart.

2) <u>Fish</u> have a <u>single circulatory system</u> — deoxygenated blood from the fish's body travels to the heart, which then pumps it <u>right round</u> the body again in a <u>single circuit</u> (via the gills where it picks up oxygen).

Lungs

Heart   Rest of body

## The Heart Pumps Blood Through the Blood Vessels

The mammalian heart has <u>four chambers</u> and <u>four major blood vessels</u>.

A fish's heart only has two chambers.

1) The <u>right atrium</u> of the heart receives <u>deoxygenated</u> blood from the <u>body</u> (through the <u>vena cava</u>).

2) The deoxygenated blood moves through to the <u>right ventricle</u>, which pumps it to the <u>lungs</u> (via the <u>pulmonary artery</u>).

3) The <u>left atrium</u> receives <u>oxygenated</u> blood from the <u>lungs</u> (through the <u>pulmonary vein</u>).

4) The oxygenated blood then moves through to the <u>left ventricle</u>, which pumps it out round the <u>whole body</u> (via the <u>aorta</u>).

The <u>left</u> ventricle has a much <u>thicker wall</u> than the <u>right</u> ventricle. It needs more <u>muscle</u> because it has to pump blood around the <u>whole body</u> at high pressure, whereas the right ventricle only has to pump it to the <u>lungs</u>. <u>Valves</u> prevent the <u>backflow</u> of blood in the heart.

Blue = deoxygenated blood.
Red = oxygenated blood.

to the lungs
to the body
pulmonary artery
aorta
vena cava
pulmonary vein

**Right Side**
right atrium
left atrium
**Left Side**

semi-lunar valves

tricuspid valve

right ventricle   left ventricle

bicuspid valve

(This is the left and right side of the person whose heart it is.)

## You Can Calculate How Much Blood is Pumped Every Minute

1) <u>Cardiac output</u> is the <u>total volume</u> of blood pumped by a ventricle every <u>minute</u>. You can calculate it using this equation:

$$\text{cardiac output} = \text{heart rate} \times \text{stroke volume}$$

in $cm^3\ min^{-1}$        in beats per minute        in $cm^3$

2) The <u>heart rate</u> is the number of <u>beats per minute</u> (bpm). The <u>stroke volume</u> is the volume of blood pumped by <u>one ventricle</u> each time it <u>contracts</u>.

3) You might be asked to find the <u>stroke volume</u> or the <u>heart rate</u> in the exam <u>instead</u> of the cardiac output — if so, you can just <u>rearrange</u> the equation above. You can use this <u>formula triangle</u> to help you:

cardiac output

heart rate   ×   stroke volume

**EXAMPLE:** What is the heart rate of a person with an average stroke volume of 72 cm³ and a cardiac output of 5420 cm³ min⁻¹?

Heart rate (bpm) = cardiac output (cm³ min⁻¹) ÷ stroke volume (cm³)
= 5420 ÷ 72 = 75 bpm

Just cover up the thing you want to find with your finger and write down what's left showing.

## Are you pumped after this page? I know I am...

Make sure you learn the diagram of the heart and all its labels. It won't be fun, but it'll help you in the exam.

Q1    Calculate the stroke volume for a heart rate of 67 bpm and a cardiac output of 4221 cm³ min⁻¹.    [2 marks]

# Respiration

You need <u>energy</u> to keep your body going. Energy comes from <u>food</u>, and it's <u>released</u> by <u>respiration</u>.

## Cellular Respiration Releases Energy

1) Respiration is <u>NOT</u> breathing in and breathing out, as you might think.

2) <u>Respiration</u> actually goes on in <u>every cell</u> of all living organisms — and it happens <u>continuously</u>.

3) It's the process of <u>transferring</u> (releasing) <u>energy</u> from the breakdown of <u>organic compounds</u> (usually <u>glucose</u>).

4) Because energy is transferred <u>to the environment</u>, respiration is an <u>exothermic reaction</u>. Some of this energy is transferred by <u>heat</u>.

5) There are <u>two types</u> of respiration, <u>aerobic</u> and <u>anaerobic</u>.

> Organic compounds are compounds containing carbon. They include carbohydrates, lipids and proteins.

The <u>energy</u> is then used for things like:
- <u>metabolic processes</u> — such as making larger molecules from smaller ones (e.g. proteins from amino acids),
- <u>contracting muscles</u> (in animals),
- <u>maintaining</u> a steady <u>body temperature</u> (in mammals and birds).

## Aerobic Respiration Needs Plenty of Oxygen

1) <u>Aerobic respiration</u> is what happens when there's <u>plenty of oxygen</u> available.

2) <u>Aerobic</u> just means "<u>with oxygen</u>" and it's the most efficient way to transfer <u>energy</u> from <u>glucose</u>.

3) This type of respiration goes on <u>all the time</u> in <u>plants</u> and <u>animals</u>. Here's the equation:

$$\text{glucose} + \text{oxygen} \longrightarrow \text{carbon dioxide} + \text{water}$$
$$C_6H_{12}O_6 + 6O_2 \longrightarrow 6CO_2 + 6H_2O$$

> This is the reverse of the photosynthesis equation (see page 47).

## Anaerobic Respiration Doesn't Use Oxygen At All

1) When you do really <u>vigorous exercise</u> your body can't supply enough <u>oxygen</u> to your muscles for aerobic respiration — even though your <u>heart rate</u> and <u>breathing rate</u> increase as much as they can. Your muscles have to start <u>respiring anaerobically</u> as well.

2) <u>Anaerobic</u> just means "<u>without</u> oxygen". It transfers much <u>less energy</u> than aerobic respiration so it's much less <u>efficient</u>. In anaerobic respiration, the glucose is only <u>partially</u> broken down, and <u>lactic acid</u> is also produced.

3) The <u>lactic acid</u> builds up in the muscles — it gets <u>painful</u> and leads to <u>cramp</u>.

4) This is the word equation for anaerobic respiration in <u>animals</u>:

$$\text{glucose} \longrightarrow \text{lactic acid}$$

## Anaerobic Respiration in Plants is Slightly Different

1) <u>Plants</u> can respire <u>without oxygen</u> too, but they produce <u>ethanol</u> (alcohol) and $CO_2$ <u>instead</u> of lactic acid.

2) This is <u>the word equation</u> for anaerobic respiration in <u>plants</u>:

> Fungi such as yeast also do anaerobic respiration like this.

$$\text{glucose} \longrightarrow \text{ethanol} + \text{carbon dioxide}$$

---

## I reckon aerobics classes should be called anaerobics instead...

You need to be able to compare anaerobic and aerobic respiration for your exam. Remember, anaerobic respiration has different products to aerobic respiration and transfers much less energy, as well as taking place without oxygen. Both aerobic and anaerobic respiration are exothermic though — don't forget that.

Q1  After five minutes of intense sprinting, a student got cramp in his leg.
Explain what caused this.

[3 marks]

# Investigating Respiration

You need to know how to <u>investigate</u> the <u>rate of respiration</u> in <u>small organisms</u> — so we've concocted a lovely little page all about it. Time to get hands on with some little critters.

## You Can Measure the Rate of Respiration Using a Respirometer

In <u>aerobic respiration</u>, organisms <u>use up oxygen</u> from the air. By measuring the amount of <u>oxygen consumed</u> by organisms in a <u>given time</u>, you can calculate their <u>rate of respiration</u>. Here's an experiment which uses <u>woodlice</u>, a <u>water bath</u> and a piece of equipment called a <u>respirometer</u>. It allows you to measure the effect of <u>temperature</u> on the <u>rate of respiration</u> of the woodlice. (You could use <u>germinating peas</u> or <u>beans</u> instead of woodlice. Germinating seeds respire to provide energy for growth.)

1) Firstly, some <u>soda lime granules</u> are added to <u>two</u> test tubes. Soda lime <u>absorbs</u> the $CO_2$ produced by the <u>respiring</u> woodlice in the experiment.

*Soda lime is corrosive. Wear safety goggles and gloves when handling it to protect your eyes and skin.*

2) A ball of <u>cotton wool</u> is placed above the <u>soda lime</u> in each tube. <u>Woodlice</u> are placed on top of the cotton wool in one tube. <u>Glass beads</u> with the <u>same mass</u> as the woodlice are used in the <u>control tube</u>. (There's more on controls on page 4.)

3) The <u>respirometer</u> is then set up as shown in the <u>diagram</u>.

*Make sure the woodlice don't come into contact with the soda lime.*

4) The <u>syringe</u> is used to set the fluid in the <u>manometer</u> to a <u>known level</u>.

5) The apparatus is then <u>left</u> for a set period of time in a <u>water bath</u> set to <u>15 °C</u>.

**A Respirometer**

syringe — calibrated scale — manometer containing coloured fluid — closed tap — live woodlice on cotton wool — soda lime granules — water bath — Test tube — Control tube — glass beads

6) During this time, there'll be a <u>decrease</u> in the <u>volume</u> of the air in the <u>test tube</u> containing the <u>woodlice</u>. This is because the woodlice <u>use up oxygen</u> in the tube as they respire. (The $CO_2$ they produce is <u>absorbed</u> by the soda lime so it doesn't affect the experiment.)

7) The decrease in volume <u>reduces the pressure</u> in the tube, causing the <u>coloured liquid</u> in the manometer to move <u>towards</u> the <u>test tube</u> containing the <u>woodlice</u>.

*You can also use cotton wool soaked in a few drops of potassium hydroxide solution to absorb the $CO_2$.*

8) The <u>distance moved</u> by the liquid in a <u>given time</u> is measured. This value can then be used to calculate the <u>volume of oxygen taken in</u> by the woodlice <u>per minute</u>. This gives you the <u>rate of respiration</u> in, e.g. cm$^3$ min$^{-1}$.

9) <u>Repeat</u> steps 1-8 with the water bath set at <u>different temperatures</u>, e.g. <u>20 °C</u> and <u>25 °C</u>. This will allow you to see how <u>changing the temperature</u> affects the rate of respiration.

Any <u>live animals</u> you use in this experiment should be treated <u>ethically</u>. E.g. it's important not to <u>leave</u> the woodlice in the respirometer for <u>too long</u>, or they may <u>run out</u> of oxygen and <u>die</u>. There's more on the ethical treatment of organisms in experiments on page 212.

## My rate of respiration has increased after all that...

Controls are mega important in experiments — they check that the thing you're observing (e.g. respiring woodlice) is what's affecting the results and nothing else. So you should make sure everything else is kept exactly the same.

Q1    A student is carrying out an experiment to measure the effect of temperature on the rate of respiration in germinating beans.

    a) What could the student use as her control?     [1 mark]

    b) What could she use to keep the beans at different temperatures?     [1 mark]

# Revision Questions for Section 8

So there you have it — all you need to know about exchange and transport.  Now it's time to test yourself...

*   Try these questions and <u>tick off each one</u> when you <u>get it right</u>.
*   When you've done <u>all the questions</u> under a heading and are <u>completely happy</u>, tick it off.

## Exchange of Materials (p.59-60) ☑

1)  Name three substances that animals have to exchange with their environment. ☑
2)  Why do multicellular organisms need specialised exchange surfaces? ☑
3)  Why do multicellular organisms need mass transport systems? ☑
4)  Where does gas exchange take place within the lungs? ☑
5)  Explain the movement of oxygen between the alveoli and the blood. ☑

## The Circulatory System (p.61-63) ☑

6)  Describe the shape of an erythrocyte. ☑
7)  What is the name of the pigment contained within red blood cells and what does it do? ☑
8)  What is the function of lymphocytes? ☑
9)  What effect would there be on the body if there weren't enough platelets? ☑
10) List four different substances that can be carried in the plasma. ☑
11) Do arteries carry blood away from or towards the heart? ☑
12) How are arteries adapted for carrying blood at high pressure? ☑
13) Why are the walls of capillaries so thin? ☑
14) What is the function of the valves found within veins? ☑
15) Write the name of the blood vessel that:
    a)  carries blood into the right atrium.
    b)  carries blood towards the lungs.
    c)  carries blood into the left atrium. ☑
16) What is the equation for cardiac output? ☑
17) How would you calculate the heart rate of an individual if you were
    given values for their cardiac output and stroke volume? ☑

## Respiration (p.64-65) ☑

18) What is the purpose of cellular respiration? ☑
19) Is respiration exothermic or endothermic?  Explain your answer. ☑
20) What is the equation for the aerobic respiration of glucose? ☑
21) Under what circumstances do muscles perform anaerobic respiration? ☑
22) When using a respirometer to measure the oxygen consumption of respiring organisms,
    what is the purpose of the soda lime in the respirometer? ☑

# Ecosystems and Interactions Between Organisms

It's tough in the wild — organisms <u>depend on each other</u> for survival.  Everybody needs good neighbours...

## Ecosystems are Organised into Different Levels

Ecosystems have <u>different levels</u> of <u>organisation</u>:

1) <u>Individual</u>  — A <u>single</u> organism.

2) <u>Population</u> — <u>All</u> the organisms of <u>one species</u> in a <u>habitat</u>.

3) <u>Community</u> — All the organisms of <u>different species</u> living in a habitat.

4) <u>Ecosystem</u> — A community of <u>organisms</u> along with all the <u>non-living</u> (<u>abiotic</u>) <u>conditions</u> (see below).

> A habitat is the place where an organism lives, e.g. a rocky shore or a field.
> A species is a group of similar organisms that can reproduce to give fertile offspring.

## Organisms in a Community Are Interdependent

1) Organisms <u>depend</u> on each other for things like <u>food</u> and <u>shelter</u> in order to <u>survive</u> and <u>reproduce</u>.  This is known as <u>interdependence</u>.  It means that a <u>change</u> in the population of <u>one species</u> can have huge <u>knock on effects</u> for <u>other species</u> in the same community.

2) <u>Mutualism</u> is a relationship between two organisms, from which <u>both</u> organisms <u>benefit</u>.  E.g. <u>bees</u> and <u>flowering plants</u> have a mutualistic relationship.  When bees visit flowers to get nectar, <u>pollen</u> is transferred to their bodies.  The bees then spread the pollen to <u>other plants</u> when they land on their flowers.  The bees get <u>food</u> and the plants get <u>help reproducing</u>.  Wahey — everyone's a winner.

3) <u>Parasites</u> live very closely with a <u>host species</u> (e.g. in or on them).  The parasite takes what it needs to survive, but the host <u>doesn't</u> benefit.  E.g. <u>fleas</u> are <u>parasites</u> of <u>mammals</u> such as <u>dogs</u>.  Fleas feed on their host's blood, but don't offer anything in return.

## Environmental Changes Affect Communities in Different Ways

The <u>environment</u> in which plants and animals live <u>changes all the time</u>.  These changes are probably caused by <u>abiotic</u> (non-living) and <u>biotic</u> (living) factors and affect communities in different ways — for some species <u>population size</u> may <u>increase</u>, for others it may <u>decrease</u>, or the <u>distribution</u> of populations (where they live) may change.  Here are some <u>examples</u> of the effects of changes in <u>abiotic</u> and <u>biotic</u> factors:

### Abiotic Factors Affect Communities...

1) <u>Temperature</u> — e.g. the distribution of <u>bird species</u> in Germany is probably changing because of a rise in average temperature.  For instance, the <u>European Bee-Eater bird</u> is a <u>Mediterranean</u> species but it's now present in parts of <u>Germany</u>.

2) <u>Amount of water</u> — e.g. <u>daisies</u> grow best in soils that are <u>slightly damp</u>.  If the soil becomes <u>waterlogged</u> or <u>too dry</u>, the population of daisies will <u>decrease</u>.

3) <u>Light intensity</u> — e.g. as trees grow and provide more <u>shade</u>, <u>grasses</u> may be replaced by <u>fungi</u> (or <u>mosses</u>, etc.) which are better able to <u>cope</u> with the <u>lower light intensity</u>.

4) <u>Levels of pollutants</u> — e.g. <u>lichen</u> are unable to survive if the concentration of <u>sulfur dioxide</u> (an <u>air pollutant</u>) is too <u>high</u>.

### ... and so do Biotic Factors

1) <u>Competition</u> — organisms <u>compete with other species</u> (and members of their own species) for the <u>same resources</u>.  E.g. red and grey <u>squirrels</u> live in the same habitat and eat the same food.  Competition with the grey squirrels for these resources in some areas means there's not enough food for the reds — the <u>population</u> of red squirrels is <u>decreasing</u>, partly as a result of this.

2) <u>Predation</u> — e.g. if the <u>number of lions</u> (predators) <u>decreases</u> then the number of <u>gazelles</u> (their prey) might <u>increase</u> because <u>fewer</u> of them will be <u>eaten</u> by the lions.

## Revision — an abiotic factor causing stress in my community...

Organisms like everything to be just right — temperature, light, food...  I'd never get away with being that fussy.

Q1    Give two abiotic factors that could affect the community in an ecosystem.                [2 marks]

# Investigating Ecosystems

Studying <u>ecology</u> gives you the chance to <u>rummage around</u> in bushes and get your hands <u>dirty</u>. It's proper fun.

## Use a Quadrat to Study The Distribution of Small Organisms

A <u>quadrat</u> is a <u>square</u> frame enclosing a <u>known area</u>, e.g. 1 m². To compare <u>how common</u> an organism is in <u>two sample areas</u> just follow these simple steps:

1) Place a <u>1 m² quadrat</u> on the ground at a <u>random point</u> within the <u>first</u> sample area. You could do this by dividing the sample area into a grid and using a random number generator to pick coordinates to place your quadrats at. This will help to make sure the results you get are <u>representative</u> of the <u>whole sample area</u>.

2) <u>Count</u> all the organisms you're interested in <u>within</u> the quadrat.

3) <u>Repeat</u> steps 1 and 2 lots of times.

4) <u>Work out</u> the <u>mean</u> number of organisms per quadrat within the first sample area.

5) <u>Repeat</u> steps 1 to 4 in the <u>second</u> sample area.

6) Finally <u>compare</u> the two means. E.g. you might find a mean of 2 daisies per m² in one area, and 22 daisies per m² (lots more) in another area.

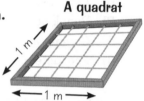

A quadrat

1 m

1 m

$$\text{Mean} = \frac{\text{total number of organisms}}{\text{number of quadrats}}$$

## Estimate Population Size by Scaling Up from a Small Sample Area

To work out the <u>population size</u> of an organism in one sample area you need to work out the <u>mean number of organisms per m²</u> (if your quadrat has an area of 1 m², this is the same as the mean number of organisms per quadrat, worked out above). Then just <u>multiply the mean</u> by the <u>total area</u> of the habitat:

**EXAMPLE:**

Students used 0.5 m² quadrats to randomly sample daisies in a field. They found a mean of 10 daisies per quadrat. The field's area was 800 m². Estimate the population of daisies in the field.

1) Work out the <u>mean number of organisms per m²</u>. 1 ÷ 0.5 = 2    2 × 10 = 20 daisies per m²

2) Multiply the <u>mean per m²</u> by the <u>total area</u> (in m²) of the habitat. 20 × 800 = 16 000 daisies in the field

## Use Belt Transects to Study Distribution Along a Gradient   PRACTICAL

Sometimes <u>abiotic factors</u> will <u>change across a habitat</u>. The change is known as a <u>gradient</u>. You can use quadrats to help find out how organisms (like plants) are <u>distributed along</u> a gradient. For example, how a species becomes <u>more or less common</u> as you move from an area of <u>shade</u> (near a hedge at the edge of a field) to an area of full sun (the middle of the field). The quadrats are laid out along a <u>line</u>, forming a <u>belt transect</u>. Here's what you do:

1) <u>Mark out a line</u> in the area you want to study, e.g. from the hedge to the middle of the field.

2) Then <u>collect data</u> along the line using <u>quadrats</u> placed <u>next to</u> each other. If your transect is <u>quite long</u>, you could place the quadrats at <u>regular intervals</u> (e.g. every 2 metres) instead. Collect data by <u>counting</u> all the organisms of the species you're interested in, or by <u>estimating percentage cover</u>. This means estimating the <u>percentage area</u> of a quadrat covered by a particular type of organism.

3) You could also <u>record</u> other data, such as the <u>mean height</u> of the plants you're counting or the <u>abiotic factors</u> in each quadrat (e.g. you could use a <u>light meter</u> to measure the light intensity).

4) <u>Repeat</u> steps 1 and 2 several times, then find the <u>mean</u> number of organisms or mean percentage cover for <u>each quadrat</u>.

5) Plot graphs to see if the <u>changing abiotic factor</u> is <u>correlated</u> with a change in the <u>distribution</u> of the species you're studying.

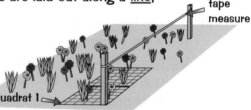

tape measure

quadrat 1

Make sure you can correctly identify the organisms you're investigating. If necessary, use books or information from the internet to help you.

## Drat, drat, and double drat — my favourite use of quadrats...

Unless you're doing a transect, it's key that you put your quadrat down in a random place before you start counting.

Q1    Describe how quadrats could be used to investigate the distribution of organisms along a gradient. [3 marks]

# Human Impacts on Biodiversity

However you look at it, we humans have a huge impact on the environment around us, including on biodiversity.

## Human Activities Affect Biodiversity

Biodiversity is the variety of living organisms in an ecosystem. Human interactions within ecosystems often affect biodiversity. Sometimes we have a positive impact on biodiversity (e.g. by carrying out conservation schemes or reforestation, see next page), but we often have a negative effect. Here are some examples:

## Fertilisers can Leach into Water and Cause Eutrophication

Nitrates are put onto fields as fertilisers (see p.73). If too much fertiliser is applied and it rains afterwards, nitrates easily find their way into rivers and lakes. The result is eutrophication — an excess of nutrients in water — which can lead to the death of many of the species present in the water, reducing the biodiversity of the habitat:

*Pollution by sewage can cause eutrophication in the same way that fertilisers do.*

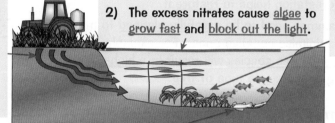

1) Fertilisers enter the water, adding excess nitrates (more than plants in the water can take in).

2) The excess nitrates cause algae to grow fast and block out the light.

3) Plants can't photosynthesise due to lack of light and start to die and decompose.

4) With more food available, microorganisms that feed on decomposing plants increase in number and use up oxygen in the water.

5) Organisms that need oxygen for aerobic respiration (e.g. fish) die.

## Fish can be Farmed in Holding Nets in Open Water

Fish farms in areas of open water (e.g. lakes or the sea) can reduce biodiversity in the surrounding area. Here's how:

1) Food is added to the nets to feed the fish, which produce huge amounts of waste. Both the food and the waste can leak into the open water, causing eutrophication and the death of wild species.

2) Fish farms in open water often act as a breeding ground for large numbers of parasites. These parasites can get out of the farm and infect wild animals, sometimes killing them.

3) Predators (e.g. sea lions) are attracted to the nets and can become trapped in them and die.

4) Sometimes farmed fish can escape into the wild, which can cause problems for wild populations of indigenous species (see below).

Sometimes fish are farmed in large tanks rather than in open water nets. These farms are low in biodiversity because often only one species is farmed, the tanks are often kept free of plants and predators, and any parasites and microorganisms are usually killed.

## The Introduction of Non-Indigenous Species Can Reduce Biodiversity

1) A non-indigenous species is one that doesn't naturally occur in an area. They can be introduced intentionally (e.g. for food or hunting) or unintentionally (e.g. as a stowaway in international cargo). The introduction of a non-indigenous species may cause problems for indigenous (native) species.

2) Non-indigenous species compete with indigenous species for resources like food and shelter. Sometimes, they are better at getting these resources and out-compete the indigenous species, which decrease in number and eventually die out. For example, signal crayfish were introduced to the UK for food, but they prey on and out-compete many indigenous river species, reducing biodiversity.

3) Non-indigenous species sometimes also bring new diseases to a habitat. These often infect and kill lots of indigenous species, reducing the habitat's biodiversity.

## My dirty gym kit definitely increases the biodiversity of my bag...

OK, there's a lot of negativity on this page, but you need to know it all for your exam. Best get cracking.

Q1      Suggest how introducing a non-indigenous species could reduce the biodiversity of an area.     [2 marks]

# Conservation and Biodiversity

Trying to conserve biodiversity can be _tricky_, given all the _challenges_ that face different ecosystems (many of which are a result of human activities). There are _benefits_ of doing this though, so it's _pretty worthwhile_...

## There Are Lots of Ways to Conserve and Maintain Biodiversity

Lots of _human activities_ can reduce biodiversity (see previous page). However, there are _plenty_ of things that we can do to _increase biodiversity_. Here are a couple of examples...

### Reforestation Can Increase Biodiversity in Deforested Areas

1) _Reforestation_ is when land where a _forest previously stood_ is _replanted_ to form a new forest.

2) Forests generally have a _high biodiversity_ because they contain a _wide variety_ of trees and plants, and these provide _food_ and _shelter_ for lots of different animal species. Deforestation _reduces_ this biodiversity by _removing_ the _trees_ (either by chopping them down or burning them). _Reforestation_ helps to _restore_ it.

3) Reforestation programmes need to be _carefully planned_ to maximise positive effects and minimise negative ones. For example, replanting a forest with a _variety of tree species_ will result in a _higher biodiversity_ than replanting using only a _single type of tree_.

### Conservation Schemes Protect At-Risk Species

1) Conservation schemes can help to _protect biodiversity_ by preventing species from dying out.

2) Conservation methods include:

- _Protecting_ a species' _natural habitat_ (so that individuals have a place to live).
- _Protecting_ species in _safe areas_ outside of their natural habitat (e.g. animals can be protected in _zoos_) and introducing _captive breeding programmes_ to increase numbers.
- The use of _seed banks_ to store and distribute the seeds of rare and endangered plants.

### Maintaining Biodiversity Has Many Benefits

There are lots of _benefits_ to both _wildlife_ and _humans_ of _maintaining biodiversity_ on a _local_ and _global_ scale.

1) _Protecting the human food supply_ — over-fishing has _greatly reduced fish stocks_ in the world's oceans. Conservation programmes can ensure that future generations will have _fish to eat_.

2) _Ensuring minimal damage to food chains_ — if _one species_ becomes _extinct_ it will affect all the organisms that feed on and are eaten by that species, so the _whole food chain_ is affected. This means _conserving one species_ may _help others_ to survive.

3) _Providing future medicines_ — many of the medicines we use today come from _plants_. Undiscovered plant species may contain _new medicinal chemicals_. If these plants are allowed to become _extinct_, e.g. through _rainforest destruction_, we could miss out on valuable medicines.

4) _Cultural aspects_ — individual species may be important in a nation's or an area's cultural heritage, e.g. the _bald eagle_ is being conserved in the USA as it is regarded as a _national symbol_.

5) _Ecotourism_ — people are drawn to visit beautiful, _unspoilt_ landscapes with a _variety_ of _animal_ and _plant species_. Ecotourism (environmentally-friendly tourism) helps _bring money_ into _biodiverse areas_ where conservation work is taking place.

6) _Providing new jobs_ — things such as ecotourism, conservation schemes and reforestation schemes provide _employment opportunities_ for _local people_.

## If a reforested area is cut down again, is that redeforestation...

Well who knew protecting biodiversity had so many advantages. That's the last time I vacuum up a spider...

Q1     Explain how reforestation affects biodiversity.          [3 marks]

# The Carbon Cycle

Recycling may be a buzz word for us but it's old school for nature. All the nutrients in our environment are constantly being recycled — there's a nice balance between what goes in and what goes out again.

## Materials are Constantly Recycled in an Ecosystem

1) An ecosystem is all the organisms living in an area, as well as all the non-living conditions, e.g. soil quality, availability of water, temperature.

There's more on ecosystems on page 67.

2) Materials are recycled through both the living (biotic) and non-living (abiotic) components of ecosystems:

   1) Living things are made of elements they take from the environment, e.g. plants take in carbon and oxygen from the air and nitrogen from the soil.

   2) They turn these elements into the complex compounds (carbohydrates, proteins and fats) that make up living organisms. Elements are passed along food chains when animals eat the plants and each other.

   3) The elements are recycled — waste products and dead organisms are broken down by decomposers (usually microorganisms) and the elements in them are returned to the soil or air, ready to be taken in by new plants and put back into the food chain.

## The Carbon Cycle Shows How Carbon is Recycled

Carbon is an important element in the materials that living things are made from. But there's only a fixed amount of carbon in the world. This means it's constantly recycled:

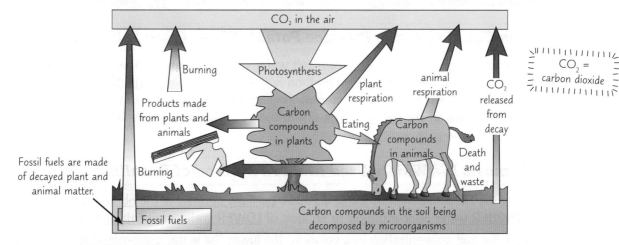

$CO_2$ = carbon dioxide

This diagram isn't half as bad as it looks. Learn these important points:

1) There's only one arrow going down from $CO_2$ in the air. The whole thing is 'powered' by photosynthesis. Green plants use the carbon from $CO_2$ to make carbohydrates, fats and proteins.
2) Eating passes the carbon compounds in the plant along to animals in a food chain.
3) Both plant and animal respiration while the organisms are alive releases $CO_2$ back into the air.
4) Plants and animals eventually die and decompose, or are killed and turned into useful products.
5) When plants and animals decompose they're broken down by microorganisms, such as bacteria and fungi. These decomposers release $CO_2$ back into the air by respiration, as they break down the material.
6) Some useful plant and animal products, e.g. wood and fossil fuels, are burned (combustion). This also releases $CO_2$ back into the air.
7) Decomposition of materials means that habitats can be maintained for the organisms that live there, e.g. nutrients are returned to the soil and waste material, such as dead leaves, doesn't just pile up.

## Carbon cycle — isn't that what Wiggo rides...

Carbon atoms are very important — they're found in plants, animals, your petrol tank and on your burnt toast.

Q1    Describe the role of microorganisms in the carbon cycle.                    [3 marks]

# The Water Cycle

Next time you get <u>soaked</u> on your way to school and moan about the <u>rain</u>, think back to this page and spare a thought for the <u>water cycle</u> — the underrated natural phenomenon that helps keep us all <u>alive</u>.

## *The Water Cycle Means Water is Endlessly Recycled*

The water here on planet Earth is constantly <u>recycled</u>. Strange but true...

1) <u>Energy</u> from the <u>Sun</u> makes water <u>evaporate</u> from the land and sea, turning it into <u>water vapour</u>. Water also evaporates from plants — this is known as <u>transpiration</u> (see p.49).

2) The warm water vapour is <u>carried upwards</u> (as warm air rises). When it gets higher up it <u>cools</u> and <u>condenses</u> to form <u>clouds</u>.

3) Water falls from the clouds as <u>precipitation</u> (usually rain, but sometimes snow or hail) onto <u>land</u>, where it provides <u>fresh water</u> for <u>plants</u> and <u>animals</u>.

4) It then <u>drains</u> into the <u>sea</u> and the whole process starts again.

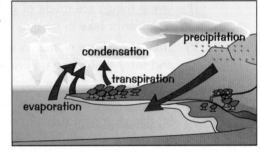

If it wasn't for the water cycle constantly recycling water, we'd quickly <u>run out</u> of the stuff. That would be <u>reeeeeally bad</u> news because all living things on our planet <u>need</u> water to <u>survive</u>.

## *A Drought Occurs When There Isn't Enough Precipitation*

Droughts can cause <u>big problems</u>, partly because we rely on <u>precipitation</u> to get <u>fresh water</u> for <u>drinking</u> (sea water is too salty). Luckily, in times of drought, there are methods we can use to produce <u>potable water</u> (water that's suitable for drinking). One of these methods is called <u>desalination</u>.

## *Desalination Can Be Used to Produce Potable Water From Salt Water*

Desalination removes <u>salts</u> (<u>mineral ions</u>) from salt water (e.g. sea water). There are a few <u>different methods</u> of desalination. One really <u>simple</u> method is <u>thermal desalination</u> (<u>distillation</u>). This is where salt water is <u>boiled</u> in a large enclosed vessel, so that the water <u>evaporates</u>. The steam <u>rises</u> to the top of the vessel, but the salts stay at the <u>bottom</u>. The steam then travels down a pipe from the top of the vessel and <u>condenses</u> back into <u>pure water</u>.

## *Reverse Osmosis Is a Widely Used Modern Method of Desalination*

1) <u>Osmosis</u> is the net movement of <u>water</u> across a <u>partially permeable membrane</u>, from an area of <u>HIGHER water concentration</u> to an area of <u>LOWER water concentration</u> (see page 18).

2) The <u>higher</u> the <u>salt concentration</u> in a solution, the <u>lower</u> the <u>water concentration</u>, so you could also say that osmosis is the net movement of water from an area of <u>LOWER salt concentration</u> to an area of <u>HIGHER salt concentration</u>.

3) <u>Reverse osmosis</u> reverses this process to <u>get rid of impurities</u> in water. Here's how:

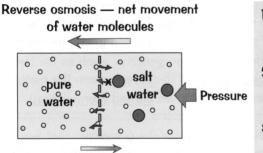

Reverse osmosis — net movement of water molecules

pure water

salt water

Pressure

Normal osmosis

1) Salt water is first <u>treated</u> to remove solids, before being fed at a very <u>high pressure</u> into a vessel containing a <u>partially permeable membrane</u>.

2) The pressure causes the water molecules to move in the <u>opposite direction</u> to <u>osmosis</u> — from a <u>higher salt concentration</u> to a <u>lower salt concentration</u>.

3) As the water is forced through the membrane, the <u>salts</u> are <u>left behind</u>, <u>removing</u> them from the water.

## *Come on out, it's only a little water cycle, it won't hurt you...*

Make sure you really understand the water cycle and how desalination produces fresh water before you turn over.

Q1    Explain how water from the sea can eventually fall as rain.    [4 marks]

# The Nitrogen Cycle

Just like carbon and water, nitrogen is constantly being recycled.

## Nitrogen is Recycled in the Nitrogen Cycle

1) The atmosphere contains 78% nitrogen gas, $N_2$. This is very unreactive and so it can't be used directly by plants or animals. Nitrogen is needed for making proteins for growth, so living organisms have to get it somehow.

2) Nitrogen in the air has to be turned into mineral ions such as nitrates before plants can use it. Plants absorb these mineral ions from the soil and use the nitrogen in them to make proteins. Nitrogen is then passed along food chains in the form of proteins, as animals eat plants (and each other).

3) Decomposers (bacteria and fungi in the soil) break down proteins in rotting plants and animals, and urea in animal waste (see below). This returns the nitrogen to the soil — so the nitrogen in these organisms is recycled.

4) Nitrogen fixation is the process of turning $N_2$ from the air into nitrogen-containing ions in the soil which plants can use.
   There are two main ways that this happens:
   a) Lightning — there's so much energy in a bolt of lightning that it's enough to make nitrogen react with oxygen in the air to give nitrates.
   b) Nitrogen-fixing bacteria in roots and soil (see below).

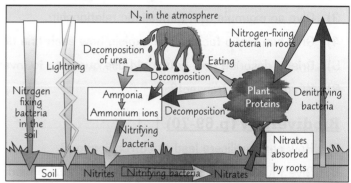

5) There are four different types of bacteria involved in the nitrogen cycle:
   a) DECOMPOSERS — decompose proteins and urea and turn them into ammonia. Ammonia forms ammonium ions in solution that plants can use.
   b) NITRIFYING BACTERIA — turn ammonia in decaying matter into nitrites and then into nitrates. Different species of nitrifying bacteria are responsible for producing nitrites and nitrates.
   c) NITROGEN-FIXING BACTERIA — turn atmospheric $N_2$ into ammonia, which forms ammonium ions.
   d) DENITRIFYING BACTERIA — turn nitrates back into $N_2$ gas. This is of no benefit to living organisms. Denitryfying bacteria are often found in waterlogged soils.

6) Some nitrogen-fixing bacteria live in the soil. Others live in nodules on the roots of legume plants (e.g. peas and beans). When these plants decompose, the nitrogen stored in them and in their nodules is returned to the soil. Nitrogen ions can also leak out of the nodules during plant growth. The plants have a mutualistic relationship (see page 67) with the bacteria — the bacteria get food (sugars) from the plant, and the plant gets nitrogen ions from the bacteria to make into proteins.

## Farmers Can Increase the Amount of Nitrates in the Soil

Like all plants, crops take up nitrates from the soil as they grow. But crops are harvested, rather than being left to die and decompose, so the nitrogen they contain isn't returned to the soil. Over time, the nitrogen content of the soil decreases, leading to poor crop growth and deficiency diseases. So farmers have ways of increasing the amount of nitrates in the soil to help their crops grow better:

1) CROP ROTATION — This is where, instead of growing the same crop in a field year after year, different crops are grown each year in a cycle. The cycle usually includes a nitrogen-fixing crop (e.g. peas or beans), which helps to put nitrates back into the soil for another crop to use the following year.

2) FERTILISERS — Spreading animal manure or compost on fields recycles the nutrients left in plant and animal waste and returns them to the soil through decomposition. Artificial fertilisers containing nitrates (and other mineral ions needed by plants) can also be used, but these can be expensive.

## It's the cyyyycle, the cyycle of liiiiife...

Bacteria do a lot of the hard work in the nitrogen cycle. Aided by a bolt or two of lightning. Naturally.

Q1     Describe how the nitrogen compounds in dead leaves are turned into nitrates in the soil.          [3 marks]

# Revision Questions for Section 9

Well, that was a bit of a mucky section if you ask me. All that <u>fieldwork</u>, <u>farming</u> and <u>bacteria</u> — I feel like I need a hot bath now to freshen up a bit. Anyway, there's no lounging about in the bath for you...

* Try these questions and <u>tick off each one</u> when you <u>get it right</u>.
* When you've done <u>all the questions</u> under a heading and are <u>completely happy</u>, tick it off.

## Ecosystems (p.67-68) ☑

1) Define the following terms:
   a) population,
   b) community,
   c) ecosystem.
2) What does it mean if two species are interdependent?
3) Give an example of a mutualistic relationship.
4) Give two biotic factors and explain how each one could affect a community.
5) Briefly describe how you could use quadrats to investigate the population size of a species.
6) What is a belt transect?

## Biodiversity (p.69-70) ☐

7) How can fertilisers lead to eutrophication?
8) Give four ways in which fish farms can reduce biodiversity.
9) What is a non-indigenous species?
10) Give three examples of conservation schemes.
11) Give three benefits of maintaining biodiversity.

## The Carbon, Water and Nitrogen Cycles (p.71-73) ☐

12) Name the process that removes carbon from the air in the carbon cycle.
13) Name two processes that put carbon back into the air.
14) Produce a labelled diagram of the water cycle.
15) Why is the ability to produce potable water important in times of drought?
16) What does desalination mean?
17) Name a common method of desalination.
18) Describe the role of nitrogen-fixing bacteria in the nitrogen cycle.
19) What is crop rotation?
20) Why is crop rotation beneficial to farmers?

# Chemical Equations

If you're going to get anywhere in chemistry you need to know about <u>chemical equations</u>...

## Chemical Changes are Shown Using Chemical Equations

One way to show a chemical reaction is to write a <u>word equation</u>. It's not as <u>useful</u> as using chemical symbols because you can't tell straight away <u>what's happened</u> to each of the <u>atoms</u>, but it's <u>dead easy</u>.

Here's an example — <u>methane</u> burns in <u>oxygen</u> giving <u>carbon dioxide</u> and <u>water</u>:

The molecules on the <u>left-hand side</u> of the equation are called the <u>reactants</u> (because they react with each other).

methane + oxygen  →  carbon dioxide + water

The molecules on the <u>right-hand side</u> are called the <u>products</u> (because they've been produced from the reactants).

## Symbol Equations Show the Atoms on Both Sides

Chemical <u>changes</u> can be shown in a kind of <u>shorthand</u> using symbol equations. Symbol equations just show the <u>symbols</u> or <u>formulas</u> of the <u>reactants</u> and <u>products</u>...

$$\text{magnesium + oxygen} \quad \xrightarrow{\phantom{xx}} \quad \text{magnesium oxide}$$
$$2Mg \quad + \quad O_2 \qquad\qquad 2MgO$$

## Symbol Equations Need to be Balanced

1) There must always be the <u>same</u> number of atoms of each element on <u>both sides</u> of the equation — atoms can't just <u>disappear</u>.

2) You <u>balance</u> the equation by putting numbers <u>in front</u> of the formulas where needed. Take this equation for reacting sulfuric acid with sodium hydroxide:

$$H_2SO_4 + NaOH \rightarrow Na_2SO_4 + H_2O$$

3) The <u>formulas</u> are all correct but the numbers of some atoms <u>don't match up</u> on both sides.

4) You <u>can't change formulas</u> like $H_2SO_4$ to $H_2SO_5$. You can only put numbers <u>in front of them</u>.

The more you <u>practise</u>, the <u>quicker</u> you get, but all you do is this:

- Find an element that <u>doesn't balance</u> and <u>pencil in a number</u> to try and sort it out.
- <u>See where it gets you</u>. It may create <u>another imbalance</u>, but if so, pencil in <u>another number</u> and see where that gets you.
- Carry on chasing <u>unbalanced</u> elements and it'll <u>sort itself out</u> pretty quickly.

**EXAMPLE:** In the equation above you'll notice you're short of <u>H atoms</u> on the RHS (Right-Hand Side).

1) The only thing you can do about that is make it <u>$2H_2O$</u> instead of just $H_2O$:

$$H_2SO_4 \quad + \quad NaOH \quad \rightarrow \quad Na_2SO_4 + 2H_2O$$

2) But that now gives <u>too many</u> H atoms and O atoms on the RHS, so to balance that up you could try putting a <u>2</u> in front of the <u>NaOH</u> on the LHS (Left-Hand Side):

$$H_2SO_4 \quad + \quad 2NaOH \quad \rightarrow \quad Na_2SO_4 + 2H_2O$$

Putting a 2 in front of the NaOH has sorted out the Na atoms too.

3) And suddenly there it is — <u>everything balances</u>.

## Revision is all about getting the balance right...

Balancing equations is all about practice. Once you have a few goes you'll see it's much less scary than it seemed before you took on, challenged and defeated this page. Go grab some chemistry glory.

Q1   Balance the equation: $Fe + Cl_2 \rightarrow FeCl_3$                     [1 mark]

Q2   Hydrogen and oxygen molecules are formed in a reaction where water splits apart.
     For this reaction: a) State the word equation.   b) Give a balanced symbol equation.   [3 marks]

# Chemical Equations Involving Ions

If you thought that was all there was to know about chemical equations, prepare to be sorely disappointed...

## State Symbols Tell You the State of a Substance in an Equation

You saw on the last page how a chemical reaction can be shown using a word equation or a symbol equation. Symbol equations can also include state symbols next to each substance — they tell you what physical state (see page 97) the reactants and products are in:

**(s) — solid    (l) — liquid    (g) — gas    (aq) — aqueous**

*'Aqueous' means 'dissolved in water'.*

Example: Aqueous hydrochloric acid reacts with solid calcium carbonate to form aqueous calcium chloride, liquid water and carbon dioxide gas: $2HCl_{(aq)} + CaCO_{3(s)} \rightarrow CaCl_{2(aq)} + H_2O_{(l)} + CO_{2(g)}$

## You Need to Learn the Formulas of Some Simple Compounds and Ions

1) It's a good idea to learn the chemical formulas of these common molecules. They crop up all the time.

- Water — $H_2O$
- Ammonia — $NH_3$
- Carbon dioxide — $CO_2$
- Hydrogen — $H_2$
- Chlorine — $Cl_2$
- Oxygen — $O_2$

2) You also need to be able to recall the formulas of certain ions.

3) For single atoms, you can use the periodic table to work out what charges their ions will form (see page 83).

*Ions form when atoms, or groups of atoms, gain or lose electrons to form charged particles (see page 83).*

4) For ions made up of groups of atoms, it's not so simple. You just have to learn these ones.

- Ammonium — $NH_4^+$
- Hydroxide — $OH^-$
- Nitrate — $NO_3^-$
- Carbonate — $CO_3^{2-}$
- Sulfate — $SO_4^{2-}$

## Ionic Equations Show Just the Useful Bits of Reactions

1) You can also write an ionic equation for any reaction involving ions that happens in solution.

2) In an ionic equation, only the reacting particles (and the products they form) are included.

3) To write an ionic equation, all you need to do is look at the balanced symbol equation and take out any aqueous ions that are present on both sides of the equation.

*You should make sure your symbol equation is balanced before you start trying to write the ionic equation (see the last page for more on how to balance symbol equations).*

**EXAMPLE:**  Write the ionic equation for the following reaction:
$$CaCl_{2\,(aq)} + 2NaOH_{(aq)} \rightarrow Ca(OH)_{2\,(s)} + 2NaCl_{(aq)}$$

1) Anything that's ionic (i.e. made of ions — see page 83) and aqueous will break up into its ions in solution. So, write out the equation showing all the aqueous ions separately.

$$Ca^{2+}_{(aq)} + 2Cl^-_{(aq)} + 2Na^+_{(aq)} + 2OH^-_{(aq)} \rightarrow Ca(OH)_{2\,(s)} + 2Na^+_{(aq)} + 2Cl^-_{(aq)}$$

2) To get to the ionic equation, cross out anything that's the same on both sides of the equation — here, those are the $Na^+$ and $Cl^-$ ions.

$$Ca^{2+}_{(aq)} + \cancel{2Cl^-}_{(aq)} + \cancel{2Na^+}_{(aq)} + 2OH^-_{(aq)} \rightarrow Ca(OH)_{2\,(s)} + \cancel{2Na^+}_{(aq)} + \cancel{2Cl^-}_{(aq)}$$

$$Ca^{2+}_{(aq)} + 2OH^-_{(aq)} \rightarrow Ca(OH)_{2\,(s)}$$

The overall charge should be the same on both sides. Here, charge on RHS = 0 and charge on LHS = (2+) + (2 × 1–) = 0.

## I'm in a Texan percussion band — we're called the state cymbals...

Ionic equations are trouble if you ask me. All those pesky ions messing things up. Better get some practice in...

Q1    Write the ionic equation for the following reaction: $HNO_{3\,(aq)} + NaOH_{(aq)} \rightarrow NaNO_{3\,(aq)} + H_2O_{(l)}$    [1 mark]

# Hazards and Risk

Chemistry's a risky business. It's not like maths, where the most dangerous thing you might come across is an awkward long division. When you're doing chemistry, you could be dealing with properly dangerous chemicals...

## You Need to Learn the Common Hazard Symbols

1) A hazard is anything that has the potential to cause harm or damage. The risk associated with that hazard is the probability of someone (or something) being harmed if they are exposed to the hazard.

2) Lots of the chemicals you'll meet in chemistry can be bad for you or dangerous in some way. That's why the chemical containers will normally have symbols on them to tell you what the dangers are.

3) Understanding these symbols means you'll be able to use suitable safe-working procedures in the lab.

 **Oxidising**
Provides oxygen which allows other materials to burn more fiercely.
Example: Liquid oxygen.

**Harmful**
Can cause irritation, reddening or blistering of the skin.
Example: Bleach.

 **Environmental Hazard**
Harmful to organisms and to the environment.
Example: Mercury.

 **Highly Flammable**
Catches fire easily.
Example: Petrol.

 **Toxic**
Can cause death by, e.g. swallowing, breathing in, absorption through skin.
Example: Hydrogen cyanide.

 **Corrosive**
Destroys materials, including living tissues (e.g. eyes and skin).
Example: Concentrated sulfuric acid.

## Experiments Involve Risks and Hazards

1) Many chemistry experiments have risks associated with them. These can include risks associated with the equipment you're using (e.g. the risk of burning from an electric heater) as well as risks associated with chemicals (see above).

2) When you plan an experiment, you need to identify all the hazards and what the risk is from each hazard. This includes working out how likely it is that something could go wrong, and how serious it would be if it did. You then need to think of ways to reduce these risks. This procedure is called a risk assessment.

Err... Doug, it's meant to be a risk assessment

Example: A student is going to react a solution of sodium hydroxide with hydrochloric acid to form a metal salt and water. Identify any hazards in this experiment, and suggest how they could reduce the risk.

Sodium hydroxide and hydrochloric acid are harmful at low concentrations and corrosive at high concentrations. Harmful substances can cause blistering or reddening of the skin, but corrosive substances are much more dangerous if they come into contact with your skin or eyes.
To reduce the risks posed by these hazards, the student should try to use low concentrations of the substances if possible, and wear gloves, a lab coat and goggles when handling the chemicals.

## I always carry out a risk assessment on my cuppa — safe-tea first...

Not only do you need to know this stuff for your exam, you need to know it if you're going to safely carry out any experiments in the lab. With all those dangerous chemicals, this page just might save you from a nasty accident.

Q1    A student is carrying out an experiment using two chemicals.
Chemical A is corrosive while chemical B is highly flammable. Suggest appropriate safety
precautions the student could take to minimise the risk associated with the chemicals.    [2 marks]

# The History of the Atom

Atoms are pretty tiny.  But what exactly are they like?  Scientists have been trying to work it out for years...

## The Theory of Atomic Structure Has Changed

Atoms are the tiny particles of matter (stuff that has a mass) which make up everything in the universe...

1)  At the start of the 19th century, John Dalton described atoms as solid spheres, and said that different spheres made up the different elements.

2)  In 1897, J J Thomson concluded from his experiments that atoms weren't solid spheres.  His measurements of charge and mass showed that an atom must contain even smaller, negatively charged particles — electrons. The 'solid sphere' idea of atomic structure had to be changed. The new theory was known as the 'plum pudding model'.

electrons

positively charged 'pudding'

delicious pudding

## Rutherford Showed that the Plum Pudding Model Was Wrong

1)  In 1909, Ernest Rutherford and his students, Hans Geiger and Ernest Marsden, conducted the famous gold foil experiment.  They fired positively charged alpha particles at an extremely thin sheet of gold.

2)  From the plum pudding model, they were expecting the particles to pass straight through the sheet or be slightly deflected at most.  This was because the positive charge of each atom was thought to be very spread out through the 'pudding' of the atom.  But, whilst most of the particles did go straight through the gold sheet, some were deflected more than expected, and a small number were deflected backwards. So the plum pudding model couldn't be right.

3)  Rutherford came up with the theory of the nuclear atom to explain this new evidence.  In this, there's a tiny, positively charged nucleus at the centre, surrounded by a 'cloud' of negative electrons — most of the atom's empty space.

A few particles are deflected backwards by the nucleus.

Most of the particles pass through empty space.

## The Refined Bohr Model Explains a Lot

1)  Scientists realised that electrons in a 'cloud' around the nucleus of an atom, as Rutherford described, would be attracted to the nucleus, causing the atom to collapse.  Niels Bohr proposed a new model of the atom where all the electrons were contained in shells.

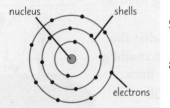

nucleus    shells

electrons

2)  Bohr suggested that electrons can only exist in fixed orbits, or shells, and not anywhere in between.  Each shell has a fixed energy.

3)  Bohr's theory of atomic structure was supported by many experiments and it helped to explain lots of other scientists' observations at the time.  It was pretty close to our currently accepted version of the atom (see next page).

## Scientific Theories Have to be Backed Up by Evidence

1)  So, our current model of the atom is completely different to what people thought the atom looked like in the past.  These different ideas were accepted because they fitted the evidence available at the time.

2)  As scientists did more experiments, new evidence was found and our theory of the structure of the atom was modified to fit it.  This is nearly always the way scientific knowledge develops — new evidence prompts people to come up with new, improved ideas.  These ideas can be used to make predictions which, if proved correct, are a pretty good indication that the ideas are right.

3)  Scientists also put their ideas and research up for peer review.  This means everyone gets a chance to see the new ideas, check for errors and then other scientists can use it to help develop their own work.

## I love a good model — Kate Moss is my personal favourite...

This is a great example of how science works.  Scientists working together to find evidence.  Lovely.

Q1    Describe the gold foil experiment and how it disproved the plum pudding model of the atom.    [4 marks]

Q2    Draw and label a diagram to show the Bohr model of the atom.    [2 marks]

# The Atom

All substances are made of <u>atoms</u>. They're really <u>tiny</u> — too small to see, even with a microscope.

## Atoms Contain Protons, Neutrons and Electrons

The atom is made up of three <u>subatomic particles</u> — protons, neutrons and electrons.

- <u>Protons</u> are <u>heavy</u> and <u>positively charged</u>.
- <u>Neutrons</u> are <u>heavy</u> and <u>neutral</u>.
- <u>Electrons</u> have <u>hardly any mass</u> and are <u>negatively charged</u>.

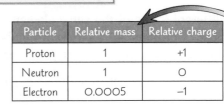

| Particle | Relative mass | Relative charge |
|----------|---------------|-----------------|
| Proton | 1 | +1 |
| Neutron | 1 | 0 |
| Electron | 0.0005 | −1 |

*Relative mass (measured in atomic mass units) measures mass on a scale where the mass of a proton or neutron is 1.*

*Protons and neutrons are still teeny tiny — they're just heavy compared to electrons.*

### The Nucleus

1) It's in the <u>middle</u> of the atom.
2) It contains <u>protons</u> and <u>neutrons</u>.
3) It has a <u>positive charge</u> because of the protons.
4) Almost the <u>whole</u> mass of the atom is <u>concentrated</u> in the nucleus.
5) Compared to the overall size of the atom, the nucleus is <u>tiny</u>.

### The Electrons

1) Electrons move <u>around</u> the nucleus in electron <u>shells</u>.
2) They're <u>negatively charged</u>.
3) They're <u>tiny</u>, but their orbitals cover <u>a lot of space</u>.
4) The <u>size</u> of their orbitals determines the size of the atom. Atoms have a radius (known as the atomic radius) of about $10^{-10}$ m.
5) Electrons have a <u>tiny</u> mass (so small that it's sometimes given as zero).

*Houston, we're in orbit.*

## In an Atom the Number of Protons Equals the Number of Electrons

1) Atoms are <u>neutral</u> — they have <u>no charge</u> overall (unlike ions).
2) This is because they have the <u>same number</u> of <u>protons</u> as <u>electrons</u>.
3) The <u>charge</u> on the electrons is the <u>same</u> size as the charge on the <u>protons</u>, but <u>opposite</u> — so the charges <u>cancel out</u>.
4) In an ion, the number of protons <u>doesn't equal</u> the number of <u>electrons</u>. This means it has an <u>overall charge</u>. For example, an ion with a <u>2− charge</u>, has <u>two more</u> electrons than protons.

*An ion is an atom or group of atoms that has lost or gained electrons.*

## Atomic Number and Mass Number Describe an Atom

1) The <u>nuclear symbol</u> of an atom tells you its <u>atomic (proton) number</u> and <u>mass number</u>.
2) The <u>atomic number</u> tells you how many <u>protons</u> an atom has. Every atom of an element has the <u>same number of protons</u>.
3) For a <u>neutral</u> atom, the number of protons equals the number of electrons, so the number of electrons equals the <u>atomic number</u>.
4) The <u>mass number</u> tells you the <u>total number</u> of <u>protons and neutrons</u> in the atom.
5) To work out the number of <u>neutrons</u> in an atom, just subtract the <u>atomic number</u> from the <u>mass number</u>.

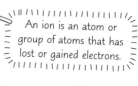

Nuclear symbol for sodium.

Mass number → 23
Atomic number → 11
**Na**
Element symbol

*In some notations and periodic tables (like the one on the data sheet in the exam), these numbers are the other way round. Just remember the bigger one is the mass number.*

## Don't trust atoms — they make up everything...

You need to learn what's in that table with the relative masses and relative charges of the different parts of the atom.

Q1 A certain neutral atom of potassium has an atomic number of 19 and a mass number of 39.
Give the number of electrons, protons and neutrons in the atom. [3 marks]

# Isotopes and Relative Atomic Mass

Atoms were reasonably straightforward weren't they?  Think again.  Here come isotopes to confuse everything.

## Isotopes are the Same Except for Extra Neutrons

1) Isotopes are different forms of the same element, which have the same number of protons but a different number of neutrons.

2) So isotopes have the same atomic number but different mass numbers.

3) A very popular example of a pair of isotopes is carbon-12 and carbon-13.

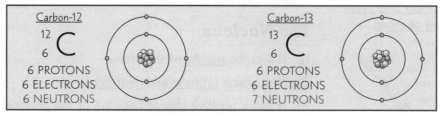

Carbon-12
$^{12}_{6}C$
6 PROTONS
6 ELECTRONS
6 NEUTRONS

Carbon-13
$^{13}_{6}C$
6 PROTONS
6 ELECTRONS
7 NEUTRONS

Remember — the number of neutrons is just the mass number minus the atomic number.

## Relative Atomic Mass Takes Isotopes Into Account

1) In the periodic table, the elements all have two numbers next to them. The bigger one is the relative atomic mass ($A_r$) of the element.

relative atomic mass

$^{4}_{2}He$    $^{12}_{6}C$

> The relative atomic mass of an element is the average mass of one atom of the element, compared to $\frac{1}{12}$ of the mass of one atom of carbon-12.

2) If an element only has one isotope, its $A_r$ will be the same as its mass number (see last page).

3) If an element has more than one isotope, its $A_r$ is the average of the mass numbers of all the different isotopes, taking into account how much there is of each one.  So, it might not be a whole number.

> For example, chlorine has two stable isotopes, chlorine-35 and chlorine-37.  There's quite a lot of chlorine-35 around and not so much chlorine-37 — so chlorine's $A_r$ works out as 35.5.

## $A_r$ Can Be Worked Out from Isotopic Abundances

1) Different isotopes of an element occur in different quantities, or isotopic abundances.

2) You need to know how to calculate the relative atomic mass of an element from its isotopic abundances.

3) To work out the relative atomic mass of an element, you need to find the average mass of all its atoms.  Here's how...

- Multiply each relative isotopic mass by its isotopic abundance, and add up the results.
- Divide by the sum of the abundances.  (If the abundances are given as percentages, this will be 100.)

**EXAMPLE:** Boron has two isotopes, boron-10 and boron-11. Given that the relative abundances or boron-10 and boron-11 are 4 and 16 respectively, work out the relative atomic mass of boron.

1) Multiply each relative isotopic mass by its relative abundance, then add up the results.

$(10 \times 4) + (11 \times 16) = 216$

2) Divide this by the sum of the isotopic abundances.

$216 \div (16 + 4) = 10.8$

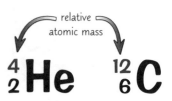

## It's elemental my dear Watson...

Atoms, elements and isotopes — make sure you know what they are and the differences between them.

Q1    Bromine has an atomic number of 35 and has two stable isotopes — bromine-79 and bromine-81. Given that 51% of bromine atoms are bromine-79, and 49% are bromine-81, work out the relative atomic mass of bromine.  Give your answer to the nearest whole number.    [2 marks]

# The Periodic Table

We haven't always known as much about chemistry as we do now. No sirree. Take the periodic table. Early chemists looked to try and find patterns in the elements' properties to understand a bit more about them.

## Dmitri Mendeleev Made the First Proper Periodic Table

1) In 1869, Dmitri Mendeleev arranged the 50 or so elements known at the time into a Table of Elements.

2) He began by sorting the elements into groups, based on their properties (and the properties of their compounds).

3) As he did this, he realised that if he put the elements in order of atomic mass, a pattern appeared — he could put elements with similar chemical properties in columns.

Mendeleev's Table of the Elements

| H | | | | | | | | | | | | | | | | | |
|---|---|---|---|---|---|---|---|---|---|---|---|---|---|---|---|---|---|
| Li | Be | | | | | | | | | | | B | C | N | O | F |
| Na | Mg | | | | | | | | | | | Al | Si | P | S | Cl |
| K | Ca | * | Ti | V | Cr | Mn | Fe | Co | Ni | Cu | Zn | * | * | As | Se | Br |
| Rb | Sr | Y | Zr | Nb | Mo | * | Ru | Rh | Pd | Ag | Cd | In | Sn | Sb | Te | I |
| Cs | Ba | * | * | Ta | W | * | Os | Ir | Pt | Au | Hg | Tl | Pb | Bi | | |

4) A few elements, however, seemed to end up in the wrong columns. In some cases this was because the atomic mass Mendeleev had was wrong (due to the presence of isotopes) — but some elements just didn't quite fit the pattern. Wherever this happened, he switched the order of the elements to keep those with the same properties in the same columns.

5) To keep elements with similar properties together, Mendeleev also had to leave some gaps (shown by the *s in the table above). He used the properties of the other elements in the columns with the gaps to predict the properties of undiscovered elements. When they were found and they fitted the pattern, it helped to confirm his ideas. For example, Mendeleev predicted the chemical and physical properties of an element he called ekasilicon, which we know today as germanium.

## This is How the Periodic Table Looks Today

1) Once protons and electrons were discovered, the atomic number (see p.79) of each element could be found, based on the number of protons in its nucleus. The modern periodic table shows the elements in order of ascending atomic number — and they fit the same patterns that Mendeleev worked out.

2) The periodic table is laid out so elements with similar chemical properties form columns called groups.

3) The group to which the element belongs corresponds to the number of electrons it has in its outer shell. E.g. Group 1 elements have 1 outer shell electron, Group 7 elements have 7, etc. Group 0 elements are the exception — they have full outer shells of 8 electrons (or 2 in the case of helium).

4) The rows are called periods. Each new period represents another full shell of electrons (see next page).

5) The period to which the element belongs corresponds to the number of shells of electrons it has.

## These jokes are tested for funniness — periodically...

You can use your old mate the periodic table to make predictions about how reactions will occur. How neat is that?

Q1 Based on its position in the periodic table, would you expect the chemical properties of potassium to be more similar to those of sodium or calcium? Explain your answer. [2 marks]

# Electronic Configurations

Like snails, electrons live in shells. Unlike snails, electrons won't nibble on your petunias...

## Electron Shell Rules:

1) Electrons always occupy shells (sometimes called energy levels).
2) The lowest energy levels are always filled first.
3) Only a certain number of electrons are allowed in each shell:

| 1st shell | 2nd shell | 3rd shell |
|-----------|-----------|-----------|
| 2 electrons | 8 electrons | 8 electrons |

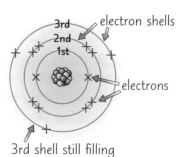

3rd shell still filling

## Working Out Electronic Configurations

The electronic configurations of the first 20 elements are shown in the diagram below.
They're not hard to work out. For a quick example, take nitrogen:

1) The periodic table tells you that the atomic number of nitrogen is seven.
   That means nitrogen has seven protons, so it must have seven electrons.

2) Follow the 'Electron Shell Rules' above. The first shell can only take 2 electrons and the second shell can take a maximum of 8 electrons. So the electronic configuration of nitrogen must be 2.5.

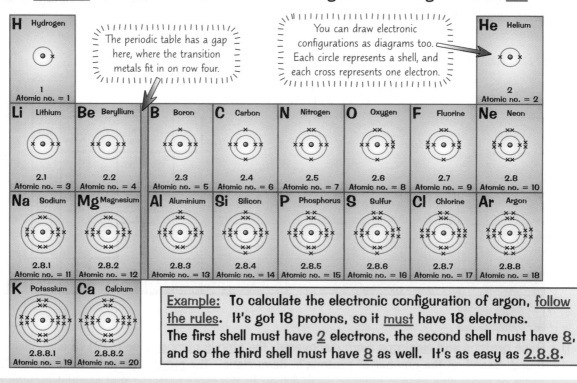

Example: To calculate the electronic configuration of argon, follow the rules. It's got 18 protons, so it must have 18 electrons. The first shell must have 2 electrons, the second shell must have 8, and so the third shell must have 8 as well. It's as easy as 2.8.8.

You can also work out the electronic configuration of an element from its period and group.

- The number of shells which contain electrons is the same as the period of the element.
- The group number tells you how many electrons occupy the outer shell of the element.

Example: Sodium is in period 3, so it has 3 shells occupied. The first two shells must be full (2.8). It's in Group 1, so it has 1 electron in its outer shell. So its electronic configuration is 2.8.1.

---

## *The electronic configuration of the fifth element — it's a bit boron...*

Electronic configurations may seem a bit complicated at first but once you learn the rules, it's a piece of cake.

Q1 Give the electronic configuration of aluminium (atomic number = 13). [1 mark]

Q2 In which group and period of the periodic table would you expect
to find the element with the electronic configuration 2.8.8.2? [2 marks]

# Ions

Some atoms are keen on getting rid of some of their <u>electrons</u>.  Others want more.  That's life.  And <u>ions</u>...

## Simple Ions Form When Atoms Lose or Gain Electrons

1) Ions are <u>charged</u> particles — they can be <u>single atoms</u> (e.g. $Na^+$) or <u>groups of atoms</u> (e.g. $NO_3^-$).

2) When <u>atoms</u> lose or gain electrons to form ions, all they're trying to do is get a <u>full outer shell</u> (also called a "<u>stable electronic structure</u>").  Atoms like full outer shells — it's atom heaven.

3) <u>Negative ions</u> (anions) form when atoms <u>gain electrons</u> — they have more electrons than protons. <u>Positive ions</u> (cations) form when atoms <u>lose electrons</u> — they have more protons than electrons.

4) The <u>number</u> of electrons lost or gained is the same as the <u>charge</u> on the ion.  E.g. If 2 electrons are <u>lost</u> the charge is 2+. If 3 electrons are <u>gained</u> the charge is 3–.

> You calculate the number of protons and neutrons in an ion in the same way as for an atom (see page 79).

- $F^-$ has a <u>single negative charge</u>, so it must have one more electron than protons. F has an atomic number of 9, so has 9 protons.  So $F^-$ must have 9 + 1 = <u>10 electrons</u>.

- $Fe^{2+}$ has a <u>2+ charge</u>, so it must have two more protons than electrons. Fe has an atomic number of 26, so has 26 protons.  So $Fe^{2+}$ must have 26 – 2 = <u>24 electrons</u>.

## Groups 1 & 2 and 6 & 7 are the Most Likely to Form Ions

1) The elements that most readily form ions are those in <u>Groups 1</u>, <u>2</u>, <u>6</u> and <u>7</u>.

2) <u>Group 1 and 2 elements</u> are <u>metals</u>. They <u>lose</u> electrons to form <u>positive ions</u>.

3) <u>Group 6 and 7 elements</u> are <u>non-metals</u>. They <u>gain</u> electrons to form <u>negative ions</u>.

4) Elements in the same <u>group</u> all have the same number of <u>outer electrons</u>.  So they have to <u>lose or gain</u> the same number to get a full outer shell.  And this means that they form ions with the <u>same charges</u>.

Group 1 elements form 1+ ions. Group 2 elements form 2+ ions. Group 6 elements form 2– ions. Group 7 elements form 1– ions.

## You Can Work Out the Formula of an Ionic Compound

1) Ionic compounds (see page 85) are made up of a <u>positively charged</u> part and a <u>negatively charged</u> part.

2) The <u>overall charge</u> of <u>any ionic compound</u> is <u>zero</u>.  So all the <u>negative charges</u> in the compound must <u>balance</u> all the <u>positive charges</u>.

3) You can use the charges on the <u>individual ions</u> present to work out the formula for the ionic compound.

4) You need to be able to write formulas using <u>chemical symbols</u>.

> Ions with names ending in -ate (e.g. nitrate) are negative ions containing oxygen and at least one other element.  Ions with names ending in -ide (e.g. chloride) are negative ions containing only one element (apart from hydroxide ions which are $OH^-$).

**EXAMPLE:** What is the chemical formula of calcium nitrate?

1) Write out the <u>formulas</u> of the calcium and nitrate ions.   $Ca^{2+}$, $NO_3^-$

2) The <u>overall charge</u> on the formula must be <u>zero</u>, so work out the ratio of Ca : $NO_3$ that gives an overall neutral charge.

To balance the 2+ charge on $Ca^{2+}$, you need two $NO_3^-$ ions:  (+2) + (2 × –1) = 0. The formula is $Ca(NO_3)_2$

> The brackets show you need two of the whole nitrate ion.

## Magnesium sulfide isn't sarcastic, it's just an ironic compound...

Don't forget about ions made up of groups of atoms, like the ones on page 76.  You can't use the periodic table to work out the charges on these, like you can with the elements in Groups 1, 2, 6 and 7.  You just need to learn them.

Q1    What is the formula of the ionic compound, lithium oxide?                    [1 mark]

# Ionic Bonding

Time to find out how particles bond together to form compounds (bet you can't wait). There are three types of bonding you need to know about — ionic, covalent and metallic. First up, it's ionic bonds.

## Ionic Bonding — Transfer of Electrons

When a metal and a non-metal react together, the metal atom loses electrons to form a positive ion (cation) and the non-metal gains these electrons to form a negative ion (anion). These oppositely charged ions are strongly attracted to one another by electrostatic forces. This attraction is called an ionic bond.

## Use Dot and Cross Diagrams to Show How Ionic Compounds are Formed

Dot and cross diagrams show the arrangement of electrons in an atom or ion. Each electron is represented by a dot or a cross. So these diagrams can show which atom the electrons in an ion originally came from.

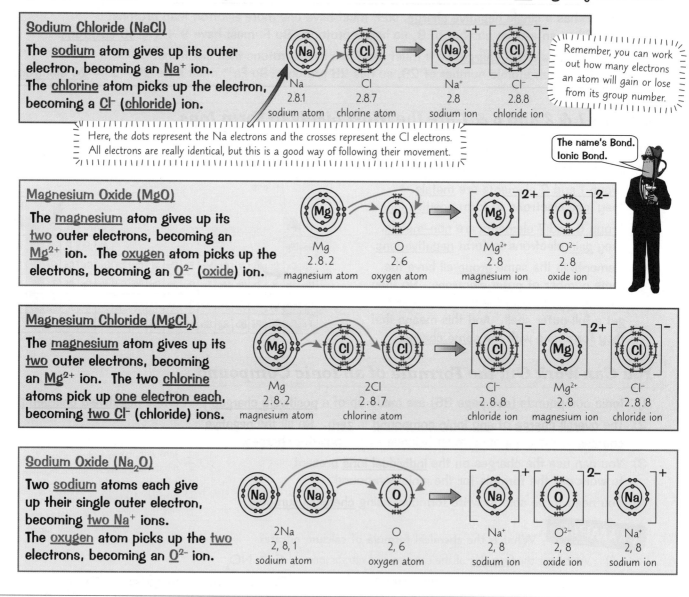

### Sodium Chloride (NaCl)

The sodium atom gives up its outer electron, becoming an Na⁺ ion. The chlorine atom picks up the electron, becoming a Cl⁻ (chloride) ion.

Na 2.8.1 sodium atom — Cl 2.8.7 chlorine atom — Na⁺ 2.8 sodium ion — Cl⁻ 2.8.8 chloride ion

Remember, you can work out how many electrons an atom will gain or lose from its group number.

Here, the dots represent the Na electrons and the crosses represent the Cl electrons. All electrons are really identical, but this is a good way of following their movement.

The name's Bond. Ionic Bond.

### Magnesium Oxide (MgO)

The magnesium atom gives up its two outer electrons, becoming an Mg²⁺ ion. The oxygen atom picks up the electrons, becoming an O²⁻ (oxide) ion.

Mg 2.8.2 magnesium atom — O 2.6 oxygen atom — Mg²⁺ 2.8 magnesium ion — O²⁻ 2.8 oxide ion

### Magnesium Chloride (MgCl₂)

The magnesium atom gives up its two outer electrons, becoming an Mg²⁺ ion. The two chlorine atoms pick up one electron each, becoming two Cl⁻ (chloride) ions.

Mg 2.8.2 magnesium atom — 2Cl 2.8.7 chlorine atom — Cl⁻ 2.8.8 chloride ion — Mg²⁺ 2.8 magnesium ion — Cl⁻ 2.8.8 chloride ion

### Sodium Oxide (Na₂O)

Two sodium atoms each give up their single outer electron, becoming two Na⁺ ions. The oxygen atom picks up the two electrons, becoming an O²⁻ ion.

2Na 2, 8, 1 sodium atom — O 2, 6 oxygen atom — Na⁺ 2, 8 sodium ion — O²⁻ 2, 8 oxide ion — Na⁺ 2, 8 sodium ion

## Any old ion, any old ion — any, any, any old ion...

You need to be able to describe how ionic compounds are formed using both words and dot and cross diagrams. It gets easier with practice, so here are some questions to get you started.

Q1   Describe, in terms of electron transfer, how sodium (Na) and chlorine (Cl) react to form sodium chloride (NaCl).   [3 marks]

Q2   Draw a dot and cross diagram to show how potassium (electronic configuration 2.8.8.1) and bromine (electronic configuration 2.8.8.7) form potassium bromide (KBr).   [3 marks]

# Ionic Compounds

I know it's covered in sodium chloride, but this page is all true — no need to take it with a pinch of salt...

## Ionic Compounds Have a Regular Lattice Structure

Ionic compounds always have giant ionic lattice structures. The ions form a closely packed regular lattice. There are very strong electrostatic forces of attraction between oppositely charged ions, in all directions.

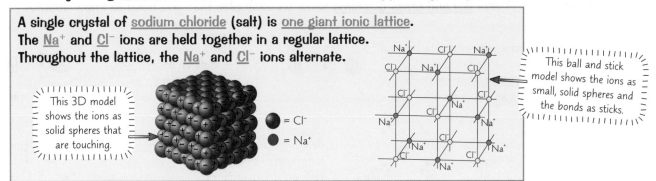

A single crystal of sodium chloride (salt) is one giant ionic lattice. The $Na^+$ and $Cl^-$ ions are held together in a regular lattice. Throughout the lattice, the $Na^+$ and $Cl^-$ ions alternate.

This 3D model shows the ions as solid spheres that are touching.

= $Cl^-$
= $Na^+$

This ball and stick model shows the ions as small, solid spheres and the bonds as sticks.

## Ionic Compounds All Have Similar Properties

1) Ionic compounds have high melting and boiling points due to the strong attraction between the ions. It takes a large amount of energy to overcome this attraction.

2) Solid ionic compounds don't conduct electricity because the ions are fixed in place and can't move. But when an ionic compound melts, the ions are free to move and will carry an electric current.

3) Many also dissolve easily in water. The ions separate and are all free to move in the solution, so they'll carry an electric current.

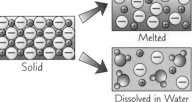

Solid

Melted

Dissolved in Water

## Models That Show Structures Have Some Limitations

It would be pretty tricky to draw out exactly what a substance looked like, so instead we use models. Each type of model has its own advantages and disadvantages...

1) 2D representations (e.g. displayed formulas) of molecules are simple and great at showing what atoms something contains, and how the atoms are connected. They don't show the shape of the substance though, and they don't give you any idea about the sizes of the atoms.

2) Dot and cross diagrams (like those on page 84 and page 86) are useful for showing how compounds or molecules are formed and where the electrons in the bonds or ions came from. But they don't usually show you anything about the size of the atoms or ions or how they're arranged.

3) 3D models of ionic solids show the arrangement of ions, but only show the outer layer of the substance.

Ball and stick models (like the one for NaCl above) show how the atoms in a substance are connected. You can draw them, or make them with plastic molecular model kits, or as computer models.

- They're great for helping to visualise structures, as they show the shape of the lattice or molecule in 3D.
- They're more realistic than 2D drawings, but they're still a bit misleading. They make it look like there are big gaps between the atoms — in reality this is where the electron clouds interact.
- They also don't show the correct scales of the atoms or ions. The atoms and ions are really different sizes, but this isn't shown well by ball and stick models.

It's easiest to make ball and stick models of small molecules. Here's one of ethanol ($C_2H_5OH$).

## Is it just me, or does that model of ethanol look like a little doggie?

Make sure you know the properties of ionic compounds inside out and back to front. They may crop up in the exam.

Q1    Explain why calcium chloride, an ionic compound, has a high melting point.    [1 mark]

# Covalent Bonding

These molecules might be simple, but you've still go to know about them. I know, the world is a cruel place.

## Learn These Examples of Simple Molecular Substances

A covalent bond is a strong bond that forms when a pair of electrons is shared between two atoms. Simple molecular substances are made up of molecules containing a few atoms joined by covalent bonds. These dot and cross diagrams show six examples that you need to know about:

Hydrogen, $H_2$
Hydrogen atoms have one electron, so they need one more to complete the first shell. They can form a single covalent bond with another hydrogen atom to achieve this.

Hydrogen Chloride, HCl
This is very similar to $H_2$ — both atoms only need one more electron to complete their outer shells.

Water, $H_2O$
In water molecules, an oxygen atom shares a pair of electrons with two H atoms to form two single covalent bonds.

Oxygen, $O_2$
An oxygen atom needs two more electrons to complete its outer shell. In oxygen gas, each oxygen atom forms a double covalent bond (a bond made of two shared electron pairs) with another oxygen atom.

Methane, $CH_4$
Carbon has four outer electrons, which is half a full shell. It can form four covalent bonds with hydrogen atoms to fill up its outer shell.

Carbon dioxide, $CO_2$
In carbon dioxide molecules, a carbon atom shares two pairs of electrons with two oxygen atoms to form two double covalent bonds.

Simple molecules are tiny — they generally have sizes around $10^{-10}$ m.
The bonds that form between these molecules are generally about $10^{-10}$ m too.

*These dot and cross diagrams only show the electrons in the outer shell of each atom.*

## Properties of Simple Molecular Substances

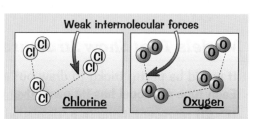
Weak intermolecular forces

Chlorine      Oxygen

1) Substances containing covalent bonds usually have simple molecular structures, like the examples above.

2) The atoms within the molecules are held together by very strong covalent bonds. By contrast, the forces of attraction between these molecules are very weak.

3) To melt or boil a simple molecular compound, you only need to break these feeble intermolecular forces and not the covalent bonds. So the melting and boiling points are very low, because the molecules are easily parted from each other.

Electrons £1,000,000

4) Most molecular substances are gases or liquids at room temperature.

5) As molecules get bigger, the strength of the intermolecular forces increases, so more energy is needed to break them, and the melting and boiling points increase.

6) Molecular compounds don't conduct electricity because they don't contain any free electrons or ions.

7) There's no easy rule about solubility in water for simple molecules — some are soluble and some aren't.

## Polymers Are Made of Covalently Bonded Carbon Chains

1) Polymers are molecules made up of long chains of covalently bonded carbon atoms. A famous example is poly(ethene).

2) They're formed when lots of small molecules called monomers join together.

$$\left(\begin{array}{c} \text{H} \ \ \text{H} \\ | \ \ \ | \\ \text{C}-\text{C} \\ | \ \ \ | \\ \text{H} \ \ \text{H} \end{array}\right)_n$$

This is known as the repeat unit. The n shows that there's loads of these units joined, one after another.

## May the intermolecular force be with you...

Remember, it's just the weak forces between molecules that are broken when a simple molecular substance melts.

Q1  Explain why oxygen, $O_2$, is a gas at room temperature.                                [2 marks]

Q2  Explain why nitrogen, $N_2$, doesn't conduct electricity.                                [1 mark]

# Giant Covalent Structures and Fullerenes

Even more covalent structures for you to feast your eyes on...  These ones are bigger, so they're better right?

## *Most Giant Covalent Structures Have Certain Properties*

1) In giant covalent structures, all the atoms are bonded to each other by strong covalent bonds.

2) They have very high melting and boiling points as lots of energy is needed to break the covalent bonds.

3) They generally don't contain charged particles, so they don't conduct electricity. ← Apart from graphite and graphene.

4) They aren't soluble in water.

5) The following examples are all carbon-based giant covalent structures.

**DIAMOND**
- Diamond is made up of a network of carbon atoms that each form four covalent bonds.
- The strong covalent bonds take lots of energy to break, so diamond has a high melting point.
- The strong covalent bonds also hold the atoms in a rigid lattice structure, making diamond really hard — it's used to strengthen cutting tools (e.g. saw teeth and drill bits).
- It doesn't conduct electricity because it has no free electrons or ions.

**GRAPHITE**
- In graphite, each carbon atom only forms three covalent bonds, creating sheets of carbon atoms arranged in hexagons.
- There aren't any covalent bonds between the layers — they're only held together weakly, so they're free to move over each other.  This makes graphite soft and slippery, so it's ideal as a lubricating material.
- Graphite's got a high melting point — the covalent bonds in the layers need loads of energy to break.
- Only three out of each carbon's four outer electrons are used in bonds, so each carbon atom has one electron that's delocalised (free) and can move.  So graphite conducts electricity and is often used to make electrodes.

**GRAPHENE**
- Graphene (a type of fullerene — see below) is one layer of graphite.
- It's a sheet of carbon atoms joined together in hexagons.
- The sheet is just one atom thick, making it a two-dimensional compound.

## *Fullerenes Form Spheres and Tubes*

1) Fullerenes are molecules of carbon, shaped like closed tubes or hollow balls.

2) They're mainly made up of carbon atoms arranged in hexagons, but can also contain pentagons (rings of five carbons) or heptagons (rings of seven carbons).

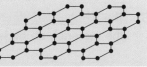
Buckminsterfullerene has the molecular formula $C_{60}$ and forms a hollow sphere made up of 20 hexagons and 12 pentagons. It's a stable molecule that forms soft brownish-black crystals.

3) Fullerenes can be used to 'cage' other molecules.  The fullerene structure forms around another atom or molecule, which is then trapped inside.  This could be used to deliver a drug directly to cells in the body.

4) Fullerenes have a huge surface area, so they could help make great industrial catalysts — individual catalyst molecules could be attached to the fullerenes (the bigger the surface area the better).

Catalysts speed up the rates of reactions without being used up (see page 133).

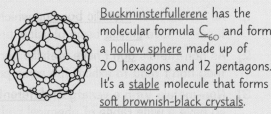
Nanotubes are also fullerenes.  They are like tiny cylinders of graphene — so they conduct electricity.  They also have a high tensile strength (they don't break when stretched) so can be used to strengthen materials without adding much weight.  For example, they can be used to strengthen sports equipment that needs to be strong but also lightweight (e.g. tennis rackets).

## *Nanotubes — not to be confused with my Irish gran, Nan O'Brady...*

Did you know that buckminsterfullerene is the state molecule of Texas?  True story bro...

Q1     Give one use of graphite and state what property of graphite makes it suitable for this use.     [2 marks]

# Metallic Bonding

Ever wondered what makes <u>metals</u> tick? Well, either way, this is the page for you.

## Metallic Bonding Involves Delocalised Electrons

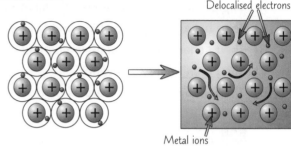

Delocalised electrons

Metal ions

1) <u>Metals</u> also consist of a <u>giant structure</u>.

2) The electrons in the <u>outer shell</u> of the metal atoms are <u>delocalised</u> (free to move around). There are strong forces of <u>electrostatic attraction</u> between the <u>positive metal ions</u> and the shared <u>negative electrons</u>.

3) These forces of attraction <u>hold</u> the <u>atoms</u> together in a <u>regular</u> structure and are known as <u>metallic bonding</u>. Metallic bonding is very <u>strong</u>.

4) Compounds that are held together by metallic bonding include metallic <u>elements</u> and <u>alloys</u>.

5) It's the <u>delocalised electrons</u> in the metallic bonds which produce <u>all</u> the properties of metals.

## Metals Have Certain Physical Properties

1) The electrostatic forces between the metal ions and the delocalised sea of electrons are very <u>strong</u>, so need <u>lots of energy</u> to be broken.

2) This means that most compounds with metallic bonds have very <u>high</u> melting and boiling points, so they're generally <u>shiny solids</u> at room temperature. They <u>aren't soluble</u> in water either.

3) Metals are also generally <u>more dense</u> than non-metals as the ions in the metallic structure are packed <u>close together</u>.

4) The <u>layers</u> of atoms in a pure metal can <u>slide over</u> each other, making metals <u>malleable</u> — this means that they can be <u>hammered</u> or <u>rolled</u> into <u>flat sheets</u>.

5) The <u>delocalised electrons</u> carry electrical current and thermal (heat) energy through the material, so metals are good <u>conductors</u> of <u>electricity</u> and <u>heat</u>.

## Metals and Non-Metals Have Different Physical Properties

1) All metals have <u>metallic bonding</u> which causes them to have <u>similar</u> basic physical properties.

2) As non-metals <u>don't</u> have metallic bonding, they don't tend to exhibit the same properties as metals.

3) Non-metals form a variety of <u>different structures</u> so have a <u>wide range</u> of chemical and physical <u>properties</u>.

4) They tend to be <u>dull looking</u>, more <u>brittle</u>, have <u>lower boiling points</u> (they're not generally solids at room temperature), <u>don't</u> generally <u>conduct electricity</u> and often have a <u>lower density</u>.

The blue boxes show the metals in the periodic table.

The white boxes show non-metals.

5) Metals and non-metals also have <u>different chemical properties</u>. Non-metals tend to <u>gain electrons</u> to form full outer shells (they hang out on the top and right-hand side of the periodic table and their outer shells are generally <u>over half-filled</u>). Metals <u>lose electrons</u> to gain full outer shells (they're found at the bottom and left-hand side of the periodic table and their outer shells are generally <u>under half-filled</u>).

---

## *I saw a metal on the bus once — he was the conductor...*

If your knowledge of metals is still feeling a bit delocalised, the questions below will help...

Q1 Copper is a metallic element. State what property of copper makes it suitable for using in electrical circuits and explain why it has this property. [2 marks]

Q2 Thomas has samples of two solids, A and B. One of the samples is a metal. Solid A is shiny and conducts electricity as a solid. Solid B is a white powder that only conducts electricity when dissolved in water. Predict, with reasoning, whether solid A or solid B is likely to be the metal. [3 marks]

# Conservation of Mass

Being a diva, I prefer the conservation of sass. Conservation of mass is more useful in science exams though.

## In a Chemical Reaction, Mass is Always Conserved

1) During a chemical reaction no atoms are destroyed and no atoms are created.

2) This means there are the same number and types of atoms on each side of a reaction equation.

3) You can see this in action if you do a reaction in a closed system (this is a system where nothing can get in or out). The total mass of the system before and after doesn't change.

4) A good way of showing this is to do a precipitation reaction. ◀

*A precipitation reaction happens when two solutions react and an insoluble solid, called a precipitate, forms in the solution.*

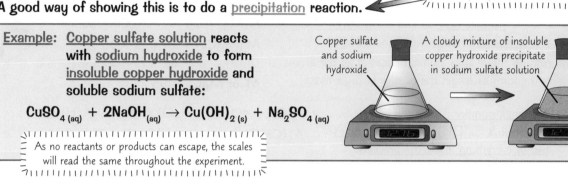

Example: Copper sulfate solution reacts with sodium hydroxide to form insoluble copper hydroxide and soluble sodium sulfate:

$$CuSO_{4(aq)} + 2NaOH_{(aq)} \rightarrow Cu(OH)_{2(s)} + Na_2SO_{4(aq)}$$

*As no reactants or products can escape, the scales will read the same throughout the experiment.*

Copper sulfate and sodium hydroxide

A cloudy mixture of insoluble copper hydroxide precipitate in sodium sulfate solution

## If the Mass Seems to Change, There's Usually a Gas Involved

In some experiments, you might observe a change of mass in an unsealed reaction vessel during a reaction. There are two reasons why this might happen:

**1** If the mass increases, it's probably because at least one of the reactants is a gas that's found in air (e.g. oxygen) and the products are solids, liquids or aqueous.

- Before the reaction, the gas is floating around in the air. It's there, but it's not contained in the reaction vessel, so you can't measure its mass.

- When the gas reacts to form part of the product, it becomes contained inside the reaction vessel.

- So the total mass of the stuff inside the reaction vessel increases.

- For example, when a metal in an unsealed container reacts with oxygen from the air, the mass inside the container increases. The mass of the metal oxide produced equals the total mass of the metal and the oxygen that reacted from the air.

$$metal_{(s)} + oxygen_{(g)} \rightarrow metal\ oxide_{(s)}$$

**2** If the mass decreases, it's probably because some, or all, of the reactants are solids, liquids or aqueous and at least one of the products is a gas.

- Before the reaction, any solid, liquid or aqueous reactants are contained in the reaction vessel.

- If the vessel isn't enclosed, then the gas can escape from the reaction vessel as it's formed. It's no longer contained in the reaction vessel, so you can't measure its mass.

- So the total mass of the stuff inside the reaction vessel decreases.

- For example, when a metal carbonate thermally decomposes in an unsealed container to form a metal oxide and carbon dioxide gas, the mass of the container will appear to decrease as the carbon dioxide escapes. But in reality, the mass of the metal oxide and the carbon dioxide produced will equal the mass of the metal carbonate that reacted.

$$metal\ carbonate_{(s)} \rightarrow metal\ oxide_{(s)} + carbon\ dioxide_{(g)}$$

*A gas will expand to fill any container it's in. So if the reaction vessel isn't sealed the gas expands out from the vessel, and escapes into the air around. There's more about this on page 97.*

## Conservation of Mass — protecting mass for future generations...

Never, ever forget that, in a reaction, the total mass of reactants is the same as the total mass of products.

Q1 A student carries out the following reaction in an unsealed container: $2HCl_{(aq)} + Na_2S_{(aq)} \rightarrow H_2S_{(g)} + 2NaCl_{(aq)}$
Predict how the mass of the reaction vessel and its contents
will change over the reaction. Explain your answer. [3 marks]

# Relative Masses and Chemical Formulas

Time for some maths. "But this is chemistry, not maths," I hear you cry. "Tough cookies," I reply.

## Relative Formula Mass, $M_r$ — Easy Peasy

The relative formula mass, $M_r$, of a compound is the relative atomic masses ($A_r$) of all the atoms in its formula added together.

*Look back at page 80 for more about relative atomic masses.*

**EXAMPLE:** Find the relative formula mass of:

a) magnesium chloride, $MgCl_2$,     b) calcium hydroxide, $Ca(OH)_2$.

*I have literally no idea what I'm doing.*

a)  Use the periodic table to find the relative atomic masses of magnesium and chlorine.
    Add up the relative atomic masses of all the atoms in the formula to get the relative formula mass.

$A_r(Mg) = 24$     $A_r(Cl) = 35.5$

$M_r(MgCl_2) = 24 + (2 \times 35.5)$
$= 24 + 71 = 95$

$M_r$ of $MgCl_2 = 95$

b)  The small number 2 after the bracket in the formula $Ca(OH)_2$ means that there's two of everything inside the brackets.

$A_r(Ca) = 40$     $A_r(O) = 16$     $A_r(H) = 1$

$M_r(Ca(OH)_2) = 40 + [(16 + 1) \times 2]$
$= 40 + 34 = 74$

$M_r$ of $Ca(OH)_2 = 74$

The $M_r$ of a compound is equal to the mass in grams of 1 mole (see next page) of the compound.
So, 1 mole of magnesium chloride would weigh 95 g, and 1 mole of calcium hydroxide would weigh 74 g.

## The Empirical Formula is the Simplest Ratio of Atoms

The empirical formula of a compound tells you the smallest whole number ratio of atoms in the compound.

**EXAMPLE:** Find the empirical formula of glucose, $C_6H_{12}O_6$.

The numbers in the molecular formula of glucose are 6, 12 and 6.
To simplify the ratio, divide them by the largest number that goes into 6, 12 and 6 exactly — that's 6.

C: $6 \div 6 = 1$
H: $12 \div 6 = 2$
O: $6 \div 6 = 1$
The empirical formula of glucose is $CH_2O$.

You can use the empirical formula of a compound, together with its $M_r$, to find its molecular formula.

**EXAMPLE:** Compound X has the empirical formula $C_2H_6N$. The $M_r$ of compound X is 88.
Find the molecular formula of compound X.

1)  Start by finding the $M_r$ of the empirical formula. The $A_r$ of carbon is 12, the $A_r$ of hydrogen is 1 and the $A_r$ of nitrogen is 14.

$M_r(C_2H_6N) = (2 \times A_r(C)) + (6 \times A_r(H)) + A_r(N)$
$= (2 \times 12) + (6 \times 1) + 14$
$= 24 + 6 + 14 = 44$

2)  Divide the $M_r$ of the compound by the $M_r$ of the empirical formula.

$88 \div 44 = 2$

3)  Now to get the molecular formula, you just multiply everything in the empirical formula by the result — in this case, by 2.

C: $2 \times 2 = 4$     H: $6 \times 2 = 12$     N: $1 \times 2 = 2$
The molecular formula of compound X is $C_4H_{12}N_2$.

## This page is a relative masterpiece...

This stuff comes up a fair bit in chemistry, so make sure you've got to grips with it by doing loads of practice questions. Start with these. Use the periodic table on the back cover to find the $A_r$ values you need.

Q1    Calculate the relative formula mass of ethanol, $C_2H_5OH$.                    [1 mark]

Q2    What is the empirical formula of a compound with the molecular formula $C_4H_8Cl_2$?    [1 mark]

# Moles

The mole might seem a bit confusing. I think it's the word that puts people off. But it's not that hard really...

## "The Mole" is Simply the Name Given to a Certain Number of Particles

1) Just like a million is this many: 1 000 000, or a billion is this many: 1 000 000 000, a mole is an amount of particles (e.g. atoms, molecules or ions) equal to a number called Avogadro's constant, and it's this many: 602 000 000 000 000 000 000 000 or $6.02 \times 10^{23}$.

2) But why is Avogadro's constant useful? The answer is that when you get that number of atoms or molecules, of any element or compound, then, conveniently, they weigh exactly the same number of grams as the relative atomic mass, $A_r$, (or relative formula mass, $M_r$) of the element or compound.

> One mole of atoms or molecules of any substance will have a mass in grams equal to the relative particle mass ($A_r$ or $M_r$) for that substance.

*Look back at page 90 if you've forgotten how to work out $M_r$.*

**Examples:**

Carbon has an $A_r$ of 12.  
Nitrogen gas, $N_2$, has an $M_r$ of 28 ($2 \times 14$).  
Hexane, $C_6H_{14}$, has an $M_r$ of 86 (($6 \times 12$) + ($14 \times 1$)).

So one mole of carbon weighs exactly 12 g.  
So one mole of nitrogen gas weighs exactly 28 g.  
So one mole of hexane weighs exactly 86 g.

So 12 g of carbon, 28 g of nitrogen gas and 86 g of hexane all contain the same number of particles, namely one mole or $6.02 \times 10^{23}$ particles.

## You Can Use Avogadro's Constant to Calculate Numbers of Particles

You need to be able to work out the number of molecules, atoms or ions in a certain number of moles.

**EXAMPLE:** How many atoms are there in 5 moles of oxygen gas?

1) Multiply Avogadro's constant by the number of moles you have to find the number of particles.

$$6.02 \times 10^{23} \times 5 = 3.01 \times 10^{24}$$

2) There are two atoms in each molecule of oxygen gas, so multiply your answer by 2.

$$3.01 \times 10^{24} \times 2 = 6.02 \times 10^{24}$$

*Give your answer in standard form (in terms of $\times 10^x$) to save you having to write out lots of O's.*

If you're asked for the number of particles in a given mass, you need to do a cheeky bit of converting first. There's a nifty formula you can use to find the number of moles in a certain mass of something.

$$\text{Number of Moles} = \frac{\text{Mass in g (of element or compound)}}{M_r \text{ (of compound) or } A_r \text{ (of element)}}$$

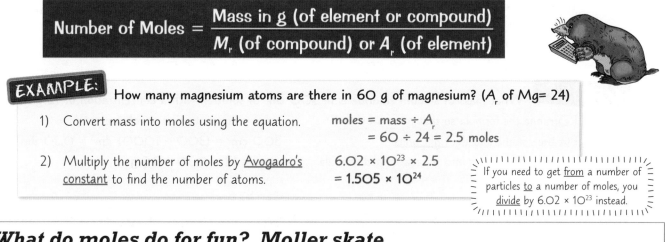

**EXAMPLE:** How many magnesium atoms are there in 60 g of magnesium? ($A_r$ of Mg = 24)

1) Convert mass into moles using the equation.

$$\text{moles} = \text{mass} \div A_r$$
$$= 60 \div 24 = 2.5 \text{ moles}$$

2) Multiply the number of moles by Avogadro's constant to find the number of atoms.

$$6.02 \times 10^{23} \times 2.5$$
$$= 1.505 \times 10^{24}$$

*If you need to get from a number of particles to a number of moles, you divide by $6.02 \times 10^{23}$ instead.*

## What do moles do for fun? Moller skate...

Moles can give you a bit of a headache — so spend a bit of time getting your head round all this if you need to.

Q1 Calculate the number of moles in 90 g of water. $M_r$ of water = 18. [1 mark]

Q2 How many molecules of ammonia are present in 3.5 moles of ammonia gas? [1 mark]

Q3 How many atoms are present in 81.4 g of calcium hydroxide, $Ca(OH)_2$? $M_r$ of $Ca(OH)_2$ = 74. [3 marks]

# More Calculations

Holy moley. I hope you like <u>moles</u>, as we're about to get stuck into another page piled high with them. Make sure you've got to grips with everything on the last page before you embark on this one.

## You Need to be Able to Rearrange the Equation for Moles

1) Just being able to plug numbers into the equation <u>moles = mass ÷ $M_r$</u> isn't going to cut it in the exams. Oh no... You need to be able to <u>rearrange</u> the formula to find out <u>other unknowns</u>, e.g. to find a mass if you've been given moles and $M_r$.

2) Putting an equation into a <u>formula triangle</u> makes rearranging equations straightforward. Here's the formula triangle that links moles, mass and relative formula mass.

3) To use a formula triangle, just cover the thing you want to find, and you're left with the expression you need to calculate it. The <u>line</u> through the triangle stands for <u>division</u>.

Or $A_r$

**EXAMPLE:**

How many moles are there in 66 g of carbon dioxide?

$M_r$ of carbon dioxide ($CO_2$) = 12 + (16 × 2) = 44

moles = mass ÷ $M_r$ = 66 ÷ 44 = 1.5 moles

**EXAMPLE:**

What mass of carbon is there in 4 moles of carbon dioxide?

mass = moles × $A_r$(C)
= 4 × 12 = 48 g

## Concentration is a Measure of How Crowded Things Are

1) The <u>more solute</u> (the solid you're dissolving) you dissolve in a given volume, the <u>more crowded</u> the particles are and the <u>more concentrated</u> the solution.

2) Concentration can be measured in <u>grams per dm³</u> (<u>g dm⁻³</u>) — so 1 gram of stuff dissolved in 1 dm³ of solution has a concentration of <u>1 g dm⁻³</u>.

3) Here's the formula for finding <u>concentration</u> from the <u>mass of solute</u>:

1 dm³
= 1 litre
= 1000 cm³

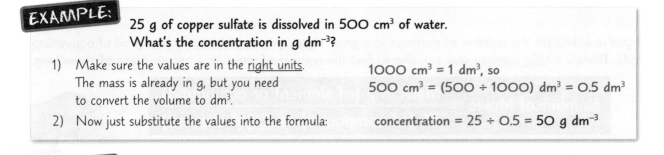

$$\text{concentration} = \text{mass of solute} \div \text{volume of solution}$$

**EXAMPLE:** 25 g of copper sulfate is dissolved in 500 cm³ of water. What's the concentration in g dm⁻³?

1) Make sure the values are in the <u>right units</u>. The mass is already in g, but you need to convert the volume to dm³.

1000 cm³ = 1 dm³, so
500 cm³ = (500 ÷ 1000) dm³ = 0.5 dm³

2) Now just substitute the values into the formula:

concentration = 25 ÷ 0.5 = 50 g dm⁻³

**EXAMPLE:** What mass of sodium chloride is in 300 cm³ of solution with a concentration of 12 g dm⁻³?

1) Rearrange the formula so that mass is by itself.

mass = concentration × volume

2) Put the volume into the <u>right units</u>.

300 cm³ = (300 ÷ 1000) dm³ = 0.30 dm³

3) Substitute the values into the rearranged formula.

mass = 12 × 0.30 = 3.6 g

## Concentration = mass of revision ÷ hours of good daytime TV...

None of the maths in these calculations is too hard. It's a bit of rearranging equations here and there, but apart from that, it's just some addition, multiplication and division — which is simple with a calculator in hand.

Q1 Calculate the mass of 0.200 moles of potassium bromide. $M_r$ of KBr = 119. [1 mark]

Q2 0.500 moles of substance X has a mass of 87.0 g. What is the relative formula mass of X? [1 mark]

Q3 What mass of sodium hydroxide is contained in 200 cm³ of a 55 g dm⁻³ solution? [2 marks]

# Calculating Empirical Formulas

You first met empirical formulas back on page 90, but now they're back and they mean business.

## Empirical Formulas can be Calculated from Masses

You can work out the empirical formula of a compound from the masses of the elements it contains.

**EXAMPLE:** A sample of a hydrocarbon contains 36 g of carbon and 6 g of hydrogen. Work out the empirical formula of the hydrocarbon.

*Remember — moles = mass ÷ $M_r$.*

1) First work out how many moles of each element you have.

$A_r(C) = 12$     moles of C = 36 ÷ 12 = 3 moles
$A_r(H) = 1$     moles of H = 6 ÷ 1 = 6 moles

2) Work out the smallest whole number ratio between the moles of C and H atoms to get the empirical formula.

Ratio C:H = 3:6. Now divide both numbers by the smallest — here it's 3. So, the ratio C:H = 1:2. The empirical formula must be $CH_2$.

## You can Use Experiments to Find Empirical Formulas

Here's an experiment you could use to calculate the empirical formula of a metal oxide, e.g. magnesium oxide.

1) Get a crucible and heat it until it's red hot. (This will make sure it's clean and there are no traces of oil or water lying around from a previous experiment.)

2) Leave the crucible to cool, then weigh it, along with its lid.

3) Add some clean magnesium ribbon to the crucible. Reweigh the crucible, lid and magnesium ribbon. The mass of magnesium you're using is this reading minus the initial reading for the mass of the crucible and lid.

4) Heat the crucible containing the magnesium. Put the lid on the crucible so as to stop any bits of solid from escaping, but leave a small gap to allow oxygen to enter the crucible.

5) Heat the crucible strongly for around 10 minutes, or until all the magnesium ribbon has turned white.

6) Allow the crucible to cool and reweigh the crucible with the lid and its contents. The mass of magnesium oxide you have is this reading, minus the initial reading for the mass of the crucible and lid.

*lid* — *crucible containing magnesium ribbon* — *gauze* — *tripod* — **HEAT**

**EXAMPLE:** A student heats 1.08 g of magnesium ribbon in a crucible so it completely reacts to form magnesium oxide. The total mass of magnesium oxide formed was 1.80 g. Calculate the empirical formula of magnesium oxide.

1) The extra mass in the magnesium oxide must have come from oxygen, so you can work out the mass of oxygen.

mass of O = 1.80 − 1.08 = 0.72 g

2) Work out the number of moles of magnesium and oxygen atoms involved in the reaction.

moles of Mg = 1.08 ÷ 24 = 0.045 moles      moles of O = 0.72 ÷ 16 = 0.045 moles

3) Work out the lowest whole number ratio between Mg and O by dividing the moles of both by the smallest number.

Mg = 0.045 ÷ 0.045 = 1          O = 0.045 ÷ 0.045 = 1

This shows that the ratio between O and Mg in the formula is 1:1, so the empirical formula of the magnesium oxide must be **MgO**.

## The empirical strikes back...

You may be given experimental results, like those in the example above, and asked to find the empirical formula of the compound formed. So read through the example thoroughly and make sure you can follow what's going on.

Q1   A 45.6 g sample of an oxide of nitrogen contains 13.9 g of nitrogen.
What is the empirical formula of the nitrogen oxide?      [3 marks]

# Limiting Reactants

Unlimited. Together we're unlimited. Unless you're a <u>limiting reactant</u>, in which case you're a big ol' limiter.

## Reactions Stop When One Reactant is Used Up

1) A reaction stops when all of one of the reactants is <u>used up</u>. Any other reactants are said to be in <u>excess</u>.

2) The reactant that's <u>used up</u> in a reaction is called the <u>limiting reactant</u> (because it limits the amount of product that's formed).

3) The amount of product formed is <u>directly proportional</u> to the amount of the <u>limiting reactant</u> used. This is because if you add <u>more of the limiting reactant</u> there will be <u>more reactant particles</u> to take part in the reaction, which means <u>more product particles</u> are made (as long as the other reactants are in excess).

## You can Calculate the Amount of Product from the Limiting Reactant

You can use a <u>balanced chemical equation</u> to work out the <u>mass of product formed</u> from a given <u>mass of a limiting reactant</u>. Here's how...

*You could also use this method to find the mass of a reactant needed to produce a known mass of a product.*

1) Write out the <u>balanced equation</u>.

2) <u>Work out relative formula masses</u> ($M_r$) of the reactant and product you're interested in.

3) Find out <u>how many moles</u> there are of the substance you <u>know</u> the mass of.

4) Use the balanced equation to work out <u>how many moles</u> there'll be of the <u>other</u> substance (i.e. how many moles of product will be made by this many moles of reactant).

5) Use the number of moles to calculate the <u>mass</u>.

### EXAMPLE:

Calculate the mass of aluminium oxide, $Al_2O_3$, formed when 135 g of aluminium is burned in air.

| | |
|---|---|
| 1) Write out the <u>balanced equation</u>: | $4Al + 3O_2 \rightarrow 2Al_2O_3$ |
| 2) Calculate the <u>relative formula masses</u> of the reactants and products you're interested in. | Al: 27    $Al_2O_3$: $(2 \times 27) + (3 \times 16) = 102$ |
| 3) <u>Calculate the number of moles</u> of aluminium in 135 g: | Moles = mass ÷ $M_r$ = 135 ÷ 27 = 5 |
| 4) Look at the <u>ratio</u> of moles in the equation: | 4 moles of Al react to produce 2 moles of $Al_2O_3$ — half the number of moles are produced. So 5 moles of Al will react to produce 2.5 moles of $Al_2O_3$. |
| 5) <u>Calculate the mass</u> of 2.5 moles of aluminium oxide: | mass = moles × $M_r$ = 2.5 × 102 = **255 g** |

### EXAMPLE:

Magnesium oxide, MgO, can be made by burning magnesium in air. What mass of magnesium is needed to make 100 g of magnesium oxide?

| | |
|---|---|
| 1) Write out the <u>balanced equation</u>. | $2Mg + O_2 \rightarrow 2MgO$ |
| 2) Work out the <u>relative formula masses</u> of the reactants and products you're interested in. | Mg: 24        MgO: 24 + 16 = 40 |
| 3) <u>Calculate the number of moles</u> of magnesium oxide in 100 g: | Moles = mass ÷ $M_r$ = 100 ÷ 40 = 2.5 |
| 4) Look at the <u>ratio</u> of moles in the equation: | 2 moles of MgO are made from 2 moles of Mg. So 2.5 moles of MgO will be formed from 2.5 moles of Mg. |
| 5) <u>Calculate the mass</u> of 2.5 moles of Mg. | mass = moles × $M_r$ = 2.5 × 24 = **60 g** |

## Relative mass — when you go to church with your parents...

A specially organically grown, hand-picked question for you, my dear. Don't say I don't spoil you.

Q1 Chlorine and potassium bromide react according to this equation: $Cl_2 + 2KBr \rightarrow Br_2 + 2KCl$
Calculate the mass of bromine produced when 23.8 g of
potassium bromide reacts with an excess of chlorine.

[4 marks]

# Balancing Equations using Masses

You've already seen how to balance equations back on page 75. But, sometimes, you may have to balance equations given the masses of the reactants and products. Your good old friend the mole will come in handy...

## You Can Balance Equations Using Reacting Masses

If you know the masses of the reactants and products that took part in a reaction, you can work out the balanced symbol equation for the reaction. Here are the steps you should take:

1) Divide the mass of each substance by its relative formula mass to find the number of moles.

> You may need to work out some unknown masses first (see below).

2) Divide the number of moles of each substance by the smallest number of moles in the reaction.

3) If needed, multiply all the numbers by the same amount to make them all whole numbers.

4) Write the balanced symbol equation for the reaction by putting these numbers in front of the formulas.

**EXAMPLE:** Paula burns a metal, X, in oxygen. There is a single product, an oxide of the metal. Given that 25.4 g of X burns in 3.2 g of oxygen, write a balanced equation for this reaction. $A_r$ of X = 63.5 and $M_r$ of X oxide = 143.0.

1) Work out the mass of metal oxide produced. Because it's the only product, the mass of metal oxide produced must equal the total mass of reactants.    25.4 + 3.2 = 28.6 g of X oxide

2) Divide the mass of each substance by its $M_r$ or $A_r$ to calculate how many moles of each substance reacted or were produced:

$$X: \frac{25.4}{63.5} = 0.40 \text{ mol} \quad O_2: \frac{3.2}{32.0} = 0.10 \text{ mol} \quad X \text{ oxide}: \frac{28.6}{143.0} = 0.20 \text{ mol}$$

3) Divide by the smallest number of moles, which is 0.10:

$$X: \frac{0.40}{0.10} = 4.0 \quad O_2: \frac{0.10}{0.10} = 1.0 \quad X \text{ oxide}: \frac{0.20}{0.10} = 2.0$$

4) The numbers are all whole numbers, so you can write out the balanced symbol equation straight away.    $4X + O_2 \rightarrow 2(X \text{ oxide})$

5) The oxide of X must have a chemical formula containing X and O atoms. In order for the equation to balance, each molecule of X oxide must contain one O atom and two X atoms. $4X + O_2 \rightarrow 2X_2O$

## You Can Work Out Limiting Reactants

**EXAMPLE:** 8.1 g of zinc oxide (ZnO) were put in a crucible with 0.30 g of carbon and heated until they reacted. Given that the balanced chemical equation for this reaction is: $2ZnO + C \rightarrow CO_2 + 2Zn$, work out the limiting reactant in this reaction.

1) Divide the mass of each substance by its $M_r$ or $A_r$ to find how many moles of each substance were reacted:

$$ZnO: \frac{8.1}{81} = 0.10 \text{ mol} \quad C: \frac{0.30}{12} = 0.025 \text{ mol}$$

2) Divide by the smallest number of moles, which is 0.025:

$$ZnO: \frac{0.10}{0.025} = 4.0 \quad C: \frac{0.025}{0.025} = 1.0$$

3) Compare the ratios between the moles of products with the balanced chemical equation.

In the balanced equation, ZnO and C react in a ratio of 2 : 1. Using the masses, there is a 4 : 1 ratio of ZnO to C. So, ZnO is in excess, and C must be the limiting reactant.

## What do moles have for pudding?  Jam moly-poly...

The best way to get to grips with the maths on this page is by practising. Luckily for you, here's a question.

Q1    During an experiment, a student heats some iron, Fe, in the presence of an unknown gas, $Y_2$. A single product forms, which is an ionic compound containing Fe and Y only. Given that during the reaction, the student heated 17.92 g of iron, and 52.00 g of product were formed, write a balanced equation for the reaction. $A_r(\text{Fe}) = 56$, $M_r(\text{product}) = 162.5$ and $M_r(Y_2) = 71$    [5 marks]

# Revision Questions for Section 10

Phew. That's <u>Section 10</u> over already. And I always say, Section 10 is always, well sometimes, the hardest...
- Try these questions and <u>tick off each one</u> when you <u>get it right</u>.
- When you've done <u>all the questions</u> under a heading and are <u>completely happy</u> with it, tick it off.

## <u>Chemical Equations, Risks and Hazards (p.75-77)</u> ☑

1) What are the chemicals on the left-hand side of a chemical equation called? ☑
2) Write out the four state symbols used in chemical equations, and state what each one means. ☑
3) Write out the formulas, complete with charges, of the carbonate and sulfate ions. ☑
4) Sketch the following hazard symbols:  a) toxic,  b) harmful. ☑

## <u>Atoms, Isotopes and Electronic Configurations (p.78-82)</u> ☐

5) Describe the main features of the plum pudding model of the atom. ☑
6) Name the three subatomic particles found in an atom, and state the relative charge of each. ☑
7) What can you say about the number of protons and electrons in a neutral atom? ☑
8) What does the mass number tell you about an atom? ☑
9) State what isotopes are, using an example to explain your answer. ☑
10) Describe how Dmitri Mendeleev organised his version of the periodic table. ☑
11) What can you say about the number of electron shells in elements in the same period? ☑
12) What does the group number of an element in the periodic table tell you about its electronic structure? ☐
13) How many electrons can fit into each of the first three electron shells? ☑

## <u>Types of Bonding and Structures (p.83-88)</u> ☑

14) What charge will the ion of a Group 6 element have? ☑
15) Describe how ionic bonding occurs. ☑
16) Draw a dot and cross diagram to show how magnesium chloride forms. ☑
17) Why do ionic compounds conduct electricity when molten or in solution, but not as solids? ☑
18) Outline the limitations associated with ball and stick models of molecules and compounds. ☑
19) Draw a dot and cross diagram to show the bonding in a molecule of water. ☑
20) Do simple molecular substances have high or low boiling points? Explain your answer. ☑
21) Describe the structures of the following substances: a) diamond,  b) graphite. ☑
22) Briefly describe what a fullerene is. ☑
23) Give three general properties of metals. ☑

## <u>Calculations and Moles (p.89-95)</u> ☑

24) Why might the mass of an unsealed system increase during a chemical reaction? ☑
25) Give a definition for the relative formula mass of a compound. ☑
26) What is the empirical formula of a compound? ☑
27) What equation links the number of moles with the mass and $M_r$ of a substance? ☑
28) What equation links the concentration of a solution with its volume and the mass of solute used? ☑
29) Outline an experiment you could use to work out the empirical formula of magnesium oxide. ☑
30) Explain what a limiting reactant is. ☑
31) Describe how to balance an equation using the masses of the reactants and products in a reaction. ☑

# States of Matter

All stuff is made of <u>particles</u> (molecules, ions or atoms). The <u>forces</u> between these particles can be weak or strong, depending on whether it's a <u>solid</u>, <u>liquid</u> or a <u>gas</u>. Want to find out more? Then read on...

## States of Matter Depend on the Forces Between Particles

1) There are <u>three states of matter</u> that you need to know about — <u>solids</u>, <u>liquids</u> and <u>gases</u>. You can model these three different states using the <u>particle model</u>.

2) In the particle model, each particle (it could be a molecule, an ion or an atom) is represented by a <u>solid sphere</u>.

3) The <u>properties</u> of each state of matter depend on the <u>forces</u> between the particles.

4) The forces between the particles can be <u>weak</u> or <u>strong</u>, depending on whether the substance is a solid, liquid or a gas.

> The force is strong with this one.
>
> SOLID

### Solids

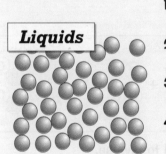

1) There are <u>strong forces</u> of attraction between particles, which hold them in <u>fixed positions</u> in a regular <u>lattice arrangement</u>.

2) The particles <u>don't move</u> from their positions, so all solids keep a <u>definite shape</u> and <u>volume</u>.

3) The particles in a solid <u>don't</u> have much <u>energy</u>.

4) They hardly move at all — in fact, they can only <u>vibrate</u> about their fixed positions. The <u>hotter</u> the solid becomes, the <u>more</u> they vibrate (causing solids to <u>expand</u> slightly when heated).

### Liquids

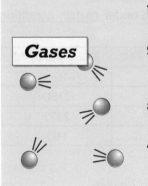

1) There is <u>some force</u> of attraction between the particles. They're <u>free</u> to <u>move</u> past each other, but they do tend to <u>stick together</u>.

2) Liquids <u>don't</u> keep a <u>definite shape</u> and will flow to fill the bottom of a container. But they do keep the <u>same volume</u>.

3) For any given substance, in the <u>liquid state</u> its particles will have <u>more energy</u> than in the <u>solid state</u> (but <u>less</u> energy than in the <u>gas state</u>).

4) The particles are <u>constantly</u> moving with <u>random motion</u>. The <u>hotter</u> the liquid gets, the <u>faster</u> they move. This causes liquids to <u>expand</u> slightly when heated.

### Gases

1) There's next to <u>no force</u> of attraction between the particles — they're <u>free</u> to <u>move</u>. They travel in <u>straight lines</u> and only interact when they <u>collide</u>.

2) Gases <u>don't</u> keep a definite <u>shape</u> or <u>volume</u> and will always <u>fill</u> any container. When particles bounce off the walls of a container they exert a <u>pressure</u> on the walls.

> This means a gas will escape from a container if it isn't air-tight.

3) For any given substance, in the <u>gas state</u> its particles will have more energy that in the <u>solid state</u> or the <u>liquid state</u>.

4) The particles move <u>constantly</u> with <u>random motion</u>. The <u>hotter</u> the gas gets, the <u>faster</u> they move. Gases either <u>expand</u> when heated, or their <u>pressure increases</u>.

## Don't ignore gases — they matter too...

Time to get to the bottom of the matter with all these states of matter. Try your hand at these questions...

Q1 Put the three states of matter, solid, liquid and gas, in order of the strength of the forces between their particles, starting with the weakest. [1 mark]

Q2 Describe the arrangement of the particles and the forces between them in a gas. [3 marks]

# Changes of State

By <u>adding</u> or <u>taking away energy</u> from a substance, you can <u>convert</u> it from one <u>physical state</u> to another.

## *Heating or Cooling a Substance can Change its State*

When a substance changes from one state of matter to another, it's a <u>physical change</u>. Physical changes are pretty easy to undo by <u>heating</u> or <u>cooling</u>.

*The red arrows show heat being added. The blue arrows show heat being given out.*

3) At a certain temperature, the particles have <u>enough energy</u> to <u>break</u> free from their positions. This is called <u>melting</u> and the solid turns into a <u>liquid</u>.

2) This makes the particles <u>vibrate more</u>, which <u>weakens</u> the <u>forces</u> that hold the solid together. This makes the solid <u>expand</u>.

1) When a <u>solid</u> is <u>heated</u>, its particles <u>gain</u> more <u>energy</u>.

**Liquid**

melting / freezing

**Solid**

subliming

evaporating / condensing

**Gas**

4) When a liquid is <u>heated</u>, again the particles get even <u>more energy</u>.

5) This energy makes the particles <u>move faster</u>, which <u>weakens</u> and <u>breaks</u> the <u>bonds</u> holding the liquid together.

6) At a certain temperature, the particles have enough energy to <u>break</u> their <u>bonds</u>. This is called <u>evaporating</u> and the liquid turns into a <u>gas</u>.

## *Atoms are Rearranged During Chemical Reactions*

1) <u>Chemical changes</u> are different to physical changes

2) Chemical changes happen during <u>chemical reactions</u>, when bonds between atoms break and the atoms <u>change places</u>. The atoms from the substances you <u>start off</u> with (the <u>reactants</u>) are rearranged to form <u>different substances</u> (the <u>products</u>).

3) Compared to physical changes, chemical changes are often <u>hard to reverse</u>.

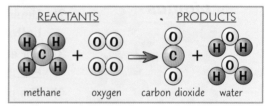

REACTANTS · PRODUCTS

methane oxygen carbon dioxide water

## *Making Predictions about Substances from their Properties*

You might be asked to <u>use data</u> to work out what <u>state</u> substances will be in under <u>certain conditions</u>.

**EXAMPLE:**

The table on the right gives information about the properties of four different substances.

**Predict the state of substance D at 1000 °C.**

| Substance | Melting point / °C | Boiling point / °C |
|-----------|--------------------|--------------------|
| A | −218.4 | −183.0 |
| B | 1535 | 2750 |
| C | 1410 | 2355 |
| D | 801 | 1413 |

1) The <u>melting point</u> of D is 801 °C and its <u>boiling point</u> is 1413 °C.

2) That means it's a solid <u>below 801 °C</u>, a gas <u>above 1413 °C</u>, and a liquid <u>in between</u>.

3) <u>1000 °C</u> is between 801 °C and 1413 °C, so... **D is a liquid at 1000 °C.**

## *I felt like changing state, so I moved from Texas to Michigan...*

Predicting the state of something at a given temperature isn't too tricky. Best get some practice in anyway...

Q1 What states of matter are you moving from and to if you are condensing a substance? [1 mark]

Q2 Using the table in the example above, predict the states of substances A, B and C at 1500 °C. [3 marks]

# Purity

Purity — one of those special science words that has a special science meaning that doesn't quite match the everyday meaning that people use in real life... *sigh*...

## Pure Substances Contain Only One Thing

Having impure thoughts again, Henry?

1) In everyday life, the word 'pure' is often used to mean 'clean' or 'natural'.

2) In chemistry, it's got a more specific meaning — a substance is pure if it's completely made up of a single element or compound.

3) If you've got more than one compound present, or different elements that aren't all part of a single compound, then you've got a mixture.

4) So, for example, fresh air might be thought of as nice and 'pure', but it's chemically impure, because it's a mixture of nitrogen, oxygen, argon, carbon dioxide, water vapour and various other gases.

5) Lots of mixtures are really useful — alloys (e.g. steel) are a great example. But sometimes chemists need to obtain a pure sample of a substance.

## You Can Test For Purity Using Melting Points

1) Every pure substance has a specific, sharp melting point and boiling point. For example, pure ice melts at 0 °C, and pure water boils at 100 °C.

2) You can use this to test the purity of a sample of a substance, by comparing the actual melting point of the sample to the expected value.

3) If a substance is a mixture then it will melt gradually over a range of temperatures, rather than having a sharp melting point, like a pure substance.

4) Impure substances will melt over a range of temperatures, because they are effectively mixtures.

5) To measure the melting point of a substance, you can use melting point apparatus. This is a piece of kit that allows you to heat up a small sample of a solid very slowly, so you can observe and record the exact temperature that it melts at.

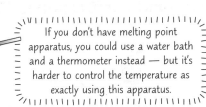

If you don't have melting point apparatus, you could use a water bath and a thermometer instead — but it's harder to control the temperature as exactly using this apparatus.

Example: Adil's teacher gives him samples of four powdered solids, labelled A, B, C and D. He uses melting point apparatus to determine the melting point of each of the solids. Adil's results are shown in the table below.

| Solid | A | B | C | D |
|---|---|---|---|---|
| Melting point (°C) | 82 | 72-79 | 101 | 63 |

Which of the four solids, A, B, C or D, was a mixture?

Answer: B — Adil's results show that solid B must be a mixture, because it melted over a range of temperatures (rather than melting at a specific temperature, as the other three solids did).

## If in doubt, heat it up until it melts — that's my motto...

There are lots of ways to extract a pure substance out of a mixture. You'll learn about some over the next few pages.

Q1    Rachel buys a carton of juice labelled '100% pure orange juice'. Explain why the use of the word 'pure' on this label doesn't match the scientific definition.

[2 marks]

Q2    Glyn is going to use melting point apparatus to test the melting point of a sample of pure benzoic acid. He says "I expect the sample to melt over a range of temperatures." Do you agree with Glyn? Explain your answer.

[1 mark]

# Distillation

Distillation is used to separate mixtures that contain <u>liquids</u>.
There are two types that you need to know about — <u>simple</u> and <u>fractional</u>.

## Simple Distillation Separates Out Solutions

PRACTICAL

<u>Simple distillation</u> is used for separating out a <u>liquid</u> from a <u>solution</u>.
Here's how to use simple distillation to get <u>pure water</u> from <u>seawater</u>:

1) Pour your sample of seawater into the <u>distillation flask</u>.

2) Set up the <u>apparatus</u> as shown in the diagram. Connect the bottom end of the <u>condenser</u> to a cold tap using <u>rubber tubing</u>. Run <u>cold water</u> through the condenser to keep it cool.

3) Gradually heat the distillation flask. The part of the solution that has the lowest boiling point will <u>evaporate</u> — in this case, that's the water.

4) The water <u>vapour</u> passes into the condenser where it <u>cools</u> and <u>condenses</u> (turns back into a liquid). It then flows into the beaker where it is <u>collected</u>.

5) Eventually you'll end up with just the <u>salt</u> left in the flask.

The <u>problem</u> with simple distillation is that you can only use it to separate things with <u>very different</u> boiling points.

If you have a <u>mixture of liquids</u> with <u>similar boiling points</u>, you need another method to separate them out — like fractional distillation...

*thermometer*

*water out*

*condenser*

*seawater*

*water in*

**heat**

*pure distilled water*

If the liquid you're heating is flammable, use an electric heater or a water bath to heat it, rather than a Bunsen burner.

## Fractional Distillation is Used to Separate a Mixture of Liquids

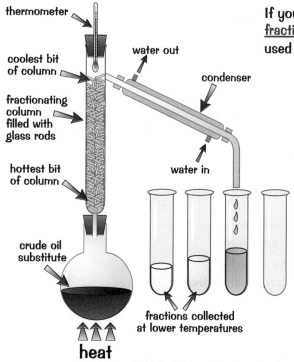

*thermometer*

*coolest bit of column*

*water out*

*condenser*

*fractionating column filled with glass rods*

*hottest bit of column*

*water in*

*crude oil substitute*

*fractions collected at lower temperatures*

**heat**

If you've got a <u>mixture of liquids</u> you can separate it using <u>fractional distillation</u>. Here's a lab demonstration that can be used to model <u>fractional distillation of crude oil</u> at a <u>refinery</u>:

1) Put your <u>mixture</u> in a flask. Attach a <u>fractionating column</u> and condenser above the flask as shown.

2) Gradually heat the flask. The <u>different liquids</u> will all have <u>different boiling points</u> — so they will evaporate at <u>different temperatures</u>.

3) The liquid with the <u>lowest boiling point</u> evaporates first. When the temperature on the thermometer matches the boiling point of this liquid, it will reach the <u>top</u> of the column.

4) Liquids with <u>higher boiling points</u> might also start to evaporate. But the column is <u>cooler</u> towards the <u>top</u>, so they will only get part of the way up before <u>condensing</u> and running back down towards the flask.

5) When the first liquid has been collected, <u>raise the temperature</u> until the <u>next one</u> reaches the top.

## Fractionating — sounds a bit too much like maths to me...

The industrial method for fraction distillation of crude oil isn't quite as... well... crude as the one shown here. If you're desperate to find out what goes on in oil refineries, have a look at page 137.

Q1    Propan-1-ol, methanol and ethanol have boiling points of 97 °C, 65 °C and 78 °C respectively.
A student uses fractional distillation to separate a mixture of these compounds.
State which liquid will be collected in the first fraction and explain why.          [2 marks]

# Filtration and Crystallisation

If you've mixed a <u>solid</u> with a <u>liquid</u>, it should be pretty easy to <u>separate</u> them out again.
Which <u>method</u> you'll need to use depends on whether or not the solid can <u>dissolve</u> in the liquid.

## Filtration is Used to Separate an Insoluble Solid from a Liquid

1) If the <u>product</u> of a reaction is an <u>insoluble solid</u>, you can use <u>filtration</u> to separate it out from the <u>liquid reaction mixture</u>.

2) It can be used in <u>purification</u> as well. For example, <u>solid impurities</u> can be separated out from a reaction mixture using <u>filtration</u>.

3) All you do is pop some <u>filter paper</u> into a <u>funnel</u> and pour your mixture into it. The liquid part of the mixture <u>runs through</u> the paper, leaving behind a <u>solid residue</u>.

Filter paper folded into a cone shape.

The solid is left in the filter paper.

## Crystallisation Separates a Soluble Solid from a Solution

Here's how you <u>crystallise</u> a product...

1) Pour the solution into an <u>evaporating dish</u> and gently <u>heat</u> the solution. Some of the <u>water</u> will evaporate and the solution will get more <u>concentrated</u>.

2) Once some of the water has evaporated, <u>or</u> when you see crystals start to form (the <u>point of crystallisation</u>), remove the dish from the heat and leave the solution to <u>cool</u>.

3) The salt should start to form <u>crystals</u> as it becomes <u>insoluble</u> in the cold, highly concentrated solution.

4) <u>Filter</u> the crystals out of the solution, and leave them in a warm place to <u>dry</u>. You could also use a <u>drying oven</u> or a <u>desiccator</u> (a desiccator contains chemicals that remove water from the surroundings).

evaporating dish

## Choose the Right Purification Method

You might have to pick one of the <u>techniques</u> covered in this section to separate a mixture. The best technique to use will depend on the <u>properties</u> of the <u>substances</u> in the mixture.

Choose wisely...

**Example:**
A <u>mixture</u> is composed of two substances, X and Y.
<u>Substance X</u> is a <u>liquid</u> at room temperature, has a <u>melting point</u> of 5 °C and a <u>boiling point</u> of 60 °C.
<u>Substance Y</u> is a <u>solid</u> at room temperature. It has a <u>melting point</u> of 745 °C and a <u>boiling point</u> of 1218 °C. Substance Y <u>dissolves completely</u> in substance X.

Suggest a <u>purification method</u> you could use to obtain:
a) A pure sample of substance X,      b) A pure sample of substance Y.

**Answer:**
a) To get **X** on its own, you need to <u>distil it</u> from the solution. You can use <u>simple distillation</u> here — there's no need for fractional distillation as there's only <u>one liquid</u> in the solution. You could obtain a pure sample of substance X using simple distillation.

b) To get a <u>soluble solid</u> out of a solution, you should use <u>crystallisation</u>.
In theory, if you <u>distilled</u> the mixture until all of substance X had evaporated off, you'd end up with just substance Y left in the flask. But there might be <u>traces</u> of substance X still hanging around — crystallisation's a better way of getting a <u>pure sample</u> of a solid from a solution.
You could obtain a pure sample of substance Y using crystallisation.

## Its mum calls it Philliptration...

Some mixtures are made up of several components, so you might need to use a combination of the methods covered in this section to get all the different components out. I never said it was easy...

Q1      You are given a solution that has been made by dissolving copper sulfate crystals in water. Describe a method that you could use to extract pure copper sulfate crystals from the solution.     [4 marks]

# Chromatography

Chromatography is one analytical method that you need to know. It's all to do with a mobile phase and a stationary phase. But I'll tell you what, my revision's feeling in a stationary phase at the moment...

## Chromatography uses Two Phases

Chromatography is a method used to separate a mixture of soluble substances and identify them. There are lots of different types of chromatography — but they all have two 'phases':

- A mobile phase — where the molecules can move. This is always a liquid or a gas.
- A stationary phase — where the molecules can't move. This can be a solid or a really thick liquid.

1) The components in the mixture separate out as the mobile phase moves over the stationary phase — they all end up in different places in the stationary phase. ◄

2) This happens because each of the chemicals in a mixture will spend different amounts of time dissolved in the mobile phase and stuck to the stationary phase.

3) How fast a chemical moves through the stationary phase depends on how it 'distributes' itself between the two phases.

*For each component in your mixture, you'll end up with one spot on your chromatogram (see next page for more on chromatograms).*

## In Paper Chromatography the Mobile Phase is a Solvent

In paper chromatography, the stationary phase is a piece of filter paper and the mobile phase is a solvent (e.g. water or ethanol).

Here's the method for setting it up:

**PRACTICAL**

1) Draw a line near the bottom of the paper — this is the baseline.
(Use a pencil to do this — pencil marks are insoluble and won't move with the solvent as ink might.)
Put a spot of the mixture to be separated on the line.

2) Put some of the solvent into a beaker. Dip the bottom of the paper (but not the spot) into the solvent.

3) Put a watch glass on the top of the beaker to stop any solvent from evaporating away.

4) The solvent will start to move up the paper. When the chemicals in the mixture dissolve in the solvent, they will move up the paper too.

5) You will see the different chemicals in the sample separate out, forming spots at different places on the paper.
(If one of your components is insoluble in the mobile phase, it won't move — it'll stay as a spot on the baseline.)

6) Remove the paper from the beaker before the solvent reaches the top. Mark the distance the solvent has moved (the solvent front) in pencil.

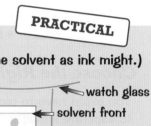
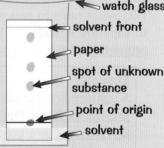

watch glass
solvent front
paper
spot of unknown substance
point of origin
solvent

*If any substances in a mixture are insoluble in one solvent, you could try re-running the experiment on the same mixture, but using a different solvent. You may find this separates out the components, allowing you to find their $R_f$ values (see next page).*

The amount of time the molecules spend in each phase depends on two things:

- How soluble they are in the solvent.
- How attracted they are to the stationary phase.

Molecules with a higher solubility in the solvent (and which are less attracted to the paper) will spend more time in the mobile phase than the stationary phase — so they'll be carried further up the paper.

## All hairdressers have to master Combatography...

Like a solvent working its way up some filter paper, let this chromatography stuff work its way into your brain...

Q1 In paper chromatography, what is the stationary phase? [1 mark]

Q2 A mixture of two chemicals, A and B, is separated using paper chromatography. Chemical A is more soluble in the solvent than B is. Which chemical, A or B, will end up closer to the solvent front? Explain your answer. [2 marks]

# Interpreting Chromatograms

So, what use is chromatography, apart from making a pretty pattern of spots? Let's find out...

## You can Calculate the $R_f$ Value for Each Chemical

1) In paper chromatography, the piece of paper that you end up with is called a chromatogram.

2) If you know that you have chemicals in your mixture that are colourless (e.g. amino acids), you might have to spray the chromatogram with a chemical called a locating agent to show where the spots are.

3) You need to know how to work out the $R_f$ values for the spots on a chromatogram.

4) An $R_f$ value is the ratio between the distance travelled by the dissolved substance (the solute) and the distance travelled by the solvent. You can find $R_f$ values using the formula:

$$R_f = \frac{\text{distance travelled by solute}}{\text{distance travelled by solvent}}$$

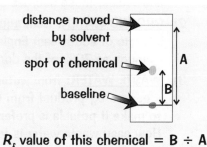

$R_f$ value of this chemical = B ÷ A

5) To find the distance travelled by the solute, measure from the baseline to the centre of the spot.

6) Chromatography is often carried out to see if a certain substance is present in a mixture. You run a pure sample of a substance that you think might be in your mixture alongside a sample of the mixture itself. If the sample has the same $R_f$ values as one of the spots, they're likely to be the same.

7) Chemists sometimes run samples of pure substances called standard reference materials (SRMs) next to a mixture to check the identities of its components. SRMs have controlled concentrations and purities.

8) You can also use chromatography to do a purity test. A pure substance won't be separated by chromatography — it'll move as one blob (while a mixture should give you multiple blobs).

## You can Combine Separation Techniques to Analyse Mixtures

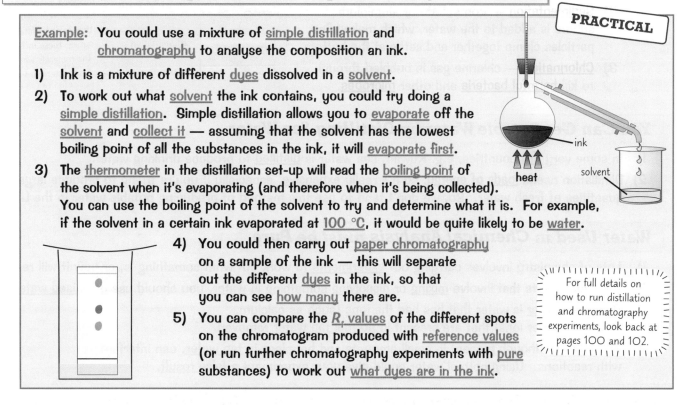

PRACTICAL

Example: You could use a mixture of simple distillation and chromatography to analyse the composition an ink.

1) Ink is a mixture of different dyes dissolved in a solvent.

2) To work out what solvent the ink contains, you could try doing a simple distillation. Simple distillation allows you to evaporate off the solvent and collect it — assuming that the solvent has the lowest boiling point of all the substances in the ink, it will evaporate first.

3) The thermometer in the distillation set-up will read the boiling point of the solvent when it's evaporating (and therefore when it's being collected). You can use the boiling point of the solvent to try and determine what it is. For example, if the solvent in a certain ink evaporated at 100 °C, it would be quite likely to be water.

4) You could then carry out paper chromatography on a sample of the ink — this will separate out the different dyes in the ink, so that you can see how many there are.

5) You can compare the $R_f$ values of the different spots on the chromatogram produced with reference values (or run further chromatography experiments with pure substances) to work out what dyes are in the ink.

For full details on how to run distillation and chromatography experiments, look back at pages 100 and 102.

## J'aime la chromatographie... hmm, I think I need an interpreter...

You could be asked to work out $R_f$ values in the exams, so make sure you know the formula in the purple box.

Q1 On a paper chromatogram, chemical X travelled 2.1 cm, chemical Y travelled 3.6 cm and the solvent front travelled 6.0 cm. Calculate the $R_f$ value of chemical Y. [2 marks]

# Water Treatment

Water, water, everywhere... well, there is if you live in a submarine.

## There are a Variety of Limited Water Resources in the UK

In the UK, there are a number of sources of water which can be purified to provide us
with potable water (water that is fit to drink). We get our water from:

1) **SURFACE WATER**: from lakes, rivers and reservoirs. In much of England
and Wales, these sources start to run dry during the summer months.

2) **GROUND WATER**: from aquifers (rocks that trap water underground).
In parts of south-east England, where surface water is very limited,
as much as 70% of the domestic water supply comes from ground water.

3) **WASTE WATER**: from water that's been contaminated by a human process,
e.g. as a by-product from some industrial processes. Treating waste water
to make it potable is preferable to disposing of the water, which can be polluting.
How easy waste water is to treat depends on the levels of contaminants in it.

## Water is Purified in Water Treatment Plants

The water that comes out of your taps doesn't just come straight from the source — first it has to
be purified. How much purification it needs will depends on the source. Ground water from aquifers
is usually quite pure, but waste water and surface water needs a lot of treatment. But, wherever
it comes from, before we can drink it most water will be purified using the following processes:

1) Filtration — a wire mesh screens out large
twigs etc., and then gravel and sand
beds filter out any other solid bits.

2) Sedimentation — iron sulfate or aluminium
sulfate is added to the water, which makes fine
particles clump together and settle at the bottom.

3) Chlorination — chlorine gas is bubbled through
to kill harmful bacteria and other microbes.

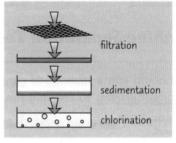

filtration

sedimentation

chlorination

*Some soluble
impurities that are
dissolved in the water
are not removed as
they can't be filtered
out — these include
the minerals which
cause water hardness.*

## You Can Get Potable Water by Distilling Sea Water

1) In some very dry countries, e.g. Kuwait, sea water is distilled to produce drinking water.

2) Distillation needs loads of energy, so it's really expensive, especially if you're trying to produce large
quantities of fresh water. So, we don't tend to use this method of producing potable water in the UK.

## Water Used in Chemical Analysis must be Pure

1) Lots of chemistry involves carrying out experiments to work out what something is, or how it will react.

2) For experiments that involve mixing or dissolving something in water, you should use deionised water.

3) Deionised water is water that has had the ions (such as calcium,
iron and copper ions) that are present in normal tap water removed.

4) These ions, although present in small amounts and harmless in tap water, can interfere
with reactions. Using normal water could give your experiment a false result.

## If water from the ground is ground water, why isn't rain sky water?

Ahhh... Every glass of tap water I drink tastes all the sweeter for knowing what it had to go through to get to me...

Q1    Outline how water is purified in a water treatment plant.     [3 marks]

Q2    A student plans to make a solution to use in an experiment by dissolving pure, solid sodium iodide
in water. Suggest why the student should **not** use tap water. State what he should use instead.     [2 marks]

# Acids and Bases

Testing the pH of a solution means using an <u>indicator</u> — and that means pretty <u>colours</u>...

## The pH Scale Goes From 0 to 14

1) The pH scale is a measure of <u>how acidic or alkaline</u> a solution is. A <u>neutral</u> substance has <u>pH 7</u>.

2) An <u>acid</u> is a substance with a <u>pH</u> of <u>less than 7</u>. Acids form $H^+$ ions in water.

3) The higher the <u>concentration of hydrogen ions</u> in a solution, the <u>more acidic</u> it is, so the lower its pH will be. In other words, as the concentration of hydrogen ions <u>increases</u>, the <u>pH decreases</u>.

4) A <u>base</u> is a substance that reacts with an acid to produce a <u>salt</u> and <u>water</u>.

5) An <u>alkali</u> is a base that is <u>soluble</u> in water. All alkalis have a <u>pH</u> of <u>more than 7</u> and they form <u>$OH^-$ ions</u> (otherwise known as <u>hydroxide ions</u>) in water.

6) In alkaline solutions, the higher the <u>concentration of $OH^-$ ions</u>, the higher the pH.

## You Can Measure the pH of a Solution

1) An <u>indicator</u> is a <u>dye</u> that <u>changes colour</u> depending on whether it's <u>above or below a certain pH</u>.

2) Indicators are simple to use — <u>add a few drops</u> to the solution you're testing, then compare the colour the solution goes to a <u>pH chart</u> for that indicator. E.g. here's the pH chart for <u>Universal indicator</u>.

pH 0   1   2   3   4   5   6   7   8   9   10   11   12   13   14

ACIDS          NEUTRAL          ALKALIS

3) Some indicators that you need to know about are:
- litmus — is <u>red</u> in <u>acidic</u> solutions, <u>purple</u> in <u>neutral</u> solutions and <u>blue</u> in <u>alkaline</u> solutions.
- methyl orange — is <u>red</u> in <u>acidic solutions</u> and <u>yellow</u> in <u>neutral</u> and <u>alkaline</u> solutions
- phenolphthalein — is colourless in acidic or neutral solutions and <u>pink</u> in <u>alkaline</u> solutions.

## Acids and Bases Neutralise Each Other

The reaction between an acid and a base is called <u>neutralisation</u>. It produces a <u>salt</u> and <u>water</u>.

$$HCl + NaOH \rightarrow NaCl + H_2O$$
acid        base        salt        water

Neutralisation reactions in <u>aqueous solution</u> can also be shown as an ionic equation (see p.76) in terms of <u>$H^+$</u> and <u>$OH^-$ ions</u>:

$$H^+_{(aq)} + OH^-_{(aq)} \rightarrow H_2O_{(l)}$$

When an acid neutralises a base (or vice versa), the <u>products</u> are <u>neutral</u>, i.e. they have a <u>pH of 7</u>. At pH 7, the concentration of hydrogen ions is <u>equal to</u> the concentration of hydroxide ions.

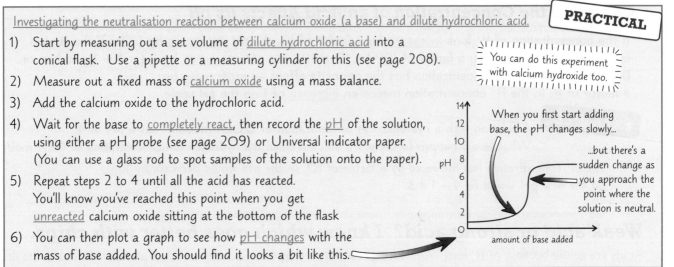

PRACTICAL

<u>Investigating the neutralisation reaction between calcium oxide (a base) and dilute hydrochloric acid.</u>

1) Start by measuring out a set volume of <u>dilute hydrochloric acid</u> into a conical flask. Use a pipette or a measuring cylinder for this (see page 208).

You can do this experiment with calcium hydroxide too.

2) Measure out a fixed mass of <u>calcium oxide</u> using a mass balance.

3) Add the calcium oxide to the hydrochloric acid.

4) Wait for the base to <u>completely react</u>, then record the <u>pH</u> of the solution, using either a pH probe (see page 209) or Universal indicator paper. (You can use a glass rod to spot samples of the solution onto the paper).

When you first start adding base, the pH changes slowly...

...but there's a sudden change as you approach the point where the solution is neutral.

5) Repeat steps 2 to 4 until all the acid has reacted. You'll know you've reached this point when you get <u>unreacted</u> calcium oxide sitting at the bottom of the flask

6) You can then plot a graph to see how <u>pH changes</u> with the mass of base added. You should find it looks a bit like this.

pH    amount of base added

## This page should have all bases covered...

pHew, you got to the end of the page, so here's an interesting(ish) fact — your skin is slightly acidic (pH 5.5).

Q1    The pH of an unknown solution is found to be 2. Is the solution acidic or alkaline?          [1 mark]

# Strong and Weak Acids

Right then. More on <u>acids</u>. Brace yourself...

## Acids Produce Hydrogen Ions in Water

All acids can <u>ionise</u> (or <u>dissociate</u>) in solution — that means splitting up to produce a <u>hydrogen ion</u>, $H^+$, and another ion. For example,

$$HCl \rightarrow H^+ + Cl^-$$
$$HNO_3 \rightarrow H^+ + NO_3^-$$

*HCl and $HNO_3$ don't produce hydrogen ions until they meet water.*

## Acids Can be Strong or Weak

1) <u>Strong acids</u> (e.g. sulfuric, hydrochloric and nitric acids) <u>ionise almost completely</u> in water, i.e. a <u>large</u> proportion of the acid molecules dissociate to release $H^+$ ions. They tend to have low pHs (pH 0-2).

2) <u>Weak acids</u> (e.g. ethanoic, citric and carbonic acids) <u>do not fully ionise</u> in solution, i.e. only a <u>small</u> proportion of the acid molecules dissociate to release $H^+$ ions. Their pHs tend to be around 2-6.

3) The ionisation of a <u>weak</u> acid is a <u>reversible reaction</u>, which sets up an <u>equilibrium</u>. Since only a few of the acid particles release $H^+$ ions, the <u>equilibrium</u> lies well to the <u>left</u>.

<u>Strong acid</u>: $HCl \longrightarrow H^+ + Cl^-$

<u>Weak acid</u>: $CH_3COOH \rightleftharpoons H^+ + CH_3COO^-$

*For more on equilibria turn to page 121.*

## Don't Confuse Strong Acids with Concentrated Acids

1) Acid <u>strength</u> (i.e. strong or weak) tells you <u>what proportion</u> of the acid molecules <u>ionise</u> in water.

2) The <u>concentration</u> of an acid is different. Concentration measures <u>how much acid</u> there is in a litre (1 $dm^3$) of water. Concentration is basically how <u>watered down</u> your acid is.

3) An acid with a <u>large number</u> of <u>acid molecules</u> compared to the volume of water is said to be <u>concentrated</u>. An acid with a <u>small number</u> of acid molecules compared to the volume of water is said to be <u>dilute</u>.

*Concentration is measured in $g\ dm^{-3}$ or $mol\ dm^{-3}$.*

4) Note that concentration describes the <u>total number</u> of dissolved acid molecules — <u>not</u> the number of molecules that produce hydrogen ions.

5) The more grams (or moles) of acid per $dm^3$, the <u>more concentrated</u> the acid is.

6) So you can have a <u>dilute strong</u> acid, or a <u>concentrated weak</u> acid.

## Changing the Concentration of an Acid Affects its pH

If the concentration of $H^+$ ions <u>increases</u> by a factor of <u>10</u>, the pH <u>decreases</u> by <u>1</u>. So if the $H^+$ ion concentration <u>increases</u> by a factor of <u>100</u> (= 10 × 10), the pH <u>decreases</u> by <u>2</u> (= 1 + 1), and so on. Decreasing the $H^+$ ion concentration has the opposite effect — a <u>decrease</u> by a factor of <u>10</u> in the $H^+$ concentration means an <u>increase</u> of <u>1</u> on the pH scale.

**EXAMPLE:** A solution with a hydrogen ion concentration of 0.001 $mol/dm^3$ has a pH of 4.
What would happen to the pH if you increased the hydrogen ion concentration to 0.01 $mol/dm^3$?

The $H^+$ concentration has increased by a factor of 10, so the pH would decrease by 1.
So the new pH would be 4 − 1 = 3.

## Weak acid or strong acid? I know which goes better with chips...

Acids are acidic because of $H^+$ ions. And strong acids are strong because they let go of all their $H^+$ ions at the drop of a hat... Well, at the drop of a drop of water.

Q1    Explain the difference between a strong acid and a weak acid.                    [2 marks]

Q2    A student added a strong acid to a solution with a pH of 6. The new solution had a pH of 3.
State whether the concentration of $H^+$ had increased or decreased and by what factor.    [2 marks]

# Reactions of Acids

You met bases, back on page 105. You've also seen how they react with acids in neutralisation reactions to form a salt and water. So I'm sure you'll be overjoyed to hear there are more of these reactions coming up.

## Salts Form When Acids React with Bases

1) A salt is formed during a neutralisation reaction (a reaction between an acid and a base). Salts are ionic compounds.

2) In general, hydrochloric acid produces chloride salts, sulfuric acid produces sulfate salts and nitric acid produces nitrate salts.

3) You need to be able to remember what happens when you add acids to various bases...

### Acid + Metal Oxide → Salt + Water

Examples:
$2HCl + CuO \rightarrow CuCl_2 + H_2O$      (Copper chloride)
$H_2SO_4 + ZnO \rightarrow ZnSO_4 + H_2O$      (Zinc sulfate)
$2HNO_3 + MgO \rightarrow Mg(NO_3)_2 + 2H_2O$      (Magnesium nitrate)

### Acid + Metal Hydroxide → Salt + Water

Examples:
$HCl + NaOH \rightarrow NaCl + H_2O$      (Sodium chloride)
$H_2SO_4 + Zn(OH)_2 \rightarrow ZnSO_4 + 2H_2O$      (Zinc sulfate)
$HNO_3 + KOH \rightarrow KNO_3 + H_2O$      (Potassium nitrate)

*These are the same as the acid/alkali neutralisation reaction you met on page 105.*

## Salts Also Form When Acids React With Metals or Metal Carbonates

You also need to know what happens when you react an acid with a metal or a metal carbonate:

### Acid + Metal → Salt + Hydrogen

Examples:
$2HCl + Mg \rightarrow MgCl_2 + H_2$      (Magnesium chloride)
$H_2SO_4 + Mg \rightarrow MgSO_4 + H_2$      (Magnesium sulfate)

*The reaction of nitric acid with metals can be more complicated — you get a nitrate salt, but instead of hydrogen gas, the other products are usually a mixture of water, NO and $NO_2$.*

1) You can test for hydrogen using a lighted splint.
2) Hydrogen makes a "squeaky pop" with a lighted splint.
3) The noise comes from the hydrogen burning with the oxygen in the air to form water.

hydrogen

squeaky pop!

♪ Eeeee! ♪

### Acid + Metal Carbonate → Salt + Water + Carbon Dioxide

Examples:
$2HCl + Na_2CO_3 \rightarrow 2NaCl + H_2O + CO_2$      (Sodium chloride)
$H_2SO_4 + K_2CO_3 \rightarrow K_2SO_4 + H_2O + CO_2$      (Potassium sulfate)
$2HNO_3 + ZnCO_3 \rightarrow Zn(NO_3)_2 + H_2O + CO_2$      (Zinc nitrate)

1) You can test to see if a gas is carbon dioxide by bubbling it through limewater.
2) If the gas is carbon dioxide, the limewater will turn cloudy.

$CO_2$ gas

acid + carbonate

limewater

## Nitrates — much cheaper than day-rates...

What a lot of reactions. Better take a peek back at page 75 for help with writing and balancing chemical equations.

Q1      Write a balanced chemical equation for the reaction of hydrochloric acid with calcium carbonate.      [2 marks]

# Making Insoluble Salts

Unfortunately for you, you've got to learn which salts are <u>soluble</u> and which ones <u>aren't</u>. Tough luck...

## The Rules of Solubility

*Soluble things dissolve in water. Insoluble things don't.*

1) How you make a salt depends on whether it's <u>soluble</u> or <u>insoluble</u>.

2) You may need to work out if, when two solutions are mixed, a salt will form as a <u>precipitate</u> (i.e. it's an insoluble salt), or whether it will just form <u>in solution</u> (i.e. it's a soluble salt).

3) This table is a pretty fail-safe way of working out whether a substance is soluble in water or not.

| Substance | Soluble or Insoluble? |
|---|---|
| common salts of sodium, potassium and ammonium | soluble |
| nitrates | soluble |
| common chlorides | soluble (except silver chloride and lead chloride) |
| common sulfates | soluble (except lead, barium and calcium sulfate) |
| common carbonates and hydroxides | insoluble (except for sodium, potassium and ammonium ones) |

## Making Insoluble Salts — Precipitation Reactions

1) To make a pure, dry sample of an <u>insoluble</u> salt, you can use a <u>precipitation reaction</u>. You just need to pick the right two <u>soluble salts</u> and <u>react</u> them together to get your <u>insoluble salt</u>.

2) E.g. to make <u>lead chloride</u> (insoluble), mix <u>lead nitrate</u> and <u>sodium chloride</u> (both soluble).

lead nitrate + sodium chloride → lead chloride + sodium nitrate

$$Pb(NO_3)_{2\,(aq)} + 2NaCl_{(aq)} \rightarrow PbCl_{2\,(s)} + 2NaNO_{3\,(aq)}$$

## Method

1) Add 1 spatula of <u>lead nitrate</u> to a test tube. Add <u>water</u> to dissolve it. You should use deionised water to make sure there are no other ions about. <u>Shake it thoroughly</u> to ensure that all the lead nitrate has <u>dissolved</u>. Then, in a separate test tube, do the same with 1 spatula of <u>sodium chloride</u>.

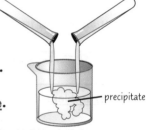
precipitate

2) Tip the <u>two solutions</u> into a small beaker, and give it a good stir to make sure it's all mixed together. The lead chloride should <u>precipitate</u> out.

filter paper
filter funnel

3) Put a folded piece of <u>filter paper</u> into a <u>filter funnel</u>, and stick the funnel into a <u>conical flask</u>.

4) <u>Pour</u> the contents of the beaker into the middle of the filter paper. Make sure that the solution doesn't go above the filter paper — otherwise some of the solid could dribble down the side.

5) <u>Swill out</u> the beaker with more deionised water, and tip this into the filter paper — to make sure you get <u>all the precipitate</u> from the beaker.

6) Rinse the contents of the filter paper with deionised water to make sure that <u>all the soluble sodium nitrate</u> has been washed away.

lead chloride

7) Then just scrape the <u>lead chloride</u> onto fresh filter paper and leave it to dry in an oven or a desiccator.

---

## *Lead chloride just doesn't behave — it's an intolerable salt...*

The theory may seem dull, but you'll probably get to make some nice salts in your class, and that's pretty cool.

Q1 State whether the following salts are soluble or insoluble:
a) potassium chloride   b) copper carbonate   c) calcium sulfate   d) ammonium hydroxide [4 marks]

Q2 Suggest two reactants you could use to form barium sulfate in a precipitation reaction. [2 marks]

# Making Soluble Salts

You met the technique for making <u>insoluble salts</u> on the last page. Time for <u>soluble salts</u> now...

## Making Soluble Salts — Use an Acid and an Insoluble Base

PRACTICAL

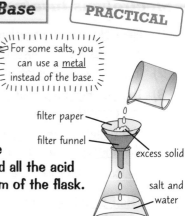

1) You can make a <u>soluble salt</u> by reacting an <u>acid</u> that contains one of the ions you want in the salt with an <u>insoluble base</u> that contains the other ion you need (often a <u>metal oxide</u> or <u>metal hydroxide</u>).

*For some salts, you can use a <u>metal</u> instead of the base.*

filter paper

filter funnel

excess solid

salt and water

2) Start by <u>heating the acid</u> in a <u>water bath</u> (see p.211) — this speeds up the reaction between the acid and the insoluble base. Do this in a <u>fume cupboard</u> to avoid releasing acid fumes into the room.

3) Then add the <u>base</u> to the <u>acid</u> — the base and acid will react to produce a <u>soluble salt</u> (and water). You will know when the base is in excess and all the acid has been neutralised because the excess solid will just <u>sink</u> to the bottom of the flask.

(It's important that the base is in excess so that you don't have any leftover acid in your product.)

4) <u>Filter</u> off the <u>excess</u> solid to get a solution containing only the <u>salt</u> and <u>water</u>.

5) <u>Heat the solution gently</u>, using a Bunsen burner, to slowly <u>evaporate</u> off some of the water. Leave the solution to cool and allow the salt to <u>crystallise</u> (see p.101). Filter off the <u>solid salt</u> and leave it to <u>dry</u>.

> **Example:** You can add <u>copper oxide</u> to warm <u>sulfuric acid</u> to make a solution of <u>copper sulfate</u>:
>
> $$CuO_{(s)} + H_2SO_{4\,(aq)} \rightarrow CuSO_{4\,(aq)} + H_2O_{(l)}$$
>
> If you evaporate off some of the water and leave this solution to <u>crystallise</u>, you should get lovely <u>blue crystals</u> of <u>hydrated copper sulfate</u>, which you can <u>filter off</u> and <u>dry</u>.

## You can Make Soluble Salts Using Acid/Alkali Reactions

1) Soluble salts (salts that dissolve in water) can be made by reacting an acid with an <u>alkali</u>.

2) But you can't tell whether the reaction has <u>finished</u> — there's no signal that all the acid has been neutralised. You also can't just add an <u>excess</u> of alkali to the acid, because the salt is <u>soluble</u> and would be contaminated with the excess alkali.

3) Instead, you need to work out <u>exactly</u> the right amount of alkali to <u>neutralise</u> the acid. For this, you need to do a <u>titration</u> using an <u>indicator</u>. Here's what you do...

- Measure out a set amount of acid into a conical flask using a <u>pipette</u>. Add a few drops of <u>indicator</u>.

- Slowly add alkali to the acid, using a <u>burette</u>, until you reach the <u>end point</u> — this is when the acid's been exactly neutralised and the indicator <u>changes colour</u>.

- Then, carry out the reaction using exactly the same volumes of alkali and acid but with no <u>indicator</u>, so the salt <u>won't be contaminated</u> with indicator.

- The <u>solution</u> that remains when the reaction is complete contains only the <u>salt</u> and <u>water</u>.

- Slowly <u>evaporate</u> off some of the water and then leave the solution to crystallise (see page 101 for more on crystallisation). Filter off the solid and dry it — you'll be left with a <u>pure</u>, <u>dry</u> salt.

*For a titration, you should use an indicator with a single, clear colour change (like phenolphthalein or methyl orange). Universal indicator is no good as its colour change is too gradual.*

## I was attacked by a nasty copper sulfate — it was a-salt...

Yet more salts for you to make. If I were you though, I'd just get my salts from a sachet at the local chippy...

Q1 Iron nitrate is a soluble salt that can be made from iron oxide (an insoluble base) and nitric acid. Suggest a method you could use to make a pure sample of iron nitrate from these reactants. **[5 marks]**

# Electrolysis

Now I hope you're sitting comfortably. We're about to embark on three pages on <u>electrolysis</u>. What a treat.

## Electrolysis Involves Oxidation and Reduction

1) <u>Electrolysis</u> is the <u>breaking down</u> of a substance using <u>electricity</u>. An electric current is passed through an <u>electrolyte</u> (a <u>molten</u> or <u>dissolved</u> ionic compound), causing it to <u>decompose</u>.

*See page 116 for more on oxidation and reduction.*

2) In electrolysis, <u>oxidation</u> (<u>loss of electrons</u>) and <u>reduction</u> (<u>gain of electrons</u>) occur.

3) The <u>positive ions</u> (<u>cations</u>) in the electrolyte move towards the <u>cathode</u> (negative electrode) and are reduced (<u>gain</u> electrons).

4) The <u>negative ions</u> (<u>anions</u>) in the electrolyte move towards the <u>anode</u> (positive electrode) and are oxidised (<u>lose</u> electrons).

*This creates a flow of charge through the electrolyte.*

5) As ions gain or lose electrons they form the uncharged substances and are <u>discharged</u> from the electrolyte.

<u>Half equations</u> show how electrons are transferred during reactions. They're really useful for showing what happens at <u>each electrode</u> during electrolysis. To write a half equation:

1) Put <u>one</u> of the things <u>being oxidised or reduced</u> on one side of an arrow, and the thing it gets <u>oxidised or reduced to</u> on the other.

2) Balance up the <u>numbers of atoms</u> just like in a normal equation.

3) Then add <u>electrons</u> (written e⁻) on to one side to balance up the charges.

*The charges on each side of the equation should balance.*

<u>Examples</u>: Sodium is losing one electron to become a sodium ion: $Na \rightarrow Na^+ + e^-$

Hydrogen ions are gaining electrons to become hydrogen: $2H^+ + 2e^- \rightarrow H_2$

## Here's How to Set Up an Electrochemical Cell

1) An <u>electrochemical cell</u> is a <u>circuit</u>, made up of the anode, cathode, electrolyte, a power source and the wires that connect the two electrodes.

2) You need to know how to <u>set up</u> an electrochemical cell. The method used depends on whether your electrolyte is a <u>solution</u> or a <u>molten ionic substance</u>.

*You could put an ammeter or bulb in series with your circuit to check you've set it up correctly.*

### IF YOUR ELECTROLYTE'S A SOLUTION

1) Get <u>two inert</u> (unreactive) <u>electrodes</u>, e.g. graphite or platinum electrodes.

2) Clean the surfaces of the electrodes using some <u>emery paper</u> (or sandpaper).

3) From this point on, be careful <u>not to touch</u> the surfaces of the electrodes with your hands — you could transfer grease back onto the strips.

4) Place both electrodes into a <u>beaker</u> filled with your <u>electrolyte</u>.

5) Connect the electrodes to a power supply using <u>crocodile clips</u> and <u>wires</u>. When you turn the power supply on, a <u>current</u> will flow through the cell.

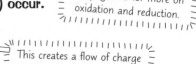

cathode (−ve)   d.c. power supply −ve +ve   anode (+ve)

*The voltage of the cell decreases as the electrolysis continues as the reactants get used up.*

### IF YOUR ELECTROLYTE'S A MOLTEN IONIC SUBSTANCE

1) Put your <u>solid ionic substance</u> (which will become your electrolyte) in a <u>crucible</u>.

2) Heat the crucible with a <u>Bunsen burner</u> until the <u>solid's molten</u>. You should do this in a <u>fume cupboard</u> to avoid releasing any toxic fumes into the room.

3) Once the solid's molten, dip two clean, <u>inert electrodes</u> into the electrolyte.

4) Then, connect the <u>electrodes</u> to a <u>power supply</u> using wires and clips — you should get a <u>current</u> flowing through the cell when you turn the power on.

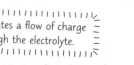

cathode   anode

molten ionic compound   HEAT

## Two electrodes and a lake of fire — electrochemical hell...

You can also carry out electrolysis experiments using non-inert electrodes. See page 112 for more about this.

Q1   At which electrode does oxidation happen during electrolysis?   [1 mark]

# Predicting Products of Electrolysis

This stuff is electrifying. You'll be on the edge of your seat with all this fun, fun, fun <u>electrolysis</u>.

## In Molten Ionic Solids, There's Only One Source of Ions

1) An <u>ionic solid can't</u> be electrolysed because the ions are in fixed positions and <u>can't move</u>.
2) <u>Molten ionic compounds can</u> be electrolysed because the ions can <u>move freely</u> and conduct electricity.
3) Positive <u>metal ions</u> are <u>reduced</u> to <u>metal atoms</u> at the cathode.
4) Negative <u>ions</u> are <u>oxidised</u> to atoms or molecules at the <u>anode</u>.
5) In the example of $PbBr_2$, you'd see a <u>brown vapour</u> of bromine gas at the anode and a silver coloured liquid at the cathode as <u>molten lead</u> is formed.

$$Pb^{2+} + 2e^- \rightarrow Pb \qquad 2Br^- \rightarrow Br_2 + 2e^-$$

*See page 83 for predicting what ions different metals and non-metals form.*

cathode (−ve)  anode (+ve)

molten lead bromide

6) It's easy to predict what products you get when you electrolyse <u>molten</u> substances — but you need to get the <u>half equations</u> (see p.110) right too. Here are some examples:

| Molten Electrolyte | Product at Cathode | Half equation at Cathode | Product at Anode | Half equation at Anode |
|---|---|---|---|---|
| potassium chloride, KCl | potassium | $K^+ + e^- \rightarrow K$ | chlorine | $2Cl^- \rightarrow Cl_2 + 2e^-$ |
| aluminium oxide, $Al_2O_3$ | aluminium | $Al^{3+} + 3e^- \rightarrow Al$ | oxygen | $2O^{2-} \rightarrow O_2 + 4e^-$ |

## Electrolysis of Aqueous Solutions is a Bit More Complicated

1) In <u>aqueous solutions</u>, as well as the <u>ions</u> from the ionic compound, there will be <u>hydrogen ions</u> ($H^+$) and <u>hydroxide ions</u> ($OH^-$) from the <u>water</u>: $H_2O_{(l)} \rightleftharpoons H^+_{(aq)} + OH^-_{(aq)}$

2) At the <u>cathode</u>, if $H^+$ ions and metal ions are present, <u>hydrogen gas</u> will be produced if the metal is <u>more reactive</u> than hydrogen (e.g. sodium). If the metal is <u>less reactive</u> than hydrogen (e.g. copper or silver), then a solid layer of the <u>pure metal</u> will be produced instead.

*You can use reactivity series to find out which metals are more or less reactive than hydrogen (see page 114).*

3) At the <u>anode</u>, if <u>$OH^-$ and halide ions</u> ($Cl^-$, $Br^-$, $I^-$) are present, molecules of chlorine, bromine or iodine will be formed. If <u>no halide ions</u> are present, then <u>oxygen</u> will be formed.

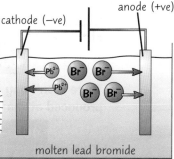

Sir Chlo Ride

Sir Chlo Rode

cathode (−ve)    anode (+ve)

NaCl solution

A solution of <u>sodium chloride</u> (NaCl) contains <u>four different ions</u>: $Na^+$, $Cl^-$, $OH^-$ and $H^+$.

- <u>Sodium</u> metal is more reactive hydrogen. So at the cathode, <u>hydrogen gas</u> is produced.

$$2H^+ + 2e^- \rightarrow H_2$$

- <u>Chloride ions</u> are present in the solution. So at the anode, <u>chlorine gas</u> is produced.

$$2Cl^- \rightarrow Cl_2 + 2e^-$$

| Aqueous Electrolyte | Product at Cathode | Half equation at Cathode | Product at Anode | Half equation at Anode |
|---|---|---|---|---|
| copper chloride, $CuCl_2$ | copper | $Cu^{2+} + 2e^- \rightarrow Cu$ | chlorine | $2Cl^- \rightarrow Cl_2 + 2e^-$ |
| sodium sulfate, $Na_2SO_4$ | hydrogen | $2H^+ + 2e^- \rightarrow H_2$ | oxygen | $4OH^- \rightarrow O_2 + 2H_2O + 4e^-$ |
| water acidified with sulfuric acid, $H_2O/H_2SO_4$ | hydrogen | $2H^+ + 2e^- \rightarrow H_2$ | oxygen | $4OH^- \rightarrow 2H_2O + O_2 + 4e^-$ |

## Faster shopping at the supermarket — use Electrolleys...

So it's kinda confusing this electrolysis malarkey — you need to take it slow and make sure you get it.

Q1  An aqueous solution of copper bromide, $CuBr_2$, is electrolysed using inert electrodes. Give the half equation to show the reaction occurring at the anode.

[2 marks]

# PRACTICAL | Electrolysis of Copper Sulfate

The products you get from electrolysis depend not only on your <u>electrolyte</u>, but also on your <u>electrodes</u> too...

## Electrolysis of Copper Sulfate with Inert Electrodes Produces Oxygen

1) A solution of <u>copper sulfate</u> ($CuSO_4$) contains <u>four different ions</u>: $Cu^{2+}$, $SO_4^{2-}$, $H^+$ and $OH^-$.

The method used to set up this electrochemical cell is on page 110.

2) When you electrolyse copper sulfate solution with inert electrodes:

- <u>Copper</u> is less reactive than hydrogen, so <u>copper metal</u> is produced at the cathode (you see a coating of copper on the electrode).

$$Cu^{2+} + 2e^- \rightarrow Cu$$

- There aren't any <u>halide ions</u> present, so <u>oxygen</u> and <u>water</u> are produced at the anode (you see bubbles of oxygen gas forming).

$$4OH^- \rightarrow O_2 + 2H_2O + 4e^-$$

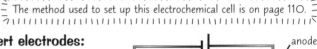
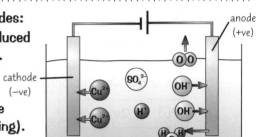

anode (+ve)

cathode (−ve)

$CuSO_4$ solution

## Non-Inert Electrodes Take Part in Electrolysis Reactions

1) If you set up an electrochemical cell in the same way as the one above, but using <u>copper electrodes</u> in a solution of copper sulfate instead of <u>inert</u> electrodes, the result is different.

2) As the reaction continues, the <u>mass</u> of the <u>anode</u> will <u>decrease</u> and the <u>mass</u> of the <u>cathode</u> will <u>increase</u>. This is because copper is transferred from the anode to the cathode.

3) The reaction takes a bit of time to happen, you'll need to leave the cell running for <u>30 minutes</u> or so to get a decent change in mass.

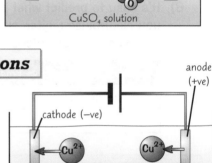

anode (+ve)

cathode (−ve)

$CuSO_{4\,(aq)}$

4) You can measure how the mass of your electrodes has changed during an experiment like this one by finding the <u>difference</u> between the <u>masses</u> of the electrodes before and after the experiment.

5) You should make sure the electrodes are <u>dry</u> the electrodes before weighing them — any copper sulfate solution on the electrodes may mean they appear to have a <u>higher mass</u> than they really do...

6) If you <u>increase the current</u> (e.g. by adding batteries) you will increase the rate of electrolysis. This means there will be a <u>bigger difference</u> between the <u>mass</u> of the two electrodes after the same amount of time.

7) The <u>electrical supply</u> acts by:
<u>Pulling electrons off</u> copper atoms at the <u>anode</u>: $Cu_{(s)} \rightarrow Cu^{2+}_{(aq)} + 2e^-$
<u>Offering electrons</u> at the <u>cathode</u> to nearby $\underline{Cu^{2+} \text{ ions}}$: $Cu^{2+}_{(aq)} + 2e^- \rightarrow Cu_{(s)}$

These two reactions mean the concentration of $Cu^{2+}$ ions in solution is constant — they're produced and removed at the same rate.

<u>Copper</u> can be extracted from its ore by <u>reduction with carbon</u> (see p.117), but copper made in this way is <u>impure</u>. <u>Electrolysis</u> is used to <u>purify</u> it — this method uses an electrochemical cell with <u>copper electrodes</u>:

When copper is <u>purified</u> using <u>electrolysis</u>, the <u>anode</u> starts off as a big lump of <u>impure copper</u>, the <u>electrolyte</u> is <u>copper(II) sulfate solution</u> (which contains $Cu^{2+}$ ions) and the <u>cathode</u> starts off as a thin piece of <u>pure copper</u>.

Here's what happens during the process:

1) The impure copper anode is <u>oxidised</u>, <u>dissolving</u> into the <u>electrolyte</u> to form <u>copper ions</u>:

$$Cu \rightarrow Cu^{2+} + 2e^-$$

2) The copper ions are <u>reduced</u> at the pure copper cathode, and add to it as a layer of <u>pure copper</u>:

$$Cu^{2+} + 2e^- \rightarrow Cu$$

3) Any <u>impurities</u> from the <u>impure copper anode</u> sink to the bottom of the cell, forming a <u>sludge</u>.

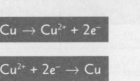

---

## A hat, some handcuffs and a truncheon — 100% pure copper...

Phew, that's the last page on electrolysis (for now...). Time to celebrate making it to the end with a question.

Q1     Explain how electrolysis is used to purify copper for use in electrical circuits.       [4 marks]

# Revision Questions for Sections 11 and 12

Sections 11 and 12 had quite a few nasty pages, but you got through 'em. Just time for a some revision questions.
- Try these questions and tick off each one when you get it right.
- When you've done all the questions under a heading and are completely happy with it, tick it off.

## States of Matter and Changes of State (p.97-98) ☑

1) Name the three states of matter. ☑
2) Describe the arrangement of particles, and the forces between them, in a solid. ☑
3) What happens to the forces between the particles in a solid as you melt it? ☑
4) What do you call the process of a substance changing from a liquid to a solid? ☑

## Purity and Separating Substances (p.99-103) ☐

5) What is the chemical definition of purity? ☑
6) Explain why air isn't considered a pure substance, according to the scientific definition of pure. ☑
7) A substance melts over a range of temperatures. Is it likely to be a pure substance or a mixture? ☑
8) Draw the apparatus you would use to carry out a simple distillation. ☑
9) Where is the hottest part of a fractionating column — at the top or at the bottom? ☑
10) Describe how to carry out filtration. ☑
11) What separation technique should you use to separate a soluble solid from a solution? ☑
12) Explain what the terms 'mobile phase' and 'stationary phase' mean in the context of chromatography. ☑
13) Write out the formula you would use to work out the $R_f$ value of a substance from a chromatogram. ☑

## Water Treatment (p.104) ☐

14) Name three different sources of water that can be made potable. ☑
15) Name three processes that are used to make water potable. ☑
16) What is deionised water? ☑

## Acids and Bases (p.105-107) ☑

17) What pH value would a neutral substance have? ☑
18) What is an alkali? ☑
19) State what colours the following indicators are in acidic solutions: a) litmus b) methyl orange ☑
20) Write the ionic equation for a neutralisation reaction. ☑
21) Write an equation to show how ethanoic acid ($CH_3COOH$) acts as a weak acid. ☑
22) Write a chemical equation to show how hydrochloric acid reacts with copper oxide. ☑
23) What would you expect to see if you bubbled carbon dioxide through limewater? ☑

## Making Salts (p.108-109) ☑

24) Name: a) three insoluble sulfates, b) two soluble hydroxides. ☑
25) Describe how you could make a pure sample of a soluble salt from an acid and an alkali. ☑

## Electrolysis (p.110-112) ☑

26) What is electrolysis? ☑
27) Towards which electrode do the anions in an electrolyte move? ☑
28) Describe how you would carry out an electrolysis where the electrolyte is a molten ionic solid. ☑
29) At which electrode does the metal form during the electrolysis of a molten ionic compound? ☑
30) Why do the masses of non-inert electrodes change during electrolysis? ☑

Section 12 — Chemical Changes

# The Reactivity Series

Reactivity series are lists of metals (sometimes with some carbon or hydrogen thrown in for fun). But they're not just any old lists in any old order. No siree... As the name suggests, they tell you all about reactivities.

## If Something Gains Oxygen it's Oxidised

Oxidation can mean the reaction with, or addition of oxygen. Reduction can be the removal of oxygen.

$$E.g.\ Fe_2O_3 + 3CO \rightarrow 2Fe + 3CO_2$$

- Iron oxide is reduced to iron (as oxygen is removed).
- Carbon monoxide is oxidised to carbon dioxide (as oxygen is added).

*Reduction and oxidation can also be to do with electrons (see page 116).*

Combustion reactions involve oxidation. They're always exothermic (see page 134).

$$E.g.\ CH_4 + 2O_2 \rightarrow CO_2 + 2H_2O$$

- Both the carbon and hydrogen are oxidised — they gain oxygen.
- The oxygen molecules are reduced as the oxygen atoms get split up by the reaction.

## The Reactivity Series Shows How Easily Metals Are Oxidised

1) A reactivity series is a table that lists metals in order of their reactivity.

2) As well as the metals, carbon is often included in reactivity series — a metal's position in the reactivity series compared to carbon dictates how it's extracted from its ore (see pages 117-118).

3) Hydrogen can be included in the reactivity series too — this shows the reactivity of metals with dilute acids (see next page).

4) Here's an example of a reactivity series:

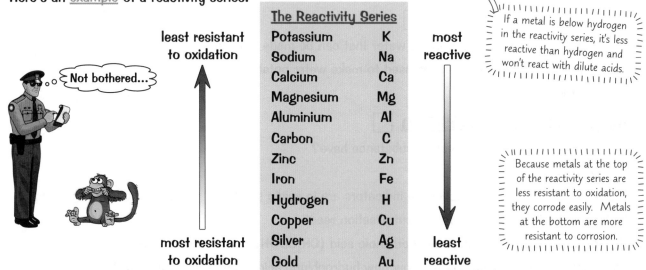

*If a metal is below hydrogen in the reactivity series, it's less reactive than hydrogen and won't react with dilute acids.*

| The Reactivity Series | |
|---|---|
| Potassium | K |
| Sodium | Na |
| Calcium | Ca |
| Magnesium | Mg |
| Aluminium | Al |
| Carbon | C |
| Zinc | Zn |
| Iron | Fe |
| Hydrogen | H |
| Copper | Cu |
| Silver | Ag |
| Gold | Au |

least resistant to oxidation ↑ most resistant to oxidation

most reactive ↓ least reactive

*Not bothered...*

*Because metals at the top of the reactivity series are less resistant to oxidation, they corrode easily. Metals at the bottom are more resistant to corrosion.*

5) The metals at the top of the reactivity series are the most reactive — they easily lose their electrons to form cations (positive ions). They're also oxidised easily.

6) The metals at the bottom of the reactivity series are less reactive — they don't give up their electrons to form cations as easily. They're more resistant to oxidation than the metals higher up the reactivity series.

7) You can determine a metal's position in the reactivity series by reacting it with water and dilute acids (see next page).

## I told a hilarious joke to some sodium — the reaction was great...

You could come across different reactivity series to the one shown above. But panic not noble chemistry pal... they all work the same. The more reactive elements are at the top of the series and the less reactive ones are at the bottom.

Q1    Identify which element has been oxidised in the following reaction: $CuO + H_2 \rightarrow Cu + H_2O$    [1 mark]

Q2    Using the reactivity series above, explain whether copper or calcium is more easily oxidised.    [1 mark]

# Reactivity of Metals

Reactive metals tend to do exciting, fizzy things when you drop them into acid or water...

## How Metals React With Acids Tells You About Their Reactivity

1) The more easily a metal atom loses its outer electrons and form a positive ion, the more reactive it will be.

2) Here's a classic experiment that you can do to show that some metals are more reactive than others. All you do is to place little pieces of various metals into dilute hydrochloric acid:

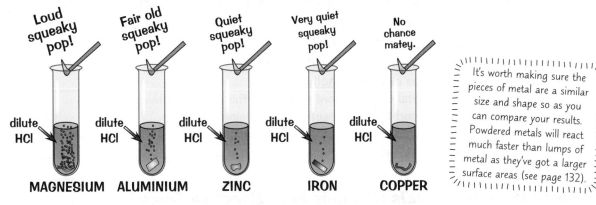

Loud squeaky pop!  Fair old squeaky pop!  Quiet squeaky pop!  Very quiet squeaky pop!  No chance matey.

dilute HCl    dilute HCl    dilute HCl    dilute HCl    dilute HCl

MAGNESIUM    ALUMINIUM    ZINC    IRON    COPPER

*It's worth making sure the pieces of metal are a similar size and shape so as you can compare your results. Powdered metals will react much faster than lumps of metal as they've got a larger surface areas (see page 132).*

3) The more reactive the metal is, the faster the reaction with the acid will go (see page 107 for more on the reactions of metals with acids).

4) Very reactive metals (e.g. magnesium) will fizz vigorously, less reactive metals (e.g. zinc) will bubble a bit, and unreactive metals (e.g. copper) will not react with dilute acids at all.

5) You can show that hydrogen is forming using the burning splint test (see page 107). The louder the squeaky pop, the more hydrogen has been made in the time period and the more reactive the metal is.

6) The speed of reaction is also indicated by the rate at which the bubbles of hydrogen are given off — the faster the bubbles form, the faster the reaction and the more reactive the metal.

*You could also follow the rate of the reaction by using a gas syringe to measure the volume of gas given off at regular time intervals (see p.128) or using a thermometer to measure by how much the temperature changes (as the reaction of acids with metals is exothermic — see p.134).*

## Some Metals Also React With Water

The reactions of metals with water also show the reactivity of metals. This is the basic reaction:

> metal + water → metal hydroxide + hydrogen
> (Or: less reactive metal + steam → metal oxide + hydrogen)

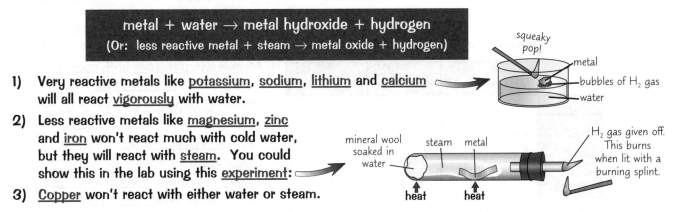

1) Very reactive metals like potassium, sodium, lithium and calcium will all react vigorously with water.

squeaky pop!
metal
bubbles of H₂ gas
water

2) Less reactive metals like magnesium, zinc and iron won't react much with cold water, but they will react with steam. You could show this in the lab using this experiment:

mineral wool soaked in water    steam    metal

H₂ gas given off. This burns when lit with a burning splint.

3) Copper won't react with either water or steam.

heat    heat

## I AM NOT HIGHLY REACTIVE — OK...

This stuff isn't too bad — who knows, you might even get to have a go at these experiments in class...

Q1    A student is given small samples of three metals, A, B and C. He places them in dilute hydrochloric acid. Nothing happens to Metal A. Metal B fizzes vigorously. The gas given off gives a loud squeaky pop when lit with a burning splint. Metal C fizzes a bit. The gas given off gives a quiet squeaky pop when lit.

   a) Put the three metals in order, from most reactive to least reactive.    [1 mark]

   b) One of the metals was zinc, one was magnesium, and one was copper. Use this information to identify metals A, B and C.    [1 mark]

# Displacement Reactions

As well as by reacting metals with <u>dilute acids</u> and <u>water</u>, you can directly compare the reactivity of metals using <u>displacement reactions</u>. This involves reacting metals with <u>metal salt solutions</u>. Exciting stuff I tell ya.

## Displacement Reactions are Redox Reactions

1) As well as talking about <u>reduction</u> and <u>oxidation</u> in terms of the loss and gain of <u>oxygen</u> (as on page 114), you can also talk about them in terms of <u>electrons</u> (as in electrolysis).

2) <u>Oxidation</u> can be the <u>loss of electrons</u>, and <u>reduction</u> can be the <u>gain of electrons</u>.

3) Reduction and oxidation happen <u>simultaneously</u> — hence the name <u>redox</u> reactions.

4) <u>Displacement reactions</u> are examples of redox reactions.

5) In displacement reactions, a <u>more reactive element</u> reacts to take the place of a <u>less reactive element</u> in a compound. In metal displacement reactions, the more reactive metal loses electrons and the less reactive metal gains electrons.

6) So, during a displacement reaction, the <u>more reactive metal</u> is <u>oxidised</u>, and the <u>less reactive metal</u> is <u>reduced</u>. For example:

> When dealing with electrons:
> Oxidation Is Loss,
> Reduction Is Gain.
>
> Remember it as OIL RIG.

> zinc is reduced
> $$Ca + ZnSO_4 \rightarrow CaSO_4 + Zn$$
> calcium is oxidised

## More Reactive Metals Displace Less Reactive Ones

1) If you put a <u>reactive metal</u> into a solution of a <u>less reactive metal salt</u>, the reactive metal will <u>replace</u> the <u>less reactive metal</u> in the salt.

> <u>Example</u>: if you put an <u>iron nail</u> in a solution of <u>copper sulfate</u>, the more reactive iron will <u>"kick out"</u> the less reactive copper from the salt. You end up with <u>iron sulfate solution</u> and <u>copper metal</u>.
>
> copper sulfate + iron → iron sulfate + copper
> $$CuSO_4 + Fe \rightarrow FeSO_4 + Cu$$

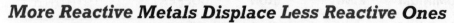

In this reaction, copper is reduced and iron is oxidised.

2) If you put a <u>less reactive metal</u> into a solution of a <u>more reactive metal salt</u>, <u>nothing</u> will happen.

> <u>Example</u>: if you put a small piece of silver metal into a solution of <u>copper sulfate</u>, nothing will happen. The more reactive metal (copper) is already in the salt.

3) You can use displacement reactions to <u>work out</u> where in the reactivity series a metal should go.

> <u>Example</u>: A student adds some <u>metals</u> to <u>metal salt solutions</u> and records whether any <u>reactions</u> happen. Use her table of results, below, to work out an <u>order of reactivity</u> for the metals.
>
> | | copper nitrate | magnesium chloride | zinc sulfate |
> |---|---|---|---|
> | copper | no reaction | no reaction | no reaction |
> | magnesium | magnesium nitrate and copper formed | no reaction | magnesium sulfate and zinc formed |
> | zinc | zinc nitrate and copper formed | no reaction | no reaction |
>
> - Magnesium <u>displaces</u> both <u>copper</u> and <u>zinc</u>, so it must be <u>more reactive</u> than both.
> - Copper <u>is displaced by</u> both <u>magnesium</u> and <u>zinc</u>, so it must be <u>less reactive</u> than both.
> - Zinc <u>can displace copper</u>, but <u>not</u> <u>magnesium</u>, so it must go between them.
>
> The <u>order of reactivity</u>, <u>from most to least</u>, is: <u>magnesium</u>, <u>zinc</u>, <u>copper</u>.

## And that's why Iron Man never goes swimming in copper sulfate...

You could be given the results of an experiment and have to use them to put the metals into an order of reactivity, or you could be told their reactivities and then asked to predict how they'll react — make sure you can do both. Time for some questions anyway — you may want to use the reactivity series on page 114 to help you...

Q1 State whether silver would displace iron from iron chloride solution and explain your answer. [1 mark]

Q2 Lithium sits between sodium and calcium in the reactivity series. State whether lithium would displace zinc from zinc sulfate solution and explain your answer. [1 mark]

# Extracting Metals Using Carbon

A few <u>unreactive metals</u>, like gold, are found in the Earth as the metals themselves, rather than as a compound. The rest of the metals we get by <u>extracting</u> them <u>from rocks</u> — and I bet you're just itching to find out how...

## Ores Contain Enough Metal to Make Extraction Worthwhile

1) A <u>metal ore</u> is a <u>rock</u> which contains <u>enough metal</u> to make it <u>economically worthwhile</u> extracting the metal from it. In many cases the ore is an <u>oxide</u> of the metal.

> <u>Example</u>: the main <u>aluminium ore</u> is called <u>bauxite</u> — it's aluminium oxide ($Al_2O_3$).

2) Most of the metals that we use are found in their <u>ores</u> in the <u>Earth's crust</u>. The ores are mined and the metals can then be <u>extracted</u> from the ores.

3) Some <u>unreactive metals</u>, such as gold and platinum, are present in the Earth's crust as <u>uncombined elements</u>. These metals can be mined straight out of the ground, but they usually need to be <u>refined</u> before they can be used.

## Some Metals can be Extracted by Reduction with Carbon

1) A metal can be <u>extracted</u> from its ore chemically by <u>reduction</u> using <u>carbon</u>.

2) When an ore is reduced, <u>oxygen is removed</u> from it, e.g.

$$2Fe_2O_3 + 3C \rightarrow 4Fe + 3CO_2$$
iron oxide + carbon → iron + carbon dioxide

*Most of the time, you actually get a mixture of carbon dioxide $CO_2$ and carbon monoxide (CO) when you reduce metal oxides with carbon.*

3) The position of the metal in the <u>reactivity series</u> determines whether it can be extracted by <u>reduction</u> with carbon.

*See page 114 for more on reactivity series.*

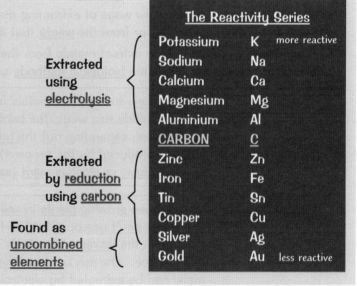

- Metals <u>higher than carbon</u> in the reactivity series have to be extracted using <u>electrolysis</u> (see next page) which is expensive.
- Metals <u>below carbon</u> in the reactivity series can be extracted by <u>reduction</u> using <u>carbon</u>. For example, <u>iron oxide</u> is reduced in a <u>blast furnace</u> to make <u>iron</u>.
- This is because carbon <u>can only take</u> the <u>oxygen</u> away from metals which are <u>less reactive</u> than carbon <u>itself</u> is.

## [Please insert ore-ful pun here]...

Make sure you've got that reactivity series sorted in your head. If a metal's below carbon in the reactivity series, then it's less reactive than carbon and can be extracted from its ore by reduction using carbon. Phew... got it?

Q1 How would you extract tin from its metal ore? Explain your answer. [2 marks]

Q2 Write a balanced chemical equation to describe the reaction that occurs when carbon is used to extract zinc from its ore, zinc oxide (ZnO). [2 marks]

# Other Methods of Extracting Metals

Electrolysis is an expensive process but, like many pricey things, it's really rather good...

## Some Metals have to be Extracted by Electrolysis

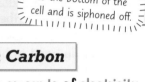

The compounds have to be molten (i.e. liquid) so that the ions are free to move.

1) Metals that are more reactive than carbon (see previous page) are extracted using electrolysis of molten compounds (see page 110 for more on this).

2) Once the metal ore is melted, an electric current is passed through it. The metal is discharged at the cathode and the non-metal at the anode.

Example: Aluminium is extracted from its ore using electrolysis with carbon electrodes. Aluminium oxide ($Al_2O_3$) has a high melting point, so the ore is first dissolved in molten cryolite (an aluminium compound with a lower melting point than $Al_2O_3$) to lower the melting point. The ions in this molten mixture are free to move. During the electrolysis, aluminium is formed at the cathode: $Al^{3+} + 3e^- \rightarrow Al$
Oxygen forms at the anode: $2O^{2-} \rightarrow O_2 + 4e^-$
The overall equation is: $2Al_2O_{3(l)} \rightarrow 4Al_{(l)} + 3O_{2(g)}$

Aluminium metal sinks to the bottom of the cell and is siphoned off.

## Electrolysis is a More Expensive Process than Reduction with Carbon

1) In order to run electrolysis to extract metals from their ores, you need large amounts of electricity. Electricity is expensive, making electrolysis a pretty pricey process. There are also costs associated with melting or dissolving the metal ore so it can conduct electricity.

2) In comparison, extracting metals using reduction with carbon is much cheaper. Carbon is cheap, and also acts as a fuel to provide the heat needed for the reduction reaction to happen.

3) This means that, in general, metals lower down the reactivity series (less reactive metals) are cheaper to extract than those higher up the reactivity series (more reactive metals).

## There are Biological Methods to Extract Metals

We can also recycle metals to save resources (see next page).

1) The supply of some metal rich ores, e.g. copper ore, is limited.

2) The demand for lots of metals is growing and this may lead to shortages in the future.

3) Scientists are looking into new ways of extracting metals from low-grade ores (ores that only contain small amounts of the metal) or from the waste that is currently produced when metals are extracted.

4) Examples of new methods to extract metals from their ores are bioleaching and phytoextraction. These are biological methods as they use living organisms.

Bioleaching: This uses bacteria to separate metals from their ores, e.g. copper can be separated from copper sulfide this way. The bacteria get energy from the bonds between the atoms in the ore, separating out the metal from the ore in the process. The leachate (the solution produced by the process) contains metal ions, which can be extracted, e.g. by electrolysis or displacement (see page 116) with a more reactive metal.

This is a bacterial method of extracting metals.

Phytoextraction: This involves growing plants in soil that contains metal compounds. The plants can't use or get rid of the metals so they gradually build up in the leaves. The plants can be harvested, dried and burned in a furnace. The ash contains metal compounds from which the metal can be extracted by electrolysis or displacement reactions.

5) Traditional methods of mining are pretty damaging to the environment (see the next page). These new methods of extraction have a much smaller impact, but the disadvantage is that they're slow.

## A policeman failed his maths test — he's a low-grade copper...

Make sure you can remember all those techniques for extracting metals, even those snazzy biological methods.

Q1 Use the reactivity series on page 117 to predict whether aluminium or iron would be more expensive to extract from its ore. Explain your answer. [3 marks]

# Recycling

Recycling's a hot topic. We don't have an infinite amount of materials, e.g. metals, to keep on making things from, so recycling's really important to make sure we don't run out of lots of important raw materials.

## Recycling Conserves Resources and Energy

1) Extracting raw materials can take large amounts of energy, lots of which comes from burning fossil fuels.

2) Fossil fuels are running out (they're a non-renewable resource) so it's important to conserve them. Not only this, but burning them contributes to acid rain and climate change (see pages 139 and 143).

3) Recycling materials saves energy as this process often only uses a small fraction of the energy needed to extract and refine the material from scratch.

4) As there's a finite amount of many raw materials, e.g. metals, on Earth, recycling conserves these resources too. Metals, like fossil fuels, are non-renewable.

5) It's particularly important to recycle materials that are rare.

## Recycling Protects the Environment

1) Extracting metals also impacts on the environment. Mines are damaging to the environment and destroy habitats — not to mention the fact that they're a bit of an eyesore. Recycling more metals means that we don't need so many mines.

2) Recycling materials also cuts down on the amount of rubbish that gets sent to landfill. Landfill takes up space and pollutes the surroundings.

## Recycling Has Important Economic Benefits

1) As you saw above, extracting materials often requires more energy than just recycling them, and energy doesn't come cheap. So recycling saves money.

2) It is particularly beneficial to the economy to recycle metals that are expensive to extract or buy.

3) Recycling is also a massive industry and creates lots of jobs. The materials to be recycled need to be transported to and processed at recycling centres. They then needs to be reprocessed into new products which can be sold.

4) Jobs are created at every stage of this process — far more than are created by simply disposing of waste by dumping it into landfill.

## Example: Recycling Aluminium

1) If you didn't recycle aluminium, you'd have to mine more aluminium ore — 4 tonnes for every 1 tonne of aluminium you need. But mining makes a mess of the landscape (and these mines are often in rainforests). The ore then needs to be transported, and the aluminium extracted (which uses loads of electricity). And don't forget the cost of sending your used aluminium to landfill.

2) So it's a complex calculation, but for every 1 kg of aluminium cans you recycle, you save:
   - 95% or so of the energy needed to mine and extract 'fresh' aluminium,
   - 4 kg of aluminium ore,
   - a lot of waste.

   *In fact, aluminium's about the most cost-effective metal to recycle.*

---

## I told a hilarious joke to some sodium — the reaction was great...

Cracking jokes like the ones you find in this book grow on trees you know. So to save trees and reduce the environmental costs of this book, I thought I'd recycle that hilarious pun from page 114. Aren't I good?

Q1    Material X is a metal. To recycle material X you need 110% of the energy used to extract and refine it. Explain why it might still be better to recycle material X.                     [2 marks]

# Life Cycle Assessments

If a company wants to manufacture a new product, it will carry out a <u>life cycle assessment</u> (LCA). Fun stuff.

## Life Cycle Assessments Show Total Environmental Costs

A <u>life cycle assessment (LCA)</u> looks at each <u>stage</u> of the <u>life</u> of a product — from making the <u>material</u> from natural raw materials, to making the <u>product</u> from the material, <u>using</u> the product and <u>disposing</u> of the product. It works out the potential <u>environmental impact</u> of each stage.

*Life cycle assessments can also be called life time assessments.*

**Choice of material**
1) <u>Metals</u> have to be <u>mined</u> and <u>extracted</u> from their ores. These processes need a lot of <u>energy</u> and cause a lot of <u>pollution</u>.
2) <u>Raw materials</u> for chemical manufacture often come from <u>crude oil</u>. Crude oil is a <u>non-renewable resource</u>, and supplies are <u>decreasing</u>. Also, obtaining crude oil from the ground and refining it into useful raw materials requires a lot of <u>energy</u> and generates <u>pollution</u>.

**Manufacture**
1) <u>Manufacturing</u> products uses a lot of <u>energy</u> and other resources.
2) It can also cause a lot of <u>pollution</u>, e.g. <u>harmful fumes</u> such as CO or HCl.
3) You also need to think about any <u>waste</u> products and how to <u>dispose</u> of them.
4) Some waste can be <u>recycled</u> and turned into other <u>useful chemicals</u>, reducing the amount that ends up polluting the environment.
5) Most chemical manufacture needs <u>water</u>. Businesses have make sure they don't put <u>polluted</u> water back into the environment at the end of the process.

**Product Use**
Using the product can also damage the environment. For example:
1) <u>Paint</u> gives off <u>toxic fumes</u>.
2) <u>Burning fuels</u> releases <u>greenhouse gases</u> and other <u>harmful substances</u>.
3) <u>Fertilisers</u> can <u>leach</u> into streams and rivers and cause damage to <u>ecosystems</u>.

**Disposal**
1) Products are often <u>disposed</u> of in a <u>landfill</u> site at the end of their life.
2) This takes up space and can <u>pollute</u> land and water.
3) Products might be <u>incinerated</u> (burnt), which causes air pollution.

*Some products can be disposed of by being recycled (see page 119).*

---

**EXAMPLE:**

A company is carrying out a life cycle assessment to work out which car, A, B or C, it should make. Using the data in the table, explain which car the company should produce to minimise the environmental impact.

| Car | $CO_2$ emissions (tonnes) | Waste solid produced (kg) | Water used (m³) | Expected lifespan of product (years) |
|-----|---------------------------|---------------------------|-----------------|--------------------------------------|
| A | 17 | 10 720 | 8.2 | 11 |
| B | 21 | 5900 | 6.0 | 17 |
| C | 34 | 15 010 | 9.5 | 12 |

- Car A produces the least $CO_2$, but produces the second highest amount of waste solids and uses the second highest amount of water. It also has the shortest life span.
- Car B produces more $CO_2$ than car A, but produces by far the least waste solid, uses the least water and also has the longest life span. On balance, this looks a better choice than car A.
- Car C produces the most $CO_2$, the most waste solid, uses the most water, and has almost as short a life span as car A. This looks like the worst choice.

So, on balance, **car B** looks like the one that will have the least environmental impact.

---

## My cycle assessment — two wheels, a bell, an uncomfortable seat...

Don't get your bike cycle and life cycle assessments confused. Life cycle assessments are the ones you'll need.

Q1     For the example above, suggest four further things (that aren't outlined in the table) that the company should consider when forming a life cycle assessment for the car.     [4 marks]

# Dynamic Equilibrium

Reversible reactions — products forming from reactants and reactants forming from products. I can't keep up...

## Reversible Reactions can go Forwards and Backwards

A reversible reaction is one where the products can react with each other to produce the original reactants. In other words, it can go both ways.

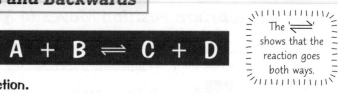

$$A + B \rightleftharpoons C + D$$

The '$\rightleftharpoons$' shows that the reaction goes both ways.

The Haber process is an example of a reversible reaction.

1) During the Haber process, nitrogen and hydrogen react to form ammonia: $N_2 + 3H_2 \rightleftharpoons 2NH_3$
   - The nitrogen ($N_2$) is obtained easily from the air, which is about 78% nitrogen.
   - The hydrogen ($H_2$) can be extracted from hydrocarbons from sources such as natural gas and crude oil.

2) The Haber process is carried out at 450 °C, with a pressure of 200 atmospheres and an iron catalyst.

## Reversible Reactions Will Reach Equilibrium

1) As the reactants (A and B) react, their concentrations fall — so the forward reaction will slow down. But as more and more of the products (C and D) are made and their concentrations rise, the backward reaction will speed up.

See the next page for more on concentrations and rate.

2) After a while the forward reaction will be going at exactly the same rate as the backward one — this is equilibrium.

3) At equilibrium both reactions are still happening, but there's no overall effect.

4) This is a dynamic equilibrium — the forward and backward reactions are both happening at the same time and at the same rate, and the concentrations of reactants and products have reached a balance and won't change.

5) Equilibrium can only be reached if the reversible reaction takes place in a 'closed system'. A closed system just means that none of the reactants or products can escape.

Forward Reaction

Same rate at equilibrium

Backward Reaction

When a reaction's at equilibrium it doesn't mean that the amounts of reactants and products are equal.
- Sometimes the equilibrium will lie to the right — this basically means "lots of the products and not much of the reactants" (i.e. the concentration of products is greater than the concentration of reactants).
- Sometimes the equilibrium will lie to the left — this basically means "lots of the reactants but not much of the products" (the concentration of reactants is greater than the concentration of products).
- The exact position of equilibrium depends on the conditions (as well as the reaction itself).

## Three Things Can Change the Position of Equilibrium

Three things can change the position of equilibrium (which changes the amounts of products and reactants present at equilibrium). These are temperature, pressure (for equilibria involving gases) and concentrations (of reactants or products).

The plural of equilibrium is 'equilibria'.

Example: ammonium chloride $\rightleftharpoons$ ammonia + hydrogen chloride

Heating this reaction moves the equilibrium to the right (more ammonia and hydrogen chloride) and cooling it moves it to the left (more ammonium chloride).

## Dynamic equilibrium — lots of activity, but not to any great effect*...

Keep an eagle eye out for that arrow that shows you that a reaction is reversible. I'd hate you to miss it.

Q1    Explain what is meant by the term 'reversible reaction'. [1 mark]

Q2    What is dynamic equilibrium? [3 marks]

*a bit like the England football team.

# Le Chatelier's Principle

This stuff might feel a bit complicated to start with, but it all comes down to one simple rule — whatever you do to a <u>reversible reaction</u>, the <u>equilibrium position</u> will <u>move</u> to try to <u>undo</u> your change. How contrary...

## The Equilibrium Position Moves to Minimise Any Changes You Make

Le Chatelier's principle states that if there's a <u>change</u> in concentration, pressure or temperature in a reversible reaction, the <u>equilibrium position will move</u> to help <u>counteract</u> that change.

**TEMPERATURE** All reactions are <u>exothermic</u> in one direction and <u>endothermic</u> in the other (see page 134).

1) If you <u>decrease the temperature</u>, the equilibrium will move in the <u>exothermic direction</u> to produce more heat.

2) If you <u>increase the temperature</u>, the equilibrium will move in the <u>endothermic direction</u> to absorb the extra heat.

For example: $N_2 + 3H_2 \rightleftharpoons 2NH_3$
This reaction is exothermic in the forward direction. If you decrease the temperature, the equilibrium will shift to the right (so you'll make more product).

**PRESSURE** Changing this only affects equilibria involving <u>gases</u>.

1) If you <u>increase the pressure</u>, the equilibrium will move towards the side that has <u>fewer moles of gas</u> to <u>reduce</u> pressure.

2) If you <u>decrease the pressure</u>, the equilibrium will move towards the side that has <u>more moles of gas</u> to <u>increase</u> pressure.

For example:
$N_2 + 3H_2 \rightleftharpoons 2NH_3$
This reaction has 4 moles of gas on the left and 2 on the right. If you increase the pressure, the equilibrium will shift to the right (so you'll make more product).

**CONCENTRATION**

1) If you <u>increase the concentration</u> of the <u>reactants</u>, the equilibrium will move to the <u>right</u> to <u>use up the reactants</u> (making <u>more products</u>).

2) If you <u>increase the concentration</u> of the <u>products</u>, the equilibrium will move to the <u>left</u> to <u>use up the products</u> (making <u>more reactants</u>).

3) <u>Decreasing</u> the concentration will have the <u>opposite effect</u>.

For example:
$N_2 + 3H_2 \rightleftharpoons 2NH_3$
If you increase the concentration of $N_2$ or $H_2$, the equilibrium will shift to the right to use up the extra reactants (so you'll make more product).

## You Can Predict How the Position of Equilibrium Will Change

You can apply the rules above to any reversible reaction to work out how <u>changing the conditions</u> will affect the <u>equilibrium position</u>. This has useful applications in <u>industry</u> — you can <u>increase yield</u> (how much product you get) by changing the conditions to shift the equilibrium position to the <u>right</u> (towards the <u>products</u>).

**EXAMPLE:** The compound $PCl_5$ can be made using this reaction: $PCl_{3(g)} + Cl_{2(g)} \rightleftharpoons PCl_{5(g)}$
Explain what would happen to the equilibrium position and to the yield of $PCl_5$ if you increased the pressure that the reaction was being performed at.

According to Le Chatelier's Principle, if you increase the pressure, the position of equilibrium will move towards the side with fewer moles of gas to reduce the pressure. In this reaction there are 2 moles of gas in the reactants and 1 in the products.

The position of equilibrium will move to the right, since that is the side with fewer moles of gas. This shifts the equilibrium towards the products, so the yield of $PCl_5$ will increase.

## Le Chatelier — relieving pressure since 1884...

Le Chatelier's principle may relieve the pressure in chemical systems, but it stands a chance of giving you a right headache in the exam. So, best make sure you understand it now by trying these questions...

Q1 This reaction is endothermic in the forward direction: $CH_3OH_{(g)} \rightleftharpoons CO_{(g)} + 2H_{2(g)}$. What will happen to the position of equilibrium if the temperature is increased? Explain your answer. [2 marks]

Q2 What would happen to the yield of $SO_3$ in the reaction below if the pressure was decreased? Explain your answer. $2SO_{2(g)} + O_{2(g)} \rightleftharpoons 2SO_{3(g)}$ [3 marks]

# Group 1 — Alkali Metals

You can predict how different elements will react by looking at where they are in the periodic table — elements in the same group will react in similar ways. Time to take a look at some of the groups, starting with Group 1...

## Group 1 Metals are Known as the 'Alkali Metals'

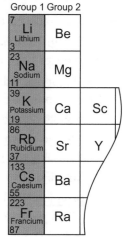

The Group 1 metals are lithium, sodium, potassium, rubidium, caesium and francium.

1) The alkali metals all have one outer electron
— so they have similar chemical properties.

2) They all have the following physical properties:

   • Low melting points and boiling points (compared with other metals).

   • Very soft — they can be cut with a knife.

3) The alkali metals form ionic compounds. They lose their single outer electron so easily that sharing it is out of the question, so they don't form covalent bonds.

## Group 1 Metals are Very Reactive

1) The Group 1 metals readily lose their single outer electron to form a 1+ ion with a stable electronic structure.

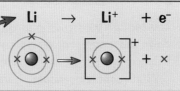

2) The more readily a metal loses its outer electrons, the more reactive it is — so the Group 1 metals are very reactive.

3) As you go down Group 1, the alkali metals get more reactive. The outer electron is more easily lost because it's further from the nucleus (the atomic radius is larger) — so it's less strongly attracted to the nucleus and less energy is needed to remove it.

## Reactions with Cold Water Produces a Hydroxide and Hydrogen Gas

1) When the alkali metals are put in water, they react vigorously.

2) The reaction produces hydrogen gas and a hydroxide of the metal (an alkali see page 105). For example, here's the overall equation for the reaction of sodium with water:

Squeaky pop!

A squeaky pop shows $H_2$ gas is present — see p.107 for more.

$$2Na + 2H_2O \rightarrow 2NaOH + H_2$$
sodium + water → sodium hydroxide + hydrogen

The same reaction happens with all of the alkali metals — make sure you can write balanced equations for them all.

3) The reactivity of Group 1 metals with water (and dilute acid) increases down the group because the outer electron is lost more easily in the reaction (see above). This results in the reaction becoming more violent:

   • Lithium will move around the surface, fizzing furiously.

   • Sodium and potassium do the same, but they also melt in the heat of the reaction. Potassium even gets hot enough to ignite the hydrogen gas being produced.

4) Because you know the reactivity trend in Group 1 (the elements get more reactive as you go down the group), you can make predictions about the reactions of elements further down the group.

> Example: You may predict that the reactions of rubidium and caesium with water will be more violent than the reaction of potassium and water. And sure enough, rubidium and caesium react violently with water and tend to explode when they get wet...

## And that's why you don't get caesium teaspoons... Amongst other reasons...

Alkali metals are so reactive, in fact, that they have to be stored in oil — otherwise they just react with the air.

Q1    A student reacts lithium with water. Describe what the student will observe. [1 mark]

Q2    Write a balanced symbol equation for the reaction between potassium (K) and water. [2 marks]

# Group 7 — Halogens

Here's a page on another periodic table group that you need to be familiar with — <u>the halogens</u>.

## Group 7 Elements are Known as the 'Halogens'

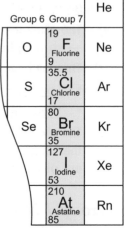

<u>Group 7</u> is made up of the elements fluorine, chlorine, bromine, iodine and astatine.

1) All Group 7 elements have <u>7 electrons in their outer shell</u> so they all have <u>similar chemical properties</u>.

2) The halogens exist as <u>diatomic molecules</u> (e.g. $Cl_2$, $Br_2$, $I_2$). Sharing one pair of electrons in a <u>covalent bond</u> (see page 86) gives both atoms a <u>full outer shell</u>.

3) As you go <u>down Group 7</u>, the <u>melting points</u> and <u>boiling points</u> of the halogens <u>increase</u>. This means that at <u>room temperature</u>:

- <u>Chlorine</u> ($Cl_2$) is a fairly reactive, poisonous, <u>green gas</u>.
- <u>Bromine</u> ($Br_2$) is a poisonous, <u>red-brown liquid</u>, which gives off an <u>orange vapour</u> at room temperature.
- <u>Iodine</u> ($I_2$) is a <u>dark grey crystalline solid</u> which gives off a <u>purple vapour</u> when heated.

> You can use the <u>trends in physical properties</u> from chlorine to iodine to <u>predict</u> the properties of halogens further down the group. For example, you can see that melting point <u>increases</u> down the group, and the colours of the halogens get <u>darker</u>, so you could predict that astatine (which comes below iodine) would be a <u>dark-coloured solid</u> at room temperature. Sure enough, astatine is a <u>black solid</u> with a melting point of around <u>300 °C</u>.

## Test for Chlorine Using Damp Blue Litmus Paper

You can test to see if a gas is <u>chlorine</u> by holding a piece of <u>damp blue litmus paper</u> over it. Chlorine will <u>bleach</u> the litmus paper, turning it <u>white</u>. It may also turn <u>red</u> for a moment first — that's because a solution of chlorine is <u>acidic</u> (see p.105 for more on acids).

damp blue litmus paper

## Reactivity Decreases Going Down Group 7

1) A halogen atom only needs to <u>gain one electron</u> to form a <u>1– ion</u> with a <u>stable electronic structure</u>.

2) The <u>easier</u> it is for a halogen atom to <u>attract</u> an electron, the <u>more reactive</u> the halogen will be.

3) As you go <u>down</u> Group 7, the halogens become <u>less reactive</u> — it gets <u>harder</u> to attract the <u>extra electron</u> to fill the outer shell when it's <u>further away</u> from the nucleus (the <u>atomic radius</u> is <u>larger</u>).

$$Cl + e^- \rightarrow Cl^-$$

## The Halogens Can React With Metals and Hydrogen

1) The halogens will react vigorously with some metals to form <u>salts</u> called 'metal halides'.

2) Halogens <u>higher up</u> in Group 7 are <u>more</u> reactive because they can attract the <u>outer electron</u> of the metal <u>more easily</u>.

3) Halogens can also react with <u>hydrogen</u> to form <u>hydrogen halides</u>. Hydrogen halides are soluble — they can <u>dissolve in water</u> to form <u>acidic solutions</u>. For example, HCl forms <u>hydrochloric acid</u> in water.

4) Since all halogens have the same number of electrons in their outer shells, they all have <u>similar reactions</u>. So you can use the reactions of <u>chlorine</u>, <u>bromine</u> and <u>iodine</u> to <u>predict</u> how <u>fluorine</u> and <u>astatine</u> will react.

| $2Na$ | + | $Cl_2$ | $\rightarrow$ | $2NaCl$ |
| Sodium | + | Chlorine | $\rightarrow$ | Sodium chloride |

Metals lose electrons and form positive ions when they react.

| $H_2$ | + | $Cl_2$ | $\rightarrow$ | $2HCl$ |
| Hydrogen | + | Chlorine | $\rightarrow$ | Hydrogen chloride |

## Halogens — one electron short of a full shell...

Another page, another periodic table group to learn the properties and the trends of. It's like Christmas come early.

Q1　　Write a balanced symbol equation for the reaction between bromine ($Br_2$) and sodium (Na).　　[2 marks]

# Halogen Displacement Reactions

The halogens are a pretty competitive lot really. In fact the more reactive ones will push the less reactive ones out of a compound. How uncivilized — has nobody ever taught them that it's bad manners to push?

## A More Reactive Halogen Will Displace a Less Reactive One

1) The elements in Group 7 take part in displacement reactions.

2) A displacement reaction is where a more reactive element 'pushes out' (displaces) a less reactive element from a compound.

3) The halogen displacement reactions are redox reactions. The halogens gain electrons (reduction) whilst halide ions lose electrons (oxidation).

4) For example, chlorine is more reactive than bromine (it's higher up Group 7). If you add chlorine water (an aqueous solution of $Cl_2$) to potassium bromide solution, the chlorine will displace the bromine from the salt solution.

5) The chlorine is reduced to chloride ions, so the salt solution becomes potassium chloride. The bromide ions are oxidised to bromine, which turns the solution orange.

chlorine water

colourless solution

potassium bromide

orange solution

bromine forming in solution

| $Cl_2$ | + | 2KBr | $\rightarrow$ | $Br_2$ | + | 2KCl |
|---|---|---|---|---|---|---|
| chlorine | + | potassium bromide | $\rightarrow$ | bromine | + | potassium chloride |

All equations for halogen displacement reactions follow this pattern.

| $Cl_2$ | + | $2Br^-$ | $\rightarrow$ | $Br_2$ | + | $2Cl^-$ |
|---|---|---|---|---|---|---|
| chlorine | + | bromide ions | $\rightarrow$ | bromine | + | chloride ions |

You can see the loss and gain of electrons by looking at the ionic equation.

## Displacement Reactions Show Reactivity Trends

You can use displacement reactions to show the reactivity trend of the halogens.

1) Start by measuring out a small amount of a halide salt solution in a test tube.

2) Add a few drops of a halogen solution to it and shake the tube gently.

3) If you see a colour change, then a reaction has happened — the halogen has displaced the halide ions from the salt. If no reaction happens, there won't be a colour change — the halogen is less reactive than the halide and so can't displace it.

4) Repeat the process using different combinations of halide salt and halogen.

5) The table below shows what should happen when you mix different combinations of chlorine, bromine and iodine water with solutions of the salts potassium chloride, potassium bromide and potassium iodide.

| Start with: | Potassium chloride solution $KCl_{(aq)}$ — colourless | Potassium bromide solution $KBr_{(aq)}$ — colourless | Potassium iodide solution $KI_{(aq)}$ — colourless |
|---|---|---|---|
| Add chlorine water $Cl_{2(aq)}$ — colourless | no reaction | orange solution ($Br_2$) formed | brown solution ($I_2$) formed |
| Add bromine water $Br_{2(aq)}$ — orange | no reaction | no reaction | brown solution ($I_2$) formed |
| Add iodine water $I_{2(aq)}$ — brown | no reaction | no reaction | no reaction |

6) Chlorine displaces both bromine and iodine from salt solutions. Bromine can't displace chlorine, but it does displace iodine. Iodine can't displace chlorine or bromine.

7) This shows the reactivity trend — the halogens get less reactive as you go down the group.

8) You can use this trend to predict how astatine might react. Since astatine is the least reactive halogen, you'd predict it wouldn't displace any other halogens from their salt solutions.

## New information displaces old information from my brain...

If you remember that the halogens get less reactive as you go down the group, you can work out what will happen when you mix any halogen with any halide salt. You need to know the colour changes that go with the reactions too.

Q1    A student added a few drops of a halogen solution to a potassium iodide solution. The solution turned brown. Explain what the student should do to help him identify the halogen solution.    [2 marks]

# Group 0 — Noble Gases

The elements in <u>Group 0</u> of the periodic table are known as the <u>noble gases</u>. 'Noble' here is just being used in the old chemistry sense of being <u>unreactive</u> — nothing to do with them being particularly honourable or good.

## Group 0 Elements are All Inert, Colourless Gases

<u>Group 0</u> elements are called the <u>noble gases</u>. Group 0 is made up of the elements helium, neon, argon, krypton, xenon and radon.

1) All of the Group 0 elements are <u>colourless gases</u> at room temperature.

2) The noble gases are all <u>monatomic</u> — that just means that their gases are made up of <u>single atoms</u> (not molecules).

3) They're also more or less <u>inert</u> — this means they <u>don't react</u> with much at all. The reason for this is that they have a <u>full outer shell</u> of electrons. This means they <u>don't</u> easily <u>give up</u> or <u>gain</u> electrons.

4) As the noble gases are inert, they're <u>non-flammable</u> — they won't set on fire.

5) These properties make the gases pretty <u>hard to observe</u> — it took a long time for them to be discovered.

| Group 6 | Group 7 | Group 0 |
|---|---|---|
| | | 4<br>**He**<br>Helium<br>2 |
| O | F | 20<br>**Ne**<br>Neon<br>10 |
| S | Cl | 40<br>**Ar**<br>Argon<br>18 |
| | Br | 84<br>**Kr**<br>Krypton<br>36 |
| | I | 131<br>**Xe**<br>Xenon<br>54 |
| | At | 222<br>**Rn**<br>Radon<br>86 |

## The Noble Gases have Many Everyday Uses...

1) <u>Noble gases</u> can be used to provide an <u>inert atmosphere</u>.

2) <u>Argon</u> does this in <u>filament lamps</u> (light bulbs). Since it's <u>non-flammable</u>, it stops the very hot filament from <u>burning away</u>. <u>Flash photography</u> uses the same principle — <u>argon</u>, <u>krypton</u> and <u>xenon</u> are used to stop the flash filament from burning up during the high temperature flashes.

3) <u>Argon</u> and <u>helium</u> can also be used to protect metals that are being <u>welded</u>. The inert atmosphere stops the hot metal reacting with <u>oxygen</u>.

4) <u>Helium</u> is used in <u>airships</u> and <u>party balloons</u>. Helium has a <u>lower density</u> than air — so it makes balloons <u>float</u>. It is also <u>non-flammable</u> which makes it safer to use than hydrogen gas.

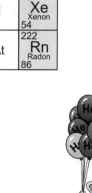

## There are Patterns in the Properties of the Noble Gases

1) As with the other groups in the periodic table, there are also <u>trends</u> in the <u>properties</u> of the noble gases.

2) For example, <u>boiling point</u>, <u>melting point</u> and <u>density</u> all <u>increase</u> as you go <u>down</u> Group 0.

3) You could be given information about a particular <u>property</u> of the noble gases (or Group 7) and asked to use it to <u>estimate the value</u> of this property for a certain element. For example:

**EXAMPLE:** Use the densities of helium ($0.2$ kg m$^{-3}$) and argon ($1.8$ kg m$^{-3}$) to predict the density of neon.

Neon comes between helium and argon in the group, so you can predict that its density will be roughly halfway between their densities:
$(0.2 + 1.8) \div 2 = 2.0 \div 2 = 1.0$

Neon should have a density of about $1.0$ kg m$^{-3}$.

*There are other methods you could use for these types of question, but don't worry — you'd get marks for any sensible answer.*

4) You could be asked about how an element <u>reacts</u> too, so remember — elements in the <u>same group</u> react in <u>similar ways</u> because they all have the same number of <u>electrons</u> in their <u>outer shells</u>. And, to find out which group an element is in, all you need to do is look at the <u>periodic table</u>. Simple.

---

## Noble gas jokes are rubbish — I never get a reaction from them...

The noble gases might seem a bit dull, given how unreactive they are, but they're not so bad. They'd be pretty good at hide and seek for a start. And what would helium balloon sellers be without them? Deflated — that's what.

Q1 The melting points of the first four noble gases are: helium = –272 °C, neon = –249 °C, argon = –189 °C and krypton = –157 °C. Predict the melting point of xenon. [1 mark]

# Revision Questions for Sections 13 and 14

Sections 13 and 14 were great weren't? Those reactivity series could prove tricky though, so try these questions.
- Try these questions and <u>tick off each one</u> when you <u>get it right</u>.
- When you've done <u>all the questions</u> under a heading and are <u>completely happy</u> with it, tick it off.

## The Reactions and Reactivity of Metals (p.114-116) ☑

1) Describe oxidation and reduction in terms of the addition and removal of oxygen. ☑
2) Identify which element is reduced in the following reaction: $CH_4 + 2O_2 \rightarrow CO_2 + 2H_2O$ ☑
3) In a reactivity series, where do you find the least reactive elements? ☑
4) True or false? The easier it is for a metal atom to form a positive ion, the more reactive it will be. ☑
5) You are given samples of four mystery metals and some dilute hydrochloric acid.
   Briefly describe how you could use these things to work out a reactivity series for the four metals. ☑
6) Describe oxidation and reduction in terms of electrons. ☑
7) Describe what happens during a displacement reaction. ☑

## Extracting Metals from their Ores (p.117-118) ☑

8) What is a metal ore and where are they usually found? ☑
9) How are metals more reactive than carbon usually extracted from their ores? ☑
10) Describe how metals less reactive than carbon are usually extracted from their ores. ☑
11) Name two biological methods that can be used to extract metals from low-grade ores. ☑

## Conserving Resources (p.119-120) ☐

12) Give two ways in which recycling is better for the environment than disposing of waste in landfill. ☑
13) State how recycling can benefit the economy. ☑
14) What is a life cycle assessment? ☑
15) Name four factors that should be considered when drawing up a life cycle assessment for a product. ☑

## Equilibria (p.121-122) ☑

16) Draw the symbol which shows that a reaction is reversible. ☑
17) State Le Chatelier's principle. ☑
18) Describe what would happen to the equilibrium position of a reversible reaction
    if you increased the concentration of the reactants. ☑

## Groups 1, 7 and 0 (p.123-126) ☐

19) Give two properties of the Group 1 metals. ☑
20) Explain why Group 1 metals are so reactive. ☑
21) Put these alkali metals in order of reactivity, starting with the least reactive:
    potassium, caesium, lithium, sodium. ☑
22) How many electrons do halogens have in their outer shells? ☑
23) Describe the appearances and physical states of the
    following halogens at room temperature and pressure:   a) chlorine,   b) bromine,   c) iodine. ☑
24) Why can halogen displacement reactions be described as redox reactions? ☑
25) If chlorine water is added to potassium bromide solution, what colour will the solution turn? ☑
26) At room temperature, what colour are the Group 0 gases? ☑
27) Why are balloons filled with helium able to float in the air? ☑
28) Does the boiling point of Group 0 elements increase or decrease going down the group? ☑

# Reaction Rates

Reactions can be <u>fast</u> or <u>slow</u> — you've probably already realised that. It's exciting stuff. Honest.

## The Rate of Reaction is a Measure of How Fast the Reaction Happens

The <u>rate of a reaction</u> is how quickly a reaction happens. It can be observed <u>either</u> by measuring how quickly the reactants are used up or how quickly the products are formed. The <u>rate of a reaction</u> can be calculated using the following formula:

$$\text{Rate of Reaction} = \frac{\text{amount of reactant used or amount of product formed}}{\text{time}}$$

*It's usually a lot easier to measure products forming.*

## You Can Do Experiments to Follow Reaction Rates

There are different ways that the rate of a reaction can be <u>measured</u>. Here are three examples:

### Precipitation

1) This method works for any reaction where mixing <u>two see-through solutions</u> produces a <u>precipitate</u>, which <u>clouds</u> the solution.

2) You <u>mix</u> the two reactant solutions and put the flask on a piece of paper that has a <u>mark</u> on it.

3) <u>Observe</u> the mark through the mixture and measure how long it takes for the mark to be <u>obscured</u>. The <u>faster</u> it disappears, the <u>faster</u> the reaction.

4) The result is <u>subjective</u> — <u>different people</u> might not agree on <u>exactly</u> when the mark 'disappears'.

*You can use this method to investigate how temperature affects the rate of the reaction between sodium thiosulfate and hydrochloric acid. See page 130.*

### Change in Mass (Usually Gas Given Off)

1) You can measure the rate of a reaction that <u>produces a gas</u> using a <u>mass balance</u>.

2) As the gas is released, the <u>lost mass</u> is easily measured on the balance. The <u>quicker</u> the reading on the balance <u>drops</u>, the <u>faster</u> the reaction.

3) You know the reaction has <u>finished</u> when the reading on the balance <u>stops changing</u>.

4) You can use your results to plot a <u>graph</u> of <u>change in mass</u> against <u>time</u>.

5) This method does release the gas produced straight into the room — so if the gas is <u>harmful</u>, you must take <u>safety precautions</u>, e.g. do the experiment in a <u>fume cupboard</u>.

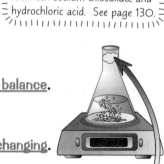

*The cotton wool lets gases through but stops any solid, liquid or aqueous reactants flying out during the reaction.*

### The Volume of Gas Given Off

1) This involves the use of a <u>gas syringe</u> to measure the <u>volume</u> of gas given off.

2) The <u>more</u> gas given off during a set <u>time interval</u>, the <u>faster</u> the reaction.

3) You can tell the reaction has <u>finished</u> when <u>no more gas</u> is produced.

4) You can use your results to plot a graph of <u>gas volume</u> against <u>time elapsed</u>.

5) You need to be careful that you're using the <u>right size</u> gas syringe for your experiment though — if the reaction is too <u>vigorous</u>, you can blow the plunger out of the end of the syringe.

## Retraction rate — how fast my mates disappear when I tell a joke...

Lots of different ways to follow reaction rates here — well... three. Precipitation, mass loss and gas formation.

Q1    Outline how you could use a mass balance to measure the rate of a reaction where a gas is formed. [3 marks]

Q2    Give one disadvantage of the precipitation method when used to follow the rate of a reaction.    [1 mark]

# Rate Experiments Involving Gases  PRACTICAL

You'll probably have to measure the rate of a reaction in class at some point. Time to learn how to do it...

## You can Measure how Surface Area Affects Rate

Here's how you can carry out an experiment to measure the effect of surface area on rate, using marble chips and hydrochloric acid.

1) Set the apparatus up as shown in the diagram on the right.

2) Measure the volume of gas produced using a gas syringe. Take readings at regular time intervals and record the results in a table.

3) You can plot a graph of your results — time goes on the x-axis and volume goes on the y-axis.

4) Repeat the experiment with exactly the same volume and concentration of acid, and exactly the same mass of marble chips, but with the marble more crunched up.

5) Then repeat with the same mass of powdered chalk.

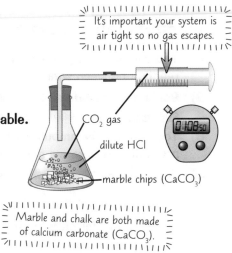

It's important your system is air tight so no gas escapes.

$CO_2$ gas

dilute HCl

marble chips ($CaCO_3$)

Marble and chalk are both made of calcium carbonate ($CaCO_3$).

### Finer Particles of Solid Mean a Higher Rate

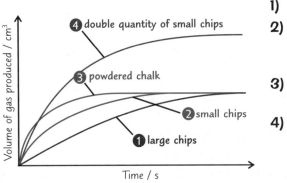

④ double quantity of small chips

③ powdered chalk

② small chips

① large chips

Volume of gas produced / cm³

Time / s

1) The sooner a reaction finishes, the faster the reaction.

2) The steeper the gradient of the graph, the faster the rate of reaction. When the line becomes flat, no more gas is being produced and the reaction has finished.

3) Using finer particles means that the marble has a larger surface area.

4) Lines 1 to 3 on the graph on the left show that the finer the particles are (and the greater the surface area of the solid reactants), the sooner the reaction finishes and so the faster the reaction.

5) Line 4 shows the reaction if a greater mass of small marble chips is added. The extra surface area gives a faster reaction and there is also more gas evolved overall.

## Changing the Concentration of Acid Affects the Rate too

The reaction between marble chips and hydrochloric acids is also good for measuring how changing the reactant concentration affects reaction rate.

You could also measure the rate of these reactions by measuring the loss of mass as the gas is produced.

### More Concentrated Solutions Mean a Higher Rate

③ highest acid concentration

②

① lowest acid concentration

Volume of gas produced / cm³

Time / s

1) You can measure the effect of concentration on rate by following the same method described above. However, this time you repeat the experiment with exactly the same mass and surface area of marble chips and exactly the same volume of acid, but using different concentrations of acid.

2) Lines 1 to 3 on the graph show that a higher concentration gives a faster reaction, with the reaction finishing sooner.

## I prefer chalk to marble chips — I like the finer things in life...

Doing rate experiments lets you collect data. Collecting data lets you plot graphs, and you can use graphs to find reaction rates. But that's all still to come. I bet you're just itching to read on...

Q1 Describe how you could investigate how the surface area of calcium carbonate affects the rate of reaction between calcium carbonate and hydrochloric acid. [3 marks]

# Rate Experiments Involving Precipitation

That's right — another page, another <u>reaction rate experiment</u> to learn. But this one involves a pretty <u>precipitation</u> reaction. Beautiful stuff, don't say I don't spoil you...

## Reaction Rate is Also Affected by Temperature

**PRACTICAL**

1) You can see how <u>temperature</u> affects reaction <u>rate</u> by looking at the reaction between sodium thiosulfate and hydrochloric acid.

2) Sodium thiosulfate and hydrochloric acid are both <u>clear</u>, <u>colourless</u> <u>solutions</u>. They react together to form a <u>yellow precipitate</u> of <u>sulfur</u>.

3) You can use the amount of <u>time</u> that it takes for the coloured precipitate to form as a measure of the <u>rate</u> of this reaction.

4) You use a method like the one on page 128 to carry out this experiment.

You can find out how temperature affects the reaction rate on page 132.

- Measure out fixed volumes of <u>sodium thiosulfate</u> and <u>hydrochloric acid</u>, using a measuring cylinder.
- Use a <u>water bath</u> to <u>gently heat</u> both solutions to the desired temperature before you mix them.
- Mix the solutions in a conical flask. Place the flask over a black mark on a piece of paper which can be seen through the solution. Watch the <u>black mark</u> disappear through the <u>cloudy</u>, <u>yellow sulfur</u> and <u>time</u> how long it takes to go.

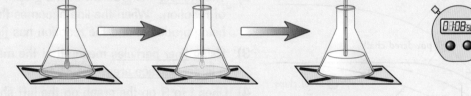

- The reaction can be repeated for solutions at <u>different temperatures</u>.
- The <u>depth</u> and <u>volumes</u> of liquid must be kept the same each time. The <u>concentrations</u> of the solutions must also be kept the same.
- You can use your results to measure what effect <u>changing the temperature</u> has on the <u>rate</u> of the reaction. The <u>shorter</u> the length of time taken for the mark to be obscured, the <u>faster</u> the rate.

## Higher Temperatures Mean a Higher Rate

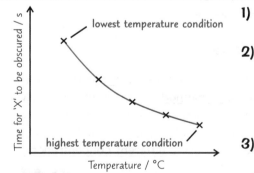

1) You can plot the <u>time taken</u> for the mark to disappear against the <u>temperature</u> of the reacting solutions.

2) If you look at the <u>graph</u>, you can see that the reactions that happened at <u>lower</u> temperatures took <u>longer</u> to obscure the mark, whereas the reactions happening at <u>higher</u> temperatures finished <u>sooner</u>.

How temperature, concentration and pressure affect the rate of a reaction can be explained using collision theory — see page 132.

3) So <u>increasing</u> the temperature <u>increases the rate</u> of the reaction.

---

## And for my next trick, I'll make this chocolate cake disappear...

When repeating this experiment, you need to keep everything exactly the same apart from the temperature — then you can sleep easy knowing that it was the temperature change that affected the reaction rate and not anything else.

Q1 Azim carries out an experiment to measure how temperature affects the rate of reaction between sodium thiosulfate and hydrochloric acid. He uses the time taken for a mark underneath the reaction vessel to be obscured as a measure of rate. How would you expect the time taken for the mark to disappear to change as the temperature of the reacting solutions was increased?

[1 mark]

# Calculating Rates

You can work out rates of reaction using <u>graphs</u>. I bet you can't wait to find out how...

## Faster Rates of Reaction are Shown by Steeper Gradients

If you have a graph of <u>amount of product formed</u> (or <u>reactant used up</u>) against <u>time</u>, then the <u>gradient</u> (slope) of the graph will be equal to the rate of the reaction — the <u>steeper</u> the slope, the <u>faster</u> the rate.

The gradient of a <u>straight line</u> is given by the equation:

**gradient = change in y ÷ change in x**

**EXAMPLE:** Calculate the rate of the reaction shown on the graph on the right.

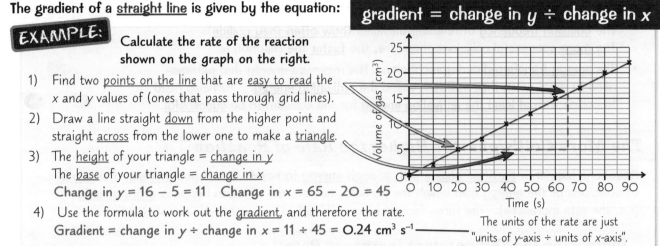

1) Find two <u>points on the line</u> that are <u>easy to read</u> the x and y values of (ones that pass through grid lines).

2) Draw a line straight <u>down</u> from the higher point and straight <u>across</u> from the lower one to make a <u>triangle</u>.

3) The <u>height</u> of your triangle = <u>change in y</u>
   The <u>base</u> of your triangle = <u>change in x</u>
   Change in y = 16 − 5 = 11    Change in x = 65 − 20 = 45

4) Use the formula to work out the <u>gradient</u>, and therefore the rate.
   Gradient = change in y ÷ change in x = 11 ÷ 45 = 0.24 cm$^3$ s$^{-1}$ ———
   The units of the rate are just "units of y-axis ÷ units of x-axis".

## Draw a Tangent to Find the Gradient of a Curve

1) If your graph (or part of it) is a <u>curve</u>, the gradient, and therefore <u>rate</u>, is different at different points along the curve.

2) To find the <u>gradient</u> of the graph at a certain point, you'll have to draw a <u>tangent</u> at that point.

3) A tangent is just a line that <u>touches the curve</u> and has the <u>same gradient</u> as the line at that point.

4) To draw a tangent, place a <u>ruler</u> on the line of best fit at the point you're interested in, so you can see the <u>whole curve</u>. Adjust the ruler so the space between the ruler and the curve is the same on both sides of the point. Draw a line <u>along the ruler</u> to make the <u>tangent</u>.

5) The rate at that point is then just the <u>gradient</u> of the <u>tangent</u>.

**EXAMPLE:** The graph below shows the concentration of product formed, measured at regular intervals during a chemical reaction. What is the rate of reaction at 3 minutes?

1) Position a <u>ruler</u> on the graph at the point where you want to know the rate — here it's <u>3 minutes</u>.

2) Adjust the ruler until the <u>space</u> between the ruler and the curve is <u>equal</u> on <u>both sides</u> of the point.

3) Draw a line along the ruler to make the <u>tangent</u>. Extend the line <u>right</u> <u>across</u> the graph.

4) Pick <u>two points</u> on the line that are easy to read. Use them to calculate the <u>gradient</u> of the tangent in order to find the <u>rate</u>:

gradient = change in y ÷ change in x
= (0.22 − 0.14) ÷ (5.0 − 2.0)
= 0.08 ÷ 3.0
= 0.027

So, the rate of reaction at 3 minutes was 0.027 mol dm$^{-3}$ min$^{-1}$.

## ...and that's why I love cows — oh sorry, I went off on a tangent ...

Lots of nifty graph skills here. Gradients aren't too hard, but make sure those tangents don't trip you up.

Q1    Work out the rate of reaction at 20 seconds using the graph (marked *) shown above.    [2 marks]

# Collision Theory

The rate of a reaction depends on these things — <u>temperature</u>, <u>concentration</u> (or <u>pressure</u> for gases) and the <u>size of the particles</u> (for solids). This page explains why these things affect the reaction rate. Let's get cracking.

## Particles Must Collide with Enough Energy in Order to React

<u>Reaction rates</u> are explained by <u>collision theory</u>. It's simple really.

<u>The rate of a chemical reaction</u> depends on:

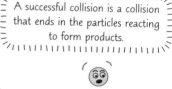

A successful collision is a collision that ends in the particles reacting to form products.

- The <u>collision frequency</u> of reacting particles (<u>how often they collide</u>). The <u>more</u> successful collisions there are, the <u>faster</u> the reaction is.
- The <u>energy transferred</u> during a collision. The minimum energy that particles need to react when they collide is called the <u>activation energy</u>. Particles need to collide with <u>at least the activation energy</u> for the collision to be <u>successful</u>.

## The More Collisions, the Higher the Rate of Reaction

Reactions happen if <u>particles collide</u> with enough <u>energy</u> to react. So, if you <u>increase</u> the <u>number</u> of collisions or the <u>energy</u> with which the particles collide, the reaction happens <u>more quickly</u> (i.e. the rate increases). The three factors below all lead to an increased rate of reaction...

### Increasing the Temperature Increases Rate

1) When the <u>temperature is increased</u> the particles <u>move faster</u>. If they move faster, they're going to have <u>more collisions</u>.

2) Higher temperatures also increase the <u>energy</u> of the collisions, since the particles are moving <u>faster</u>. Reactions <u>only happen</u> if the particles collide with <u>enough energy</u>.

3) This means that at <u>higher</u> temperatures there will be more <u>successful collisions</u> (<u>more particles</u> will <u>collide</u> with <u>enough energy</u> to react). So <u>increasing</u> the temperature <u>increases</u> the rate of reaction.

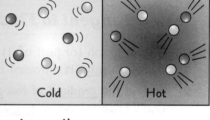

Cold          Hot

### Increasing Concentration (or Pressure) Increases Rate

1) If a <u>solution</u> is made more <u>concentrated</u> it means there are more particles of <u>reactant</u> in the same volume. This makes collisions <u>more likely</u>, so the reaction rate <u>increases</u>.

2) In a <u>gas</u>, increasing the <u>pressure</u> means that the particles are <u>more crowded</u>. This means that the frequency of <u>collisions</u> between particles will <u>increase</u> — so the rate of reaction will also <u>increase</u>.

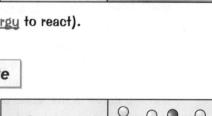

Low concentration
(Low pressure)

High concentration
(High pressure)

### Smaller Solid Particles (or More Surface Area) Means a Higher Rate

1) If one reactant is a <u>solid</u>, breaking it into <u>smaller</u> pieces will <u>increase its surface area to volume ratio</u> (i.e. more of the solid will be exposed, compared to its overall volume).

2) The particles around it will have <u>more area to work on</u>, so the frequency of collisions will <u>increase</u>.

3) This means that the rate of reaction is faster for solids with a larger <u>surface area to volume</u> ratio.

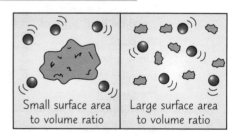

Small surface area
to volume ratio

Large surface area
to volume ratio

## Collision theory — it's always the other driver...

Remember — more collisions mean a faster reaction. But don't be fooled as not every collision results in a reaction.

Q1    Describe the two factors, in terms of collisions, that affect the rate of reaction.                [2 marks]

Q2    Explain why breaking a solid reactant into smaller pieces increases the rate of a reaction.          [3 marks]

# Catalysts

Catalysts are very important for <u>commercial reasons</u> — they <u>increase reaction rate</u> and <u>reduce energy costs</u> in industrial reactions. If that's not reason enough to learn this page, I don't know what is. (Oh, apart from "exams"...)

## A Catalyst Increases the Rate of a Reaction

1) A <u>catalyst</u> is a substance which increases the <u>rate of a reaction</u>, <u>without</u> being chemically changed or used up in the reaction.

2) Using a catalyst <u>won't</u> change the products of the reaction — so the reaction <u>equation</u> will stay the <u>same</u>.

3) Because it <u>isn't</u> used up, you only need a <u>tiny bit</u> to catalyse large amounts of reactants.

4) Catalysts tend to be very <u>fussy</u> about which reactions they catalyse though — you can't just stick any old catalyst in a reaction and expect it to work.

5) Catalysts work by <u>decreasing</u> the <u>activation energy</u> (see last page) needed for a reaction to occur.

6) They do this by providing an <u>alternative reaction pathway</u> that has a <u>lower activation energy</u>.

7) As a result, <u>more</u> of the particles have at least the <u>minimum amount of energy</u> needed for a reaction to occur when the particles collide.

8) You can see this if you look at a <u>reaction profile</u>.

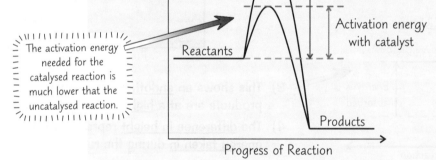

*Reaction profiles show the energy levels of the reactants and the products in a reaction. There are more reaction profiles on the next page.*

*The activation energy needed for the catalysed reaction is much lower that the uncatalysed reaction.*

Energy

Activation energy without catalyst

Activation energy with catalyst

Reactants

Products

Progress of Reaction

*MEOW*
*THE FURRIES 2016*
*RED CARPET EDITION*
*HOW TO GET THAT A-LIST RED CARPET LOOK*

## Enzymes Control Cell Reactions

1) <u>Enzymes</u> are <u>biological catalysts</u>.

2) This means that they <u>catalyse</u> (<u>speed up</u>) the <u>chemical reactions</u> in living cells.

3) Reactions catalysed by enzymes include <u>respiration</u>, <u>photosynthesis</u> and <u>protein synthesis</u>.

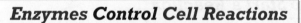

- Enzymes from <u>yeast cells</u> are used in the <u>fermentation</u> process which is used to make <u>alcoholic drinks</u>.

- They catalyse the reaction that converts <u>sugars</u> (such as glucose) into <u>ethanol</u> and <u>carbon dioxide</u>.

## I wish there was a catalyst for making my takeaway arrive...

Catalysts are really handy. Some reactions take a very long time to happen by themselves which isn't good for industrial reactions. Catalysts help to produce a acceptable amount of product in an acceptable length of time.

Q1    Give the definition of a catalyst.    [2 marks]

Q2    The decomposition of hydrogen peroxide can be catalysed by manganese dioxide.
Explain why only a small amount of manganese dioxide is needed for the catalysis
of this reaction, even when starting with a large quantity of hydrogen peroxide.    [1 mark]

Q3    Give the definition of an enzyme and explain what they do.    [2 marks]

# Endothermic and Exothermic Reactions

So, endothermic and exothermic reactions are all about taking in and giving out energy to the surroundings. I think endothermic reactions are a bit self centred really — they just take, take, take...

> Combustion reactions (where something burns in oxygen — see page 138) are always exothermic.

## Reactions are Exothermic or Endothermic

An **EXOTHERMIC** reaction is one which gives out energy to the surroundings, usually in the form of heat and usually shown by a rise in temperature of the surroundings.

An **ENDOTHERMIC** reaction is one which takes in energy from the surroundings, usually in the form of heat and usually shown by a fall in temperature of the surroundings.

## Reaction Profiles Show if a Reaction's Exo- or Endothermic

Reaction profiles show the energy levels of the reactants and the products in a reaction. You can use them to work out if energy is released (exothermic) or taken in (endothermic).

1) This shows an exothermic reaction — the products are at a lower energy than the reactants.

2) The difference in height represents the energy given out in the reaction.

EXOTHERMIC

Energy

Reactants

Energy is released

Products

Progress of reaction

ENDOTHERMIC

Energy

Products

Energy is absorbed

Reactants

Progress of reaction

3) This shows an endothermic reaction because the products are at a higher energy than the reactants.

4) The difference in height represents the energy taken in during the reaction.

## Activation Energy is the Energy Needed to Start a Reaction

1) The activation energy is the minimum amount of energy needed for bonds to break (see page 136) and a reaction to start.

2) On a reaction profile, it's the energy difference between the reactants and the highest point on the curve.

3) It's a bit like having to climb up one side of a hill before you can ski/snowboard/sledge/fall down the other side.

4) If the energy input is less than the activation energy there won't be enough energy to start the reaction — so nothing will happen.

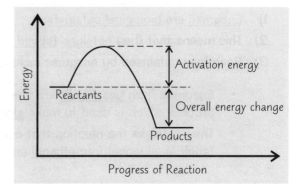

Energy

Reactants

Activation energy

Overall energy change

Products

Progress of Reaction

## Endothermic reactions — they just get cooler and cooler...

Remember, "exo-" = exit, "-thermic" = heat, so an exothermic reaction is one that gives out heat — and endothermic means just the opposite. To make sure you really understand these terms, try this question.

Q1 A student carries out an experiment which results in a change in temperature of the reaction mixture. Use the energy profile for the reaction shown on the right to help explain whether the temperature of the reaction mixture increased or decreased.

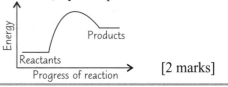

[2 marks]

Section 15 — Rates of Reaction and Energy Changes

# Measuring Temperature Changes

Sometimes it's not enough to just know if a reaction is endothermic or exothermic. You may also need to know how much energy is absorbed or released — you can do experiments to find this out. Fun, fun, fun...

## Temperature Changes can be Measured

You can follow the change in temperature of a reaction mixture as a reaction takes place. You can do this in the following way:

- Put a polystyrene cup into a large beaker of cotton wool (the cotton wool gives insulation to help limit energy transfer to or from the reaction mixture).
- Add a known volume of your first reagent to the cup.
- Measure the initial temperature of the solution.
- Add a measured mass/volume of your second reagent and stir the reaction mixture.
- Put a lid on the cup to reduce any energy lost by evaporation.
- Record the maximum or minimum temperature (depending on whether it's increasing or decreasing) that the mixture reaches during the reaction.
- Calculate the temperature change.

*lid*
*large beaker*
*thermometer*
*reaction mixture*
*polystyrene cup*
*cotton wool*

You can also use this method to see the effect that different variables have on the amount of energy transferred, e.g. the mass or concentration of the reactants.

## The Change in Temperature Depends on the Reagents Used

You can measure the temperature change for different types of reaction. Whether there's an increase or decrease in temperature depends on which reagents take part in the reaction.

### Dissolving Salts in Water

1) You can measure the temperature change when dissolving salts in water by adding the salt to a polystyrene cup of water and measuring the change in temperature when the salt has dissolved.
2) Dissolving ammonium chloride decreases the temperature of the reaction mixture — it's endothermic.
3) Dissolving calcium chloride causes the temperature of the solution to rise — it's exothermic.

### Neutralisation Reactions

1) In a neutralisation reaction (see page 105), an acid and a base react to form a salt and water. Most neutralisation reactions are exothermic, e.g. $HCl + NaOH \rightarrow NaCl + H_2O$
2) However, the neutralisation reaction between ethanoic acid and sodium carbonate is endothermic.

### Displacement Reactions

1) In a displacement reaction (see page 116), a more reactive element displaces a less reactive element in a compound. These types of reactions are accompanied by a release of energy — they're exothermic.
2) Zinc powder and copper sulfate react in a displacement reaction forming zinc sulfate and copper.

### Precipitation Reactions

1) Precipitates are insoluble solids which can sometimes form when two solutions are mixed together.
2) Precipitation reactions are exothermic. For example, the reaction between lead(II) nitrate solution and potassium iodide forming a lead iodide precipitate would result in an increase in the temperature of the surroundings.

## Energy transfer — make sure you take it all in...

Fluffy cotton wool doesn't sound very sciencey but it's really important. Best check to make sure you know why...

Q1 When measuring the temperature change of a reaction, why it is important to put the polystyrene cup in a beaker of cotton wool and to keep a lid on the cup? [1 mark]

# Bond Energies

Energy transfer in chemical reactions is all to do with <u>making and breaking bonds</u>.

## Energy Must Always be Supplied to Break Bonds

There's more on energy transfer on page 134.

1) During a chemical reaction, <u>old bonds are broken</u> and <u>new bonds are formed</u>.

2) Energy must be <u>supplied</u> to break <u>existing bonds</u> — so bond breaking is an <u>endothermic</u> process.

3) Energy is <u>released</u> when new bonds are <u>formed</u> — so bond formation is an <u>exothermic</u> process.

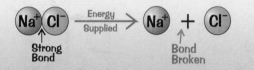

BOND BREAKING — <u>ENDOTHERMIC</u>

Na⁺Cl⁻ —Energy Supplied→ Na⁺ + Cl⁻

Strong Bond          Bond Broken

BOND FORMING — <u>EXOTHERMIC</u>

Mg²⁺ + O²⁻ ⟶ Mg²⁺O²⁻ + Energy Released

Strong Bond Formed

4) In <u>endothermic</u> reactions, the energy <u>used</u> to break bonds is <u>greater</u> than the energy <u>released</u> by forming them.

5) In <u>exothermic</u> reactions, the energy <u>released</u> by forming bonds is <u>greater</u> than the energy used to <u>break</u> 'em.

## Bond Energy Calculations — Need to be Practised

1) <u>Every</u> chemical bond has a particular <u>bond energy</u> associated with it. This <u>bond energy</u> varies slightly depending on the <u>compound</u> the bond occurs in.

2) You can use these <u>known bond energies</u> to calculate the <u>overall energy change</u> for a reaction.

> Overall Energy Change = Energy required to break bonds − Energy released by forming bonds

3) A <u>positive</u> energy change means an <u>endothermic</u> reaction and a <u>negative</u> energy change means an <u>exothermic</u> reaction.

4) You need to <u>practise</u> a few of these, but the basic idea is really very simple...

**EXAMPLE:** Using the bond energy values below, calculate the energy change for the following reaction, where hydrogen and chlorine react to produce hydrogen chloride:

$$H—H + Cl—Cl \rightarrow 2H—Cl$$

H—H: 436 kJ mol⁻¹     Cl—Cl: 242 kJ mol⁻¹     H—Cl: 431 kJ mol⁻¹

1) Work out the energy required to break the <u>original bonds</u> in the reactants.

$(1 × H—H) + (1 × Cl—Cl) = 436 + 242$
$= 678$ kJ mol⁻¹

2) Work out the energy released by forming the <u>new bonds</u> in the products.

$(2 × H—Cl) = 2 × 431$
$= 862$ kJ mol⁻¹

3) Work out the overall change.

overall energy change = energy required to break bonds − energy released by forming bonds
$= 678 − 862 = −184$ kJ mol⁻¹

> In this reaction, the energy released by forming bonds is greater than the energy used to break them so the reaction is exothermic.

## A student and their mobile — a bond that can never be broken...

This stuff might look hard at the moment, but with a bit of practice it's dead easy and it'll win you easy marks if you understand all the theory behind it. See how you get on with this question:

Q1 During the Haber Process, $N_2$ reacts with $H_2$ in the following reaction: $N_2 + 3H_2 \rightleftharpoons 2NH_3$
The bond energies for these molecules are:
N≡N: 941 kJ mol⁻¹
H–H: 436 kJ mol⁻¹
N–H: 391 kJ mol⁻¹
Calculate the overall energy change for the forward reaction.

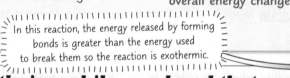

[3 marks]

# Fractional Distillation

Fossil fuels like coal, oil and gas are called non-renewable fuels — they take so long to make that they're being used up much faster than they're being formed. They're finite resources — one day they'll run out.

## Crude Oil is Separated into Different Hydrocarbon Fractions

1) Crude oil is our main source of hydrocarbons and is used as a raw material (sometimes called a feedstock) to create lots of useful substances used in the petrochemical industry.

2) It's formed underground, over millions of years (at high temperatures and pressures) from the buried remains of plants and animals. It's a non-renewable (finite) resource, so one day it will run out.

3) Crude oil is a complex mixture of lots of different hydrocarbons — compounds which contain just carbon and hydrogen. The hydrocarbons found in crude oil have their carbon atoms arranged in either chains or rings and are mostly alkanes (hydrocarbons with the general formula $C_nH_{2n+2}$).

4) Crude oil can be separated out into fractions — simpler, more useful mixtures containing groups of hydrocarbons of similar lengths (i.e. they have similar numbers of carbon and hydrogen atoms). The fractions from crude oil, e.g. petrol, kerosene and diesel, are examples of non-renewable fossil fuels.

   Methane, the main component of natural gas, is another non-renewable fossil fuel. ← Natural gas is a mixture of gases which forms underground in a similar way to crude oil.

5) The different fractions in crude oil are separated by fractional distillation. The oil is heated until most of it has turned into gas. The gases enter a fractionating column (and the liquid bit, bitumen, is drained off at the bottom).

6) In the column there's a temperature gradient (i.e. it's hot at the bottom and gets cooler as you go up).

7) The longer hydrocarbons have higher boiling points. They turn back into liquids and drain out of the column early on, when they're near the bottom. The shorter hydrocarbons have lower boiling points. They turn to liquid and drain out much later on, near to the top of the column where it's cooler.

8) You end up with the crude oil mixture separated out into different fractions. Each fraction contains a mixture of hydrocarbons, mostly alkanes, with similar boiling points.

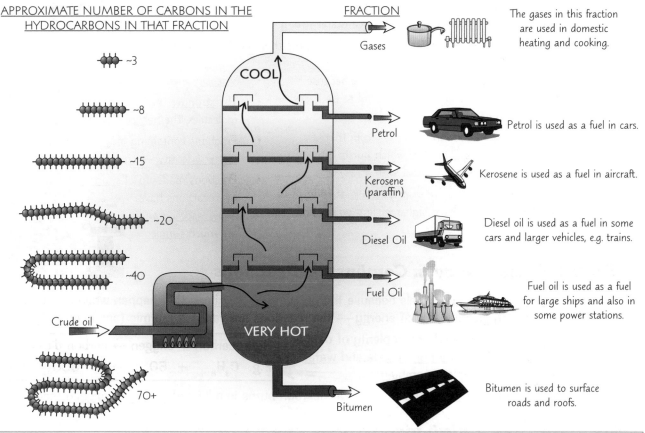

APPROXIMATE NUMBER OF CARBONS IN THE HYDROCARBONS IN THAT FRACTION

~3

~8

~15

~20

~40

Crude oil

70+

FRACTION

Gases — The gases in this fraction are used in domestic heating and cooking.

COOL

Petrol — Petrol is used as a fuel in cars.

Kerosene (paraffin) — Kerosene is used as a fuel in aircraft.

Diesel Oil — Diesel oil is used as a fuel in some cars and larger vehicles, e.g. trains.

Fuel Oil — Fuel oil is used as a fuel for large ships and also in some power stations.

VERY HOT

Bitumen — Bitumen is used to surface roads and roofs.

## How much petrol is there in crude oil? Just a fraction...

Crude oil is pretty useful, so it's worth having a good read of this page to make sure you know all about it.

Q1    Explain how crude oil is separated into fractions during fractional distillation.    [5 marks]

# Hydrocarbons

The <u>physical properties</u> of crude oil fractions all depend on how <u>big</u> the hydrocarbons in that fraction are.

## Compounds in a Homologous Series Share Similar Chemical Properties

1) A <u>homologous series</u> is a <u>family</u> of molecules which have the same <u>general formula</u> and share similar <u>chemical properties</u>.

2) The molecular formulas of <u>neighbouring compounds</u> in a homologous series differ by a <u>$CH_2$</u> unit.

3) The physical properties of compounds in a homologous series vary between the different molecules. For example, the <u>bigger</u> a molecule is, the <u>higher</u> the <u>boiling point</u> will be (see below).

4) <u>Alkanes</u> and <u>alkenes</u> are two different homologous series of hydrocarbons.

| Alkane | Molecular formula | Boiling point (°C) | Fraction in crude oil |
|---|---|---|---|
| Methane | $CH_4$ | −162 | Gases |
| Ethane | $C_2H_6$ | −89 | Gases |
| Dodecane | $C_{12}H_{26}$ | 216 | Kerosene |
| Icosane | $C_{20}H_{42}$ | 343 | Diesel Oil |
| Tetracontane | $C_{40}H_{82}$ | 524 | Fuel Oil |

## The Size of a Hydrocarbon Determines its Properties

1) The <u>size</u> of a hydrocarbon determines which <u>fraction</u> of crude oil it will separate into (see last page).

2) Each fraction contains hydrocarbons (mostly <u>alkanes</u>) with <u>similar</u> numbers of <u>carbon</u> atoms, so all of the molecules in a fraction will have <u>similar properties</u> and behave in similar ways.

3) The <u>physical properties</u> are determined by the <u>intermolecular forces</u> that hold the chains together.

- The <u>intermolecular forces</u> of attraction break a lot more <u>easily</u> in <u>small</u> molecules than they do in bigger molecules. That's because the forces are much <u>stronger</u> between big molecules than they are between small molecules.

- It makes sense if you think about it — even if a big molecule can overcome the forces attracting it to another molecule at a <u>few points</u> along its length, it's still got lots of <u>other</u> places where the force is still strong enough to hold it in place.

- That's why <u>big</u> molecules have <u>higher boiling points</u> than small molecules do.

not many intermolecular forces to break

lots of intermolecular forces to break

- <u>Shorter</u> hydrocarbons are <u>easy to ignite</u> because they have lower boiling points, so tend to be gases at room temperature.

- These gas molecules mix with <u>oxygen</u> in the air to produce a gas mixture which bursts into flames if it comes into contact with a <u>spark</u>.

- <u>Longer</u> hydrocarbons are usually <u>liquids</u> at room temperature. They have higher boiling points and are much <u>harder</u> to ignite.

- <u>Viscosity</u> measures how easily a substance <u>flows</u>.

- The <u>stronger</u> the force is between hydrocarbon molecules, the <u>harder</u> it is for the liquid to <u>flow</u>.

- Fractions containing <u>longer</u> hydrocarbons have a <u>higher viscosity</u> — they're <u>thick</u> like treacle.

- Fractions made up of <u>shorter</u> hydrocarbons have a <u>low viscosity</u> and are much <u>runnier</u>.

## Fuels Release Energy in Combustion Reactions

1) <u>Hydrocarbons</u> make great fuels because the <u>combustion reactions</u> that happen when you burn them in <u>oxygen</u> give out lots of energy — the reactions are very <u>exothermic</u> (see page 134).

2) When you burn hydrocarbons in plenty of oxygen, the only products are <u>carbon dioxide</u> and <u>water</u> — this is called <u>complete combustion</u>.

> Hydrocarbon + oxygen → carbon dioxide + water
> E.g. $C_3H_8$ + $5O_2$ → $3CO_2$ + $4H_2O$

3) <u>Incomplete combustion</u> occurs when a hydrocarbon burns in a <u>limited supply of oxygen</u> (see next page).

## *My sister has a high viscosity — she's pretty thick...*

So, the difference in properties is all down to the intermolecular forces between the hydrocarbon chains. For long hydrocarbons, just remember the three H's — <u>h</u>igher boiling points, <u>h</u>igher viscosity and <u>h</u>arder to ignite.

Q1     Write a balanced symbol equation to show the complete combustion of $C_9H_{20}$ (nonane).      [2 marks]

# Pollutants

You get loads of nasties like carbon monoxide, oxides of nitrogen and sulfur dioxide when you burn fossil fuels.

## Incomplete Combustion Produces Toxic Carbon Monoxide and Soot

1) Complete combustion reactions of hydrocarbons produce only carbon dioxide and water (see last page).

2) If there's not enough oxygen around for complete combustion, you get incomplete combustion. This can happen in some appliances, e.g. boilers, that use carbon compounds as fuels.

3) The products of incomplete combustion contain less oxygen than carbon dioxide.

4) As well as carbon dioxide and water, incomplete combustion produces carbon monoxide (CO), a toxic gas, and carbon in the form of soot.

> *In reality, incomplete combustion reactions will usually produce a mixture of $H_2O$, $CO_2$, CO and C.*

- Carbon monoxide can combine with red blood cells and stop your blood from doing its proper job of carrying oxygen around the body.
- A lack of oxygen in the blood supply to the brain can lead to fainting, a coma or even death.

- During incomplete combustion, tiny particles of carbon can be released into the atmosphere. When they fall back to the ground, they deposit themselves as the horrible black dust we call soot.
- Soot makes buildings look dirty, reduces air quality and can cause or worsen respiratory problems.

## Sulfur Dioxide Causes Acid Rain

1) When fossil fuels are burned, they release mostly $CO_2$ (a big cause of global warming, see page 143).

2) But they also release other harmful gases — especially sulfur dioxide and various nitrogen oxides.

3) The sulfur dioxide ($SO_2$) comes from sulfur impurities in the fossil fuels.

4) When sulfur dioxide mixes with clouds, it forms dilute sulfuric acid. This then falls as acid rain.

5) Acid rain causes lakes to become acidic and many plants and animals die as a result.

6) Acid rain kills trees, damages limestone buildings and stone statues and can also make metal corrode.

## Oxides of Nitrogen Are Also Pollutants

1) Nitrogen oxides are created from a reaction between the nitrogen and oxygen in the air, caused by the energy released by combustion reactions, for example, in the internal combustion engines of cars.

2) Nitrogen oxides are harmful pollutants — they can contribute to acid rain and, at ground level, can cause photochemical smog.

3) Photochemical smog is a type of air pollution that can cause breathing difficulties, headaches and tiredness.

## Hydrogen can be Used as a Clean, Renewable Fuel

Hydrogen gas can also be used to power vehicles. It's often used as a fuel in fuel cells.

**Pros:** Hydrogen is a very clean fuel. In a hydrogen fuel cell, hydrogen combines with oxygen to produce energy, and the only waste product is water — no nasty pollutants like carbon dioxide, toxic carbon monoxide or soot (which are produced when fossil fuels are burnt). Hydrogen's obtained from water which is a renewable resource, so it's not going to run out (unlike fossil fuels). Hydrogen can even be obtained from the water produced by the cell when it's used in fuel cells.

> *You get the hydrogen from the electrolysis of water.*

**Cons:** You need a special, expensive engine. Hydrogen gas also needs to be manufactured which is expensive and often uses energy from another source — this energy often comes from burning fossil fuels which produces pollutants. Also, hydrogen's hard to store and not widely available.

---

## Do you want to hear a joke about nitrogen monoxide? NO?

Acid rain's bad news for sculptors, fish and trees alike. It's bad news for you too, as you need to know it...

Q1    Name two pollutants formed by incomplete combustion.                    [2 marks]

# Cracking

Crude oil fractions from fractional distillation are split into <u>smaller molecules</u> — this is called <u>cracking</u>.
It's dead important — otherwise we might not have enough fuel for cars and planes and things.

## *Cracking is Splitting Up Long-Chain Hydrocarbons*

1) <u>Cracking</u> turns long saturated (alkane) molecules into <u>smaller unsaturated</u> (<u>alkene</u>) and <u>alkane</u> molecules (which are much more <u>useful</u>).

2) It's a form of <u>thermal decomposition</u>, which is when one substance <u>breaks down</u> into at least two new ones when you <u>heat it</u>. This means breaking <u>strong covalent bonds</u>, so you need <u>lots of energy</u>. A <u>catalyst</u> is often added to speed things up.

3) A lot of the longer molecules produced from <u>fractional distillation</u> are <u>cracked</u> into smaller ones because there's <u>more demand</u> for products like <u>petrol</u> and <u>diesel</u> than for bitumen and fuel oil.

4) Cracking also produces lots of <u>alkene</u> molecules, which can be used to make <u>polymers</u> (mostly plastics).

## *Cracking Involves Heat, Moderate Pressures and a Catalyst*

1) <u>Vaporised hydrocarbons</u> are passed over <u>powdered catalyst</u> at about <u>400 °C – 700 °C</u> and <u>70 atm</u>.

2) <u>Aluminium oxide</u> is the <u>catalyst</u> used. The <u>long-chain</u> molecules <u>split apart</u> or "crack" on the <u>surface</u> of the bits of catalyst.

*You don't need to remember the conditions used for cracking.*

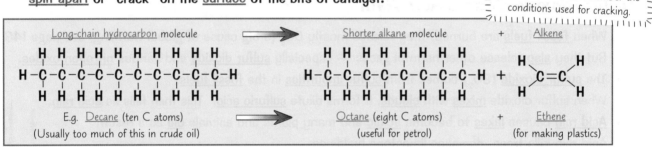

E.g. Decane (ten C atoms)    Octane (eight C atoms)    +    Ethene
(Usually too much of this in crude oil)    (useful for petrol)    (for making plastics)

3) You can use the apparatus shown below to crack <u>alkanes</u> in the lab. During this reaction, the alkane is heated until it is <u>vaporised</u>. It then breaks down when it comes into contact with the catalyst, producing a mixture of <u>short-chain alkanes</u> and <u>alkenes</u>.

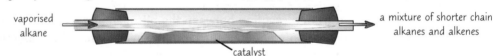

vaporised alkane                                    a mixture of shorter chain alkanes and alkenes

catalyst

## *Cracking Helps Match Supply and Demand*

The examiner might give you a <u>table</u> like the one below to show the <u>supply</u> and <u>demand</u> for various fractions obtained from crude oil. You could be asked which fraction is <u>more likely to be cracked</u> to provide us with petrol and diesel oil (demand for petrol and diesel oil is greater than the amount in crude oil).

| Fraction | Approx % in crude oil | Approx % demand |
|---|---|---|
| Gases | 2 | 4 |
| Petrol | 16 | 27 |
| Kerosene | 13 | 8 |
| Diesel Oil | 19 | 23 |
| Fuel Oil and Bitumen | 50 | 38 |

OK, you could use the <u>kerosene fraction</u> to supply the extra <u>petrol</u> and the <u>fuel oil and bitumen fraction</u> to supply the extra <u>diesel oil</u>.

Or you could crack the <u>fuel oil and bitumen</u> to supply <u>both</u> the extra <u>petrol</u> and the extra <u>diesel oil</u>. This might be cleverer, as there's a lot more fuel oil/bitumen than kerosene.

---

## *Aluminium oxide's hilarious, it's always cracking the alkanes up...*

In that case, I better crack open another packet of biscuits so that the supply matches my stomach's large demand...

Q1    Why does the process of cracking require lots of energy?    [1 mark]

Q2    When a molecule of $C_{17}H_{36}$ is cracked under certain conditions, two molecules are made. If one of the product molecules is $C_5H_{10}$, what is the chemical formula of the other product?    [1 mark]

# The Atmosphere

Scientists have looked at <u>evidence</u> from rocks, air bubbles in ice and fossils to see how our <u>atmosphere</u> has <u>changed</u> over many, many years. Here's one theory about how our atmosphere might have evolved.

## Phase 1 — Volcanoes Gave Out Steam and $CO_2$

<u>Holiday report</u>: Not nice. Take strong walking boots and a coat.

1) The Earth's surface was originally <u>molten</u> for many millions of years. There was almost no atmosphere.

2) Eventually the Earth's surface cooled and a <u>thin crust</u> formed, but <u>volcanoes</u> kept erupting, releasing gases from <u>inside the Earth</u>. This '<u>degassing</u>' released mainly <u>carbon dioxide</u>, but also <u>steam</u>, <u>methane</u> and <u>ammonia</u>.

3) When things eventually settled down, the early atmosphere was <u>mostly $CO_2$</u> and water vapour. There was very little oxygen.

4) The water vapour later <u>condensed</u> to form the <u>oceans</u>.

## Phase 2 — Green Plants Evolved and Produced Oxygen

<u>Holiday Report</u>: A bit slimy underfoot. Take wellies and a lot of suncream.

1) A lot of the early $CO_2$ <u>dissolved</u> into the oceans.

2) <u>Nitrogen gas ($N_2$)</u> was then put into the atmosphere in two ways — it was formed by ammonia reacting with oxygen, and was released by denitrifying bacteria.

3) <u>$N_2$</u> isn't very <u>reactive</u>. So the amount of $N_2$ in the atmosphere <u>increased</u>, because it was being <u>made</u> but not <u>broken down</u>.

4) Next, <u>green plants</u> evolved over most of the Earth. As they photosynthesised, they <u>removed $CO_2$</u> and <u>produced $O_2$</u>.

5) Thanks to the plants, the amount of $O_2$ in the air gradually <u>built up</u> and much of the $CO_2$ eventually got <u>locked up</u> in <u>fossil fuels</u> and <u>sedimentary rocks</u>.

## Phase 3 — Ozone Layer Allows Evolution of Complex Animals

1) The build-up of <u>oxygen</u> in the atmosphere <u>killed off</u> early organisms that couldn't tolerate it.

2) But it did allow the <u>evolution</u> of more <u>complex</u> organisms that <u>made use</u> of the oxygen.

3) The oxygen also created the <u>ozone layer ($O_3$)</u>, which <u>blocked</u> harmful rays from the Sun and <u>enabled</u> even <u>more complex</u> organisms to evolve.

4) There is virtually <u>no $CO_2$</u> left now.

<u>Holiday report</u>: A nice place to be. Get there before the crowds ruin it.

## Test for Oxygen Using a Glowing Splint

You can <u>test</u> for oxygen by checking if the gas will <u>relight</u> a <u>glowing splint</u>.

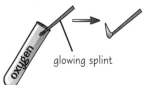

glowing splint

## I went to a restaurant on the moon — nice view, no atmosphere...

We can breathe easy knowing that our atmosphere has developed into a lovely oxygen rich one. Aaaahh.

Q1 The atmosphere of Earth was originally composed mostly of carbon dioxide.
Explain how the proportion of carbon dioxide in the atmosphere decreased over time. [3 marks]

# The Greenhouse Effect

The greenhouse effect isn't a bumper crop of tomatoes and a prize winning marrow...

## Human Activity Affects the Composition of Air

1) The human population is increasing, so there are more people respiring, giving out more carbon dioxide.

2) More people means that more energy is needed for lighting, heating, cooking, transport and so on. People's lifestyles are changing too. More and more countries are becoming industrialised and well-off. This means the average energy demand per person is also increasing (since people have more electrical gadgets, more people have cars or travel on planes, etc.). This increased energy consumption comes mainly from the burning of fossil fuels, which releases more $CO_2$.

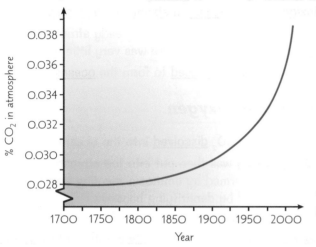

3) More people also means more land is needed to build houses and grow food. This space is often made by chopping down trees — this is called deforestation. But plants are the main things taking carbon dioxide out of the atmosphere (as they photosynthesise) — so fewer plants means less carbon dioxide is taken out of the atmosphere.

*So, as the consumption of fossil fuels increases, as does the concentration of $CO_2$ in the atmosphere.*

4) $CO_2$ is also produced by volcanoes erupting.

5) The graph shows how $CO_2$ levels in the atmosphere have risen over the last 300 years.

## The Greenhouse Effect Helps to Keep the Earth Warm

*The greenhouse effect is very important — it's what keeps the Earth warm enough for us to live on.*

1) The Sun gives out electromagnetic radiation.

2) Some electromagnetic radiation, at most wavelengths, passes through the atmosphere.

3) The electromagnetic radiation with short wavelengths is absorbed by the Earth — warming our planet.

1 The Earth radiates some of the heat radiation it absorbs as longer wavelength, infrared (IR) radiation.

3 Some of the IR radiation is reflected back to Earth by the greenhouse gases.

4 Some IR radiation is re-emitted back into space.

2 Some of this IR radiation is absorbed by greenhouse gases.

5 The absorption and reflection of IR radiation by greenhouse gases is what keeps the Earth warm. It's called the greenhouse effect.

Greenhouse gases are the gases in the atmosphere that can absorb and reflect heat radiation. They're only present in small amounts. Carbon dioxide, water vapour and methane are three greenhouse gases.

4) If the concentration of greenhouse gases in the atmosphere increases, you get an enhanced greenhouse effect. This is where more heat radiation from the Earth is absorbed and less is re-emitted back into space. This causes the atmosphere to heat up (see next page).

## The White House effect — heated political debates...

Is all this hot air isn't making you a bit hot and bothered? If so, here are some questions to cheer you up.

Q1 Give the definition of a greenhouse gas. [1 mark]

Q2 Give two reasons why the increasing human population has affected levels of atmospheric $CO_2$. [2 marks]

# Climate Change

Is it me, or is it getting <u>hot</u> in here...?

## *Increasing Greenhouse Gases Causes Climate Change*

1) You saw on the last page that the level of <u>carbon dioxide</u> in the atmosphere is <u>increasing</u>, but that's not the whole story...

2) The greenhouse gas methane is also causing problems. The concentration of <u>methane</u> has risen lots in recent years due to increased human activity. Methane is produced the <u>digestive processes</u> of certain <u>livestock</u> (e.g. cattle, goats and camels). So, the more livestock we farm, the more methane is produced.

3) Though it's currently only present in <u>tiny amounts</u> in our atmosphere, the increasing concentration of methane is an issue as it's a super effective <u>greenhouse gas</u>.

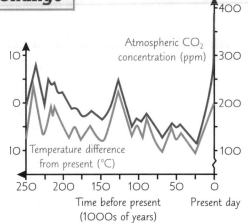

4) There's a <u>scientific consensus</u> that extra greenhouse gases from <u>human activity</u> have caused the average <u>temperature</u> of the Earth to <u>increase</u>, due to the enhanced greenhouse effect — see previous page. This effect is known as global warming.

5) Global warming is a type of <u>climate change</u> and causes other types of climate change, e.g. changing rainfall patterns. It could also cause severe <u>flooding</u> due to the polar ice caps melting. It's a BIG problem that could affect the whole world, so we need to deal with it seriously.

> Most of the scientific community agree that global warming is <u>anthropogenic</u> (caused by humans). But some scientists believe that the current rises in global temperature are just <u>natural fluctuations</u> and that we don't have <u>enough data</u> to prove that global warming is caused by increasing $CO_2$ emissions or human activity.

## *Historical Data is Much Less Accurate Than Current Records*

1) <u>Current global temperature</u> and <u>carbon dioxide levels</u> can be worked out pretty accurately as they're based on measurements taken all over the world.

2) Historical data is <u>less accurate</u> — less data was taken over fewer locations and the methods used to collect the data were less accurate. If you go back far enough, there are <u>no records</u> of global temperature and carbon dioxide levels at all...

3) But there are ways to <u>estimate past data</u>. For example, you can analyse <u>fossils</u>, <u>tree rings</u> or <u>gas bubbles</u> trapped in <u>ice sheets</u> to estimate past levels of atmospheric carbon dioxide.

4) The problem with using these kinds of measurements is that they're much <u>less precise</u> than current measurements made using <u>instrumental sampling</u>. They're also much <u>less representative</u> of global levels.

## *We Can Try To Use Less Fossil Fuels*

1) In order to prevent or <u>slow down climate change</u>, we need to <u>cut down</u> on the amount of greenhouse gases we're releasing into the atmosphere.

2) To <u>reduce carbon dioxide emissions</u>, we can try to limit our own use of fossil fuels. This could be doing things on a personal level, like <u>walking</u> or <u>cycling</u> instead of driving or <u>turning your central heating down</u>.

3) On a larger scale, the UK government has formed plans to encourage the public and industry to become more <u>energy efficient</u>, to create financial incentives to reduce $CO_2$ emissions, to use more renewable energy and to increase research into new energy sources.

## *Give the climate some privacy — it's changing...*

It's not all depressing news. There are steps we can take to cut our carbon dioxide emissions, so chin up.

Q1    What is global warming and how is it caused?         [2 marks]

Q2    Give two measures we can take to reduce carbon dioxide emissions.     [2 marks]

# Revision Questions for Sections 15 and 16

That's <u>Sections 15</u> and <u>16</u> down, which you've now covered pretty much all the chemistry in this book. Yay!

- Try these questions and <u>tick off each one</u> when you <u>get it right</u>.
- When you've done <u>all the questions</u> under a heading and are <u>completely happy</u> with it, tick it off.

## Rates of Reaction (p.128-132) ☑

1) How could you follow the rate of a reaction where two colourless solutions react to form a precipitate? ☑

2) Draw a diagram of the equipment you would use to measure the rate of reaction between hydrochloric acid and marble chips. ☑

3) How does the rate of the reaction between sodium thiosulfate and hydrochloric acid change with temperature? ☑

4) Describe how you would find the rate of a reaction from a straight line graph. ☑

5) What effect will raising the temperature have on the rate of a reaction? ☑

6) How does concentration affect the rate of a reaction? ☑

7) In a gaseous reaction, why would a decrease in pressure result in a slower rate of reaction? ☑

## Catalysts (p.133) ☑

8) What effect does a catalyst have on the activation energy needed for a reaction to take place? ☑

9) Give two examples of reactions catalysed by enzymes. ☑

## Energy Changes in Chemical Reactions (p.134-136) ☑

10) What change in temperature would you expect to observe in an exothermic reaction? ☑

11) What is activation energy? ☑

12) Describe how you could measure the temperature changes in a neutralisation reaction. ☑

13) Is energy required for the breaking of bonds or the forming of bonds? ☑

## Fuels (p.137-140) ☑

14) Name two applications of hydrocarbons. ☑

15) How is crude oil formed? ☑

16) What is the purpose of fractional distillation? ☑

17) What is fuel oil used for? ☑

18) What is the definition of a homologous series? ☑

19) Explain why long hydrocarbons have a high boiling point. ☑

20) Give the word equation for the complete combustion of hydrocarbons. ☑

21) Why does incomplete combustion occur? ☑

22) Name a gas that contributes to the production of acid rain. ☑

23) What is cracking? ☑

## The Atmosphere and Climate Change (p.141-143) ☑

24) Name the gases given out by volcanoes millions of years ago. ☑

25) How was nitrogen gas originally put into the atmosphere? ☑

26) What change in the early atmosphere allowed the complex organisms to evolve? ☑

27) How could you test an unknown gas to see if it was oxygen? ☑

28) Outline how the greenhouse effect works. ☑

29) How has human activity led to an increase in the concentration of methane in the atmosphere? ☑

30) What methods have scientists used to predict past climates? ☑

# Distance, Displacement, Speed and Velocity

To understand the difference between <u>distance</u> and <u>displacement</u>, or <u>speed</u> and <u>velocity</u>, you've got to know the difference between a <u>scalar</u> quantity and a <u>vector</u> quantity.  Then you can race through this page.

## Vectors Have Magnitude and Direction

1) Vector quantities have a <u>magnitude</u> (size) and a <u>direction</u>.

2) Lots of <u>physical quantities</u> are vector quantities:

   <u>Vector quantities</u>:  force, velocity, displacement, weight, acceleration, momentum, etc.

3) Some physical quantities <u>only</u> have magnitude and <u>no direction</u>.  These are called <u>scalar quantities</u>:

   <u>Scalar quantities</u>:  speed, distance, mass, energy, temperature, time, etc.

> <u>Velocity</u> is a <u>vector</u>, but <u>speed</u> is a <u>scalar</u> quantity.
> Both bikes are travelling at the same <u>speed</u>, *v*.
> They have <u>different velocities</u> because
> they are travelling in different <u>directions</u>.

## Distance is Scalar, Displacement is a Vector

1) <u>Distance</u> is just <u>how far</u> an object has moved.  It's a <u>scalar</u> quantity so it doesn't involve <u>direction</u>.

2) Displacement is a <u>vector</u> quantity.  It measures the distance and direction in a <u>straight line</u> from an object's <u>starting point</u> to its <u>finishing point</u> — e.g. the plane flew 5 metres <u>north</u>.  The direction could be <u>relative to a point</u>, e.g. <u>towards the school</u>, or a <u>bearing</u> (a <u>three-digit angle from north</u>, e.g. <u>035°</u>).

3) If you walk 5 m <u>north</u>, then 5 m <u>south</u>, your <u>displacement</u> is <u>0 m</u> but the <u>distance</u> travelled is <u>10 m</u>.

## Speed and Velocity are Both How Fast You're Going

1) <u>Speed and velocity</u> both measure <u>how fast</u> you're going, but <u>speed</u> is a <u>scalar</u> and <u>velocity</u> is a <u>vector</u>:

   > <u>Speed</u> is just <u>how fast</u> you're going (e.g. 30 mph or 20 m/s) with no regard to the direction.
   > <u>Velocity</u> is speed in a given <u>direction</u>, e.g. 30 mph north or 20 m/s, 060°.

2) This means you can have objects travelling at a <u>constant speed</u> with a <u>changing velocity</u>.
   This happens when the object is <u>changing direction</u> whilst staying at the <u>same speed</u>.

3) For an object travelling at a <u>constant</u> speed, <u>distance</u>,
   (average) <u>speed</u> and <u>time</u> are related by the formula:

> distance travelled (m) = (average) speed (m/s) × time (s)

4) Objects <u>rarely</u> travel at a <u>constant speed</u>.  E.g. when you <u>walk</u>, <u>run</u> or travel in a <u>car</u>, your speed is <u>always changing</u>.  Make sure you have an idea of the <u>typical speeds</u> for different transport methods:

| | | | | |
|---|---|---|---|---|
| 1) | <u>Walking</u> — <u>1.4 m/s</u> (5 km/h) | | 5) | <u>Cars</u> on a <u>motorway</u> — <u>31 m/s</u> (112 km/h) |
| 2) | <u>Running</u> — <u>3 m/s</u> (11 km/h) | | 6) | <u>Trains</u> — up to <u>55 m/s</u> (200 km/h) |
| 3) | <u>Cycling</u> — <u>5.5 m/s</u> (20 km/h) | | 7) | <u>Wind</u> speed — <u>5 – 20 m/s</u> |
| 4) | <u>Cars</u> in a <u>built-up area</u> — <u>13 m/s</u> (47 km/h) | | 8) | Speed of <u>sound</u> in <u>air</u> — <u>340 m/s</u> |

---

## *My life's feeling pretty scalar — I've no idea where I'm headed...*

This all seems pretty basic, but it's vital you understand it if you want to make it through the rest of this topic.

Q1     Name two examples of: a) a scalar quantity          b) a vector quantity                    [4 marks]

Q2     A sprinter runs 200 m in 25 s.  Calculate his average speed.                              [2 marks]

# Acceleration

Uniform acceleration sounds fancy, but it's just speeding up (or slowing down) at a constant rate.

## Acceleration is How Quickly You're Speeding Up

1) Acceleration is definitely not the same as velocity or speed.

2) Acceleration is the change in velocity in a certain amount of time.

3) You can find the average acceleration of an object using:

Acceleration (m/s²)

$$a = \frac{(v - u)}{t}$$

Change in velocity (m/s) where $u$ is the initial velocity in m/s and $v$ is the final velocity in m/s

Time (s)

*Initial velocity is just the starting velocity of the object.*

4) Deceleration is just negative acceleration (if something slows down, the change in velocity is negative).

### You Need to be Able to Estimate Accelerations

You might have to estimate the acceleration (or deceleration) of an object:

**EXAMPLE:** A car is travelling at 15 m/s, when it collides with a tree and comes to a stop. Estimate the deceleration of the car.

1) Estimate how long it would take the car to stop.
2) Put these numbers into the acceleration equation.
3) As the car has slowed down, the change in velocity and so the acceleration is negative — the car is decelerating.

The car comes to a stop in ~1 s.

$a = (v - u) \div t$
$= (0 - 15) \div 1$
$= -15$ m/s²

*The ~ symbol just means it's an approximate value (or answer).*

So the deceleration is about 15 m/s²

From the deceleration, you can estimate the forces involved too — more about that on page 149.

## Uniform Acceleration Means a Constant Acceleration

1) Constant acceleration is sometimes called uniform acceleration.

2) Acceleration due to gravity ($g$) is uniform for objects in free fall. It's roughly equal to 10 m/s² near the Earth's surface and has the same value as gravitational field strength (p.150).

3) You can use this equation for uniform acceleration:

Final velocity (m/s)

$$v^2 - u^2 = 2 \times a \times x$$

Acceleration (m/s²)

Distance (m)

Initial velocity (m/s)

**EXAMPLE:** A van travelling at 23 m/s starts decelerating uniformly at 2.0 m/s² as it heads towards a built-up area 112 m away. What will its speed be when it reaches the built-up area?

1) First, rearrange the equation so $v^2$ is on one side.
2) Now put the numbers in — remember $a$ is negative because it's a deceleration.
3) Finally, square root the whole thing.

$v^2 = u^2 + (2 \times a \times x)$
$v^2 = 23^2 + (2 \times -2.0 \times 112)$
$= 81$
$v = \sqrt{81} = 9$ m/s

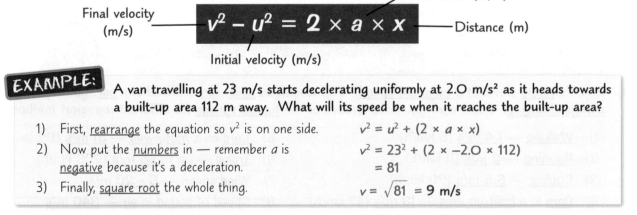

## Uniform problems — get a clip-on tie or use the equation above...

You might not be told what equation to use in the exam, so make sure you can spot when to use the equation for uniform acceleration. Make a list of the information you're given to help you see what to do.

Q1    A ball is dropped from a height, $h$, above the ground. The speed of the ball just before it hits the ground is 5 m/s. Calculate the height the ball is dropped from. (acceleration due to gravity ≈ 10 m/s²)    [2 marks]

# Distance/Time Graphs

A graph speaks a thousand words, so it's much better than writing 'An object starts from rest and moves at a steady speed of 10 m/s for 2 s until it has reaches a distance of 20 m, then remains stationary for 5 s before increasing its velocity with a constant acceleration for 2.5 s.'

## Distance/Time Graphs Tell You How Far Something has Travelled

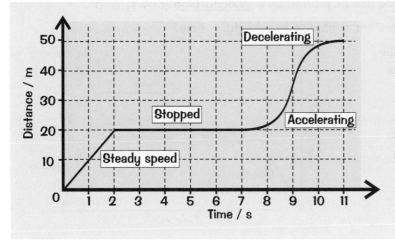

The different parts of a distance/time graph describe the motion of an object:

- The gradient (slope) at any point gives the speed of the object.
- Flat sections are where it's stopped.
- A steeper graph means it's going faster.
- Curves represent acceleration.
- A curve getting steeper means it's speeding up (increasing gradient).
- A levelling off curve means it's slowing down (decreasing gradient).

## The Speed of an Object can be Found From a Distance/Time Graph

You can find the speed at any time on a distance/time graph:

1) If the graph is a straight line, the speed at any point along that line is equal to the gradient of the line.

> For example, in the graph above, the speed at any time between 0 s and 2 s is:
>
> $$\text{Speed} = \text{gradient} = \frac{\text{change in the vertical}}{\text{change in the horizontal}} = \frac{20}{2} = \underline{10 \text{ m/s}}$$

2) If the graph is curved, to find the speed at a certain time you need to draw a tangent to the curve at that point, and then find the gradient of the tangent.

*A tangent is a line that is parallel to the curve at that point.*

3) You can also calculate the average speed of an object when it has non-uniform motion (i.e. it's accelerating) by dividing the total distance travelled by the time it takes to travel that distance.

**EXAMPLE:** The graph shows the distance/time graph for a cyclist on his bike.
Calculate:
a) the speed of the bike 25 s into the journey.
b) the average speed of the cyclist from 0 to 30 s.

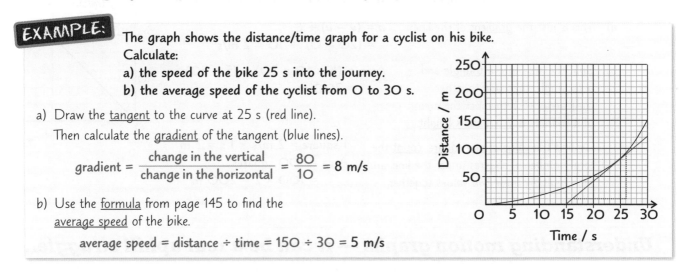

a) Draw the tangent to the curve at 25 s (red line).
Then calculate the gradient of the tangent (blue lines).

$$\text{gradient} = \frac{\text{change in the vertical}}{\text{change in the horizontal}} = \frac{80}{10} = 8 \text{ m/s}$$

b) Use the formula from page 145 to find the average speed of the bike.

$$\text{average speed} = \text{distance} \div \text{time} = 150 \div 30 = 5 \text{ m/s}$$

## Tangent — a man who's just come back from holiday...

For practice, try sketching distance/time graphs for different scenarios. Like walking home or running from a bear.

Q1  Sketch a distance/time graph for an object that initially accelerates, then travels at a constant speed, then decelerates to a stop.                    [2 marks]

# Velocity/Time Graphs

Huzzah, more graphs — <u>velocity/time graphs</u> this time. These look a lot like the <u>distance/time graphs</u> on page 147, so make sure you check the labels on the axes really carefully. You don't want to mix them up.

## Velocity/Time Graphs can have a Positive or Negative Gradient

How an object's <u>velocity</u> changes over time can be plotted on a <u>velocity/time</u> (or *v/t*) graph.

1) <u>Gradient = acceleration</u>, since acceleration = change in velocity ÷ time.

2) <u>Flat sections</u> represent a <u>steady speed</u>.

3) The <u>steeper</u> the graph, the <u>greater</u> the acceleration or deceleration.

4) <u>Uphill</u> sections (/) are <u>acceleration</u>.

5) <u>Downhill</u> sections (\) are <u>deceleration</u>.

6) A <u>curve</u> means <u>changing acceleration</u>.

> If the graph is curved, you can use a tangent to the curve (p.147) at a point to find the acceleration at that point.

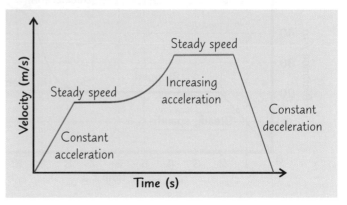

## The Distance Travelled is the Area Under the Graph

1) The <u>area</u> under any section of the graph (or all of it) is equal to the <u>distance travelled</u> in that <u>time interval</u>.

2) For bits of the graph where the acceleration's <u>constant</u>, you can split the area into <u>rectangles</u> and <u>triangles</u> to work it out.

3) If the section under the graph is <u>irregular</u>, it's easier to find the area by <u>counting the squares</u> under the line and <u>multiplying</u> the number by the value of <u>one square</u>.

These two partially shaded squares add up to make one square.

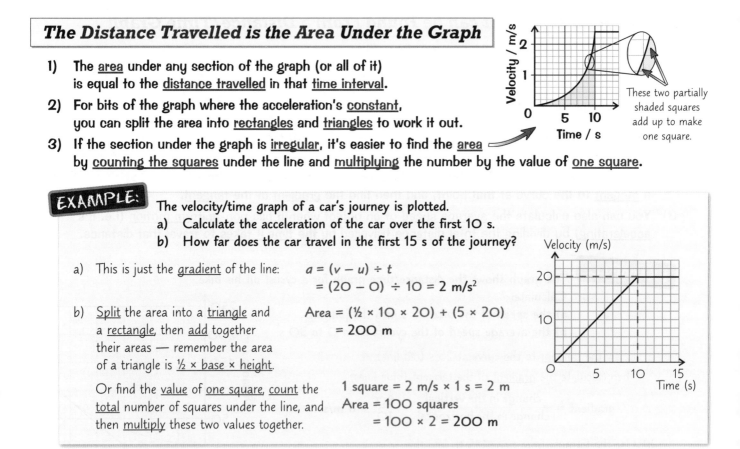

**EXAMPLE:**

The velocity/time graph of a car's journey is plotted.
a) Calculate the acceleration of the car over the first 10 s.
b) How far does the car travel in the first 15 s of the journey?

a) This is just the <u>gradient</u> of the line:
$a = (v − u) ÷ t$
$= (20 − 0) ÷ 10 = 2$ m/s²

b) <u>Split</u> the area into a <u>triangle</u> and a <u>rectangle</u>, then <u>add</u> together their areas — remember the area of a triangle is ½ × base × height.

Area = (½ × 10 × 20) + (5 × 20)
= 200 m

Or find the <u>value</u> of <u>one square</u>, <u>count</u> the <u>total</u> number of squares under the line, and then <u>multiply</u> these two values together.

1 square = 2 m/s × 1 s = 2 m
Area = 100 squares
= 100 × 2 = 200 m

## Understanding motion graphs — it can be a real uphill struggle...

Make sure you know the differences between distance/time and velocity/time graphs, and how to interpret them.

Q1  A stationary car starts accelerating increasingly for 10 s until it reaches a speed of 20 m/s.
It travels at this speed for 20 s until the driver sees a hazard and brakes.
He decelerates uniformly, coming to a stop 4 s after braking.
a) Draw the velocity/time graph for this journey.  [3 marks]
b) Using the graph, calculate the deceleration of the car when it brakes.  [2 marks]

# Newton's First and Second Laws

In the 1660s, a chap called Isaac Newton worked out his dead useful Laws of Motion. Here are the first two.

## A Force is Needed to Change Motion

This may seem simple, but it's important. Newton's First Law says that a resultant force (p.181) is needed to make something start moving, speed up or slow down:

> If the resultant force on a stationary object is zero, the object will remain stationary. If the resultant force on a moving object is zero, it'll just carry on moving at the same velocity (same speed and direction).

So, when a train or car or bus or anything else is moving at a constant velocity, the resistive and driving forces on it must all be balanced. The velocity will only change if there's a non-zero resultant force acting on the object.

1) A non-zero resultant force will always produce acceleration (or deceleration) in the direction of the force.

2) This "acceleration" can take five different forms: starting, stopping, speeding up, slowing down and changing direction.

## Acceleration is Proportional to the Resultant Force

1) The larger the resultant force acting on an object, the more the object accelerates — the force and the acceleration are directly proportional. You can write this as $F \propto a$.

2) Acceleration is also inversely proportional to the mass of the object — so an object with a larger mass will accelerate less than one with a smaller mass (for a fixed resultant force).

3) There's an incredibly useful formula that describes Newton's Second Law:

Resultant force (N)   Mass (kg)

$$F = m \times a$$ — Acceleration (m/s$^2$)

## Large Decelerations can be Dangerous

1) Large decelerations of objects and people (e.g. in car crashes) can cause serious injuries. This is because a large deceleration requires a large force — $F = m \times a$.

2) The force can be lowered by slowing the object down over a longer time, i.e. decreasing its deceleration.

3) Safety features in vehicles are designed to increase collision times, which reduces the force, and so reduces the risk of injury. For example, seat belts stretch slightly and air bags slow you down gradually. Crumple zones are areas at the front and back of a vehicle which crumple up easily in a collision, increasing the time taken to stop.

> **EXAMPLE:** Estimate the resultant force acting on a car stopping quickly from 15 m/s.
>
> 1) Estimate the deceleration of the car — you did that for this example on page 146.
>    The car comes to a stop in ~1 s.
>    $a = (v - u) \div t = (0 - 15) \div 1 = -15$ m/s$^2$
>
> 2) Estimate the mass of the car.
>    Mass of a car is ~1000 kg.
>
> 3) Put these numbers into Newton's 2nd Law.
>    $F = m \times a$
>    $= 1000 \times -15 = -15\ 000$ N
>
> *The force here is negative as it acts in the opposite direction to the motion of the car.*

4) The brakes of a vehicle do work on its wheels (see p.180). This transfers energy from the vehicle's kinetic energy store to the thermal energy store of the brakes. Very large decelerations may cause the brakes to overheat (so they don't work as well). They could also cause the vehicle to skid.

## Accelerate your learning — force yourself to revise...

Newton's First Law means that an object moving at a steady speed doesn't need a net force to keep moving.

Q1    Find the resultant force needed to accelerate an 80 kg man on a 10 kg bike at 0.25 m/s$^2$.    [2 marks]

# Weight and Circular Motion

Now for something a bit more <u>attractive</u> — the force of <u>gravity</u>.  Enjoy...

## Weight and Mass are Not the Same

1) <u>Mass</u> is just the <u>amount of 'stuff'</u> in an object.  For any given object this will have the same value <u>anywhere</u> in the universe.

2) Mass is a <u>scalar</u> quantity.  It's measured in <u>kilograms</u> with a <u>mass</u> balance (an old-fashioned pair of balancing scales).

3) <u>Weight</u> is the <u>force</u> acting on an object due to <u>gravity</u> (the <u>pull</u> of the <u>gravitational force</u> on the object).  Close to Earth, this <u>force</u> is caused by the <u>gravitational field</u> around the Earth.

4) Weight is a <u>force</u> measured in <u>newtons</u>.  You can think of the force as acting from a <u>single point</u> on the object, called its <u>centre of mass</u> (a point at which you assume the <u>whole</u> mass is concentrated).

5) Weight is measured using a calibrated <u>spring</u> balance (or <u>newton meter</u>).

> Gravity attracts all masses, but you only notice it when one of the masses is really big (like a planet).

## Weight Depends on Mass and Gravitational Field Strength

1) You can calculate the <u>weight</u> of an object if you know its <u>mass</u> ($m$) and the <u>strength</u> of the <u>gravitational field</u> that it is in ($g$):

> Weight (N) = mass (kg) × gravitational field strength (N/kg)

2) Gravitational field <u>strength</u> varies with <u>location</u>.  It's <u>stronger</u> the <u>closer</u> you are to the mass causing the field (and <u>more massive</u> objects create <u>stronger</u> fields).

3) This means that the weight of an object <u>changes</u> with its location.

**EXAMPLE:** What is the weight, in newtons, of a 2.0 kg chicken on Earth ($g$ = 10 N/kg)?

Calculate the weight on <u>Earth</u> using the equation for <u>weight</u> given above.

$W = m \times g = 2.0 \times 10 = 20$ N

The chicken has a weight of 16 N on a mystery planet.
What is the gravitational field strength of the planet?

1) <u>Rearrange</u> the weight equation for $g$.

2) <u>Substitute</u> the values in.

$g = W \div m$
$= 16 \div 2.0 = 8.0$ N/kg

> Remember — the mass of the chicken is the same on every planet, it's the weight of the chicken that changes.

## Circular Motion — Velocity is Constantly Changing

1) Velocity is both the <u>speed</u> and <u>direction</u> of an object (p.145).

2) If an object is travelling in a circle (at a <u>constant speed</u>) it is <u>constantly changing direction</u>, so it is constantly <u>changing velocity</u>.  This means it's <u>accelerating</u>.

3) This means there <u>must</u> be a <u>resultant force</u> (p.181) acting on it.

4) This force acts towards the centre of the circle.

5) This force that keeps something moving in a circle is called a <u>centripetal force</u>.

> It's pronounced sen-tree-pee-tal.

The velocity's in this direction, but...

...the force is always towards the centre of the circle.

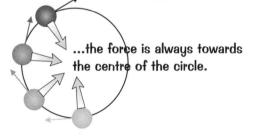

## I don't think you understand the gravity of this situation...

Remember that weight is a force due to gravity and that it changes depending on the strength of the gravitational field the object is in.  Gravity can cause circular motion (in things like moons and satellites).

Q1     Calculate the weight in newtons of a 25 kg mass:
      a) on Earth ($g \approx 10$ N/kg)         b) on the Moon ($g \approx 1.6$ N/kg)        [4 marks]

# Investigating Motion

Doing an <u>experiment</u> for yourself can really help you to understand what's going on with <u>F = ma</u> (p.149).

## *You can Investigate the Motion of a Trolley on a Ramp*  PRACTICAL

1) Measure the <u>mass</u> of the <u>trolley</u>, the <u>unit masses</u> and the <u>hanging hook</u>.
   Measure the <u>length</u> of the piece of <u>card</u> which will <u>interrupt</u> the light gate beams. Then set up
   your <u>apparatus</u> as shown in the diagram below, but <u>don't</u> attach the string to the trolley.

2) <u>Adjust</u> the <u>height</u> of the ramp until the trolley <u>just</u> starts to move.

3) Mark a <u>line</u> on the ramp just before the
   first <u>light gate</u> — this is to make sure the
   trolley travels the <u>same distance</u> every
   time. The light gate will record the <u>initial</u>
   <u>speed</u> of the trolley as it <u>begins to move</u>.

trolley with card

light gates (connected to a data logger)

ramp

string

pulley

hanging mass on hook

4) <u>Attach the trolley</u> to the hanging mass
   by the string. Hold the trolley <u>still</u>
   at the start line, and then <u>let go</u> of it so that it starts to roll down the slope.

5) Each <u>light gate</u> will record the <u>time</u> when the trolley passes through it and the
   <u>speed</u> of the trolley at that time. The <u>acceleration</u> of the trolley can then be
   found using <u>acceleration = change in speed ÷ time</u>, with the following values:

   • the <u>initial speed</u> of the trolley as it passes through the <u>first light gate</u> (it'll be <u>roughly</u> 0 m/s),
   • the <u>final speed</u> of the trolley, which equals the <u>speed</u> of the trolley through the <u>second light gate</u>,
   • the <u>time</u> it takes the trolley to travel <u>between</u> the two light gates.

By changing the <u>height</u> of the ramp so that the trolley <u>just</u> begins to move, it means that
any <u>other</u> forces that are applied (like the <u>force due to gravity</u> caused by the <u>hanging mass</u>)
will be the <u>main</u> cause of the trolley <u>accelerating</u> as it travels down the ramp (page 149).
The size of this <u>acceleration</u> depends on the <u>mass</u> of the <u>trolley</u> and the <u>size</u> of the accelerating <u>force</u>.

• **To investigate the effect of the <u>trolley's mass</u>:** <u>add masses</u> one at a time to the trolley. Keep the
  <u>mass</u> on the <u>hook</u> constant (so the <u>accelerating force</u> is <u>constant</u> — where the force is equal to the
  <u>mass on hook × acceleration due to gravity</u>). <u>Repeat</u> steps 2-5 of the experiment above each time.

• **To investigate the effect of the <u>accelerating force</u>:** start with <u>all</u> the masses loaded onto the <u>trolley</u> and
  <u>transfer</u> the masses to the <u>hook</u> one at a time. Again, <u>repeat steps 2-5</u> each time you <u>move</u> a mass.

  You <u>transfer</u> the masses because you need to keep the mass of the <u>whole system</u> (the mass of the trolley + the mass on the hook) the <u>same</u>.
  This is because the <u>accelerating force</u> causes <u>BOTH</u> the <u>trolley</u> and the <u>hanging masses</u> to accelerate.

You should find that as the <u>accelerating force increases</u>, the acceleration <u>increases</u> (for a given
trolley mass). So <u>force</u> and <u>acceleration</u> are <u>proportional</u>. As the <u>mass</u> of the trolley <u>increases</u>
its <u>acceleration decreases</u> (for a given force) — <u>mass</u> and <u>acceleration</u> are <u>inversely proportional</u>.

## *You can use Different Equipment to Measure Distance and Time*

Light gates (p.210) are often the best option for <u>short</u> time intervals. They get rid of the <u>human error</u> caused
by <u>reaction times</u> (p.155). But light gates aren't the only way to find the <u>speed</u> of an object:

1) For finding something like a person's <u>walking speed</u>, the distances and times you'll look at are quite
   <u>large</u>. You can use a <u>rolling tape measure</u> (one of those clicky wheel things) and <u>markers</u> to measure
   and mark out distances. And for any times longer than <u>five seconds</u>, you can use a regular <u>stopwatch</u>.

2) If you're feeling a bit high-tech, you could also record a <u>video</u> of the moving object and look at how <u>far</u>
   it travels each <u>frame</u>. If you know how many <u>frames per second</u> the camera records, you can find the
   <u>distance</u> travelled by the object in a given number of frames and the <u>time</u> that it takes to do so.

## *My acceleration increases with nearby cake...*

Make sure you know multiple methods for measuring the speed (distance travelled in a time) of an object.

Q1     Why is it better to use a light gate instead of a stopwatch to measure short time intervals?     [1 mark]

# Inertia and Newton's Third Law

Inertia and Newton's Third Law can seem simple on the surface, but they can quickly get confusing. Make sure you really understand what's going on with them — especially if an object is in equilibrium.

## Inertia is the Tendency for Motion to Remain Unchanged

1) Until acted on by a resultant force, objects at rest stay at rest and objects moving at a constant velocity will stay moving at that velocity (Newton's First Law).

2) This tendency to keep moving with the same velocity is called inertia.

3) An object's inertial mass measures how difficult it is to change the velocity of an object.

4) Inertial mass can be found using Newton's Second Law of $F = ma$ (p.149). Rearranging this gives $m = F \div a$, so inertial mass is just the ratio of force over acceleration.

## Newton's Third Law: Reaction Forces are Equal and Opposite

Newton's Third Law says:

> When two objects interact, the forces they exert on each other are equal and opposite.

1) If you push something, say a shopping trolley, the trolley will push back against you, just as hard.

2) And as soon as you stop pushing, so does the trolley. Kinda clever really.

3) So far, so good. The slightly tricky thing to get your head round is this — if the forces are always equal, how does anything ever go anywhere? The important thing to remember is that the two forces are acting on different objects.

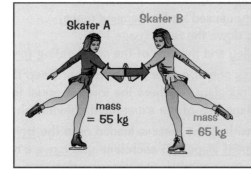

Skater A

Skater B

mass = 55 kg

mass = 65 kg

When skater A pushes on skater B (the 'action' force), she feels an equal and opposite force from skater B's hand (the 'normal contact' force). Both skaters feel the same sized force, in opposite directions, and so accelerate away from each other.

Skater A will be accelerated more than skater B, though, because she has a smaller mass — remember $a = F \div m$.

These equally-sized forces in opposite directions also explain the principle of conservation of momentum (see pages 153-154).

4) It's a bit more complicated for an object in equilibrium (p.182). Imagine a book sat on a table:

The weight of the book pulls it down, and the normal reaction force from the table pushes it up. These forces are equal to each other — the book is in equilibrium and doesn't move. This is NOT Newton's third law. These forces are different types and they're both acting on the book.

The pairs of forces due to Newton's third law in this case are:

- The book is pulled down by its weight due to gravity from Earth ($W_B$) and the book also pulls back up on the Earth ($W_E$).
- The normal contact force from the table pushing up on the book ($R_B$) and the normal contact force from the book pushing down on the table ($R_T$).

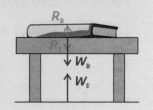

$R_B$

$R_T$

$W_B$

$W_E$

## I have a reaction to forces — they bring me out in a rash...

Newton's 3rd law really trips people up, so make sure you understand exactly what objects the forces are acting on and how that results in movement (or lack of it). Then have a crack at this question to practise what you know.

Q1  A full shopping trolley and an empty one are moving at the same speed. Explain why it is easier to stop the empty trolley than the full trolley over the same amount of time.          [1 mark]

# Momentum

A <u>large rugby player</u> running very <u>fast</u> has much more <u>momentum</u> than a skinny one out for a Sunday afternoon stroll. It's something that <u>all</u> moving objects have, so you better get your head around it.

## Momentum = Mass × Velocity

Momentum is a <u>property</u> that <u>all moving objects have</u>. (Think of it as how much '<u>oomph</u>' something has.) It's defined as the <u>product</u> of the object's <u>mass</u> and <u>velocity</u>:

$$p = m \times v \qquad \text{momentum (kg m/s) = mass (kg) × velocity (m/s)}$$

1) The <u>greater</u> the <u>mass</u> of an object, or the <u>greater</u> its <u>velocity</u>, the <u>more momentum</u> the object has.

2) Momentum is a <u>vector</u> quantity — it has size <u>and</u> direction.

**EXAMPLE:**
A 50 kg cheetah is running at 60 m/s. Calculate its momentum.

$p = m \times v = 50 \times 60$
$= 3000$ kg m/s

**EXAMPLE:**
A boy has a mass of 30 kg and a momentum of 75 kg m/s. Calculate his velocity.

$v = p \div m = 75 \div 30 = 2.5$ m/s

## Total Momentum Before = Total Momentum After

A closed system is just a fancy way of saying that no external forces act.

In a <u>closed system</u>, the total momentum <u>before</u> an event (e.g. a collision) is the same as <u>after</u> the event. This is called <u>conservation of momentum</u>. You can use this to help you calculate things like the <u>velocity</u> or <u>mass</u> of objects in a collision.

In snooker, balls of the <u>same size</u> and <u>mass</u> collide with each other. Each collision is an <u>event</u> where the <u>momentum</u> of <u>each ball changes</u>, but the <u>overall</u> momentum <u>stays the same</u> (momentum is <u>conserved</u>).

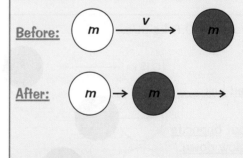

<u>Before:</u>

The red ball is <u>stationary</u>, so it has <u>zero momentum</u>. The white ball is moving with a velocity $v$, so has a <u>momentum</u> of $p = m \times v$.

<u>After:</u>

The white ball hits the red ball, causing it to <u>move</u>. The red ball now has <u>momentum</u>. The white ball <u>continues</u> moving, but at a much <u>smaller velocity</u> (and so a much <u>smaller momentum</u>).

The <u>combined</u> momentum of the red and white balls is equal to the <u>original</u> momentum of the white ball, $m \times v$.

**EXAMPLE:**
A 1500 kg car, travelling at 25 m/s, crashes into the back of a parked car. The parked car has a mass of 1000 kg. The two cars lock together and continue moving in the same direction as the original moving car. Calculate the velocity that the two cars move with.

1) Calculate the <u>momentum</u> before the collision.

2) Find the <u>combined mass</u> of the cars.

3) <u>Rearrange</u> the equation to find the <u>velocity</u> of the cars.

$p = m \times v = 1500 \times 25 = 37\ 500$ kg m/s

Total momentum before = total momentum after

New mass of joined cars = 2500 kg = M

$v = p \div M = 37\ 500 \div 2500 = 15$ m/s

## Learn this stuff — it'll only take a moment... um...

Conservation of momentum is incredibly handy — there's more on using it on the next page.

Q1 Calculate the momentum of a 60 kg woman running at 3 m/s. [2 marks]

Q2 Describe how momentum is conserved by a gun recoiling (moving backwards) as it shoots a bullet. [4 marks]

# Changes in Momentum

A <u>force</u> causes the <u>momentum</u> of an object to <u>change</u>. A <u>bigger force</u> makes it change <u>faster</u>.

## Forces Cause Changes in Momentum

1) When a resultant <u>force</u> acts on an object for a certain amount of time, it causes a <u>change in momentum</u>. <u>Newton's 2nd Law</u> can explain this:

   - A <u>resultant force</u> on an object causes it to <u>accelerate</u>: force = mass × acceleration (see p.149).

   - <u>Acceleration</u> is just <u>change in velocity</u> over <u>time</u>, so: force = $\dfrac{\text{mass} \times \text{change in velocity}}{\text{time}}$.
   
     This means a force applied to an object over any time interval will change the object's <u>velocity</u>.

   - <u>Mass × change in velocity</u> is equal to <u>change in momentum</u>, so you end up with the equation:

   $$\text{force (N)} = \frac{\text{change in momentum (kg m/s)}}{\text{time (s)}} \quad \text{or} \quad F = \frac{(mv - mu)}{t}$$

2) The <u>faster</u> a given change in momentum happens, the <u>bigger the force</u> causing the change must be (i.e. if $t$ gets <u>smaller</u> in the equation above, $F$ gets <u>bigger</u>).

3) So if someone's momentum changes <u>very quickly</u>, like in a <u>car crash</u>, the <u>forces</u> on the body will be very <u>large</u>, and more likely to cause <u>injury</u>. There's more about this on p.149.

4) You can also think of changes in momentum in collisions in terms of <u>acceleration</u> — a change in momentum normally involves a <u>change in velocity</u>, which is what acceleration is (see p.146).

5) As you know, $F = ma$, so the <u>larger the acceleration</u> (or deceleration), the <u>larger the force</u> needed to produce it.

## Conservation of Momentum Shows Newton's Third Law

The equation above can help to show <u>Newton's Third Law</u> (<u>reaction</u> forces are <u>equal</u> and <u>opposite</u>). Take the <u>snooker balls</u> from the previous page.

1) <u>Before</u> the collision, the <u>white</u> ball has a momentum of 0.15 × 4 = 0.6 kg m/s. The <u>red</u> ball has a momentum of <u>zero</u>.

2) The <u>total momentum</u> of the system is 0.6 kg m/s.

3) When the balls collide, the <u>white</u> ball exerts a <u>force</u> on the <u>red</u> ball. This force causes the <u>red ball</u> to <u>start moving</u>.

4) Due to <u>Newton's 3rd Law</u>, the <u>red</u> ball also exerts an <u>equal</u> but <u>opposite</u> force on the <u>white</u> ball. This force causes the <u>white</u> ball to <u>slow down</u>.

5) The collision lasts <u>0.1 s</u>. <u>After</u> the collision, the white ball <u>continues moving</u> at 1 m/s. The red ball <u>begins moving</u> at 3 m/s.

6) The total momentum is (0.15 × 1) + (0.15 × 3) = 0.6 kg m/s. Momentum is <u>conserved</u>.

7) You can <u>calculate</u> the size of the <u>force</u> that caused this <u>change of velocity</u> (and so <u>change of momentum</u>) for each ball:

8) The <u>force exerted on the white ball</u> (by the red ball) is <u>equal and opposite</u> to the force exerted <u>on the red ball</u> (by the white ball). This shows <u>Newton's Third Law</u>.

white ball
$$F = \frac{(mv - mu)}{t}$$
$$= \frac{(0.15 \times 1) - (0.15 \times 4)}{0.1}$$
$$= \frac{-0.45}{0.1} = -4.5 \text{ N}$$

red ball
$$F = \frac{(mv - mu)}{t}$$
$$= \frac{(0.15 \times 3) - (0.15 \times 0)}{0.1}$$
$$= \frac{0.45}{0.1} = 4.5 \text{ N}$$

## Homework this week — play pool to investigate momentum...

*Sigh* if only. Momentum is a pretty fundamental bit of physics — learn it well. Then have a go at this question.

Q1    Calculate the force a tennis racket needs to apply to a 58 g tennis ball to accelerate it from rest to 34 m/s in 11.6 ms.

[3 marks]

# Stopping Distances and Reaction Times

The stopping distance of a vehicle is the distance covered between the driver first spotting a hazard and the vehicle coming to a complete stop. It's made up of the thinking distance and the braking distance.

## Stopping Distance = Thinking Distance + Braking Distance

The longer it takes a car to stop after seeing a hazard, the higher the risk of crashing. The distance it takes to stop a car (stopping distance) is divided into the thinking distance and the braking distance:

The thinking distance is the distance the car travels in the driver's reaction time (the time between noticing the hazard and applying the brakes). It's affected by two main factors:

1) Your reaction time — this is increased by tiredness, alcohol, drugs and distractions.

2) Your speed — the faster you're going, the further you'll travel during your reaction time.

The braking distance is the distance taken to stop once the brakes have been applied. It's affected by:

1) Your speed — the faster you're going, the longer it takes to stop.

2) The mass of the car — a car full of people and luggage won't stop as quickly as an empty car.

3) The condition of the brakes — worn or faulty brakes won't be able to brake with as much force.

4) How much friction is between your tyres and the road — you're more likely to skid if the road is dirty, if it's icy or wet or if the tyres are bald (tyres must have a minimum tread depth of 1.6 mm).

In the exam, you may need to spot the factors affecting thinking and braking distance in different situations. E.g. if a parent is driving her children to school early in the morning on an autumn day, her thinking distance could be affected by tiredness, or by her children distracting her. Her braking distance could be affected by ice, or by leaves on the road reducing the friction/grip.

## The Ruler Drop Experiment Measures Reaction Times

Everyone's reaction time is different and many different factors affect it (see above).

One way of measuring reaction times is to use a computer-based test (e.g. clicking a mouse when the screen changes colour). Another is the ruler drop test:

1) Sit with your arm resting on the edge of a table (this should stop you moving your arm up or down during the test). Get someone else to hold a ruler so it hangs between your thumb and forefinger, lined up with zero. You may need a third person to be at eye level with the ruler to check it's lined up.

2) Without giving any warning, the person holding the ruler drops it. Close your thumb and finger to try to catch the ruler as quickly as possible.

3) The measurement on the ruler at the point where it was caught is how far the ruler dropped in the time it took you to react.

ruler hanging between thumb and forefinger

finger in line with zero

4) The longer the distance, the longer the reaction time.

5) You can calculate how long the ruler was falling for (the reaction time) using the equations on p.146 because its acceleration is constant (and equal to $g$, 10 m/s$^2$).

ruler is dropped without warning

6) It's hard to do this experiment accurately, so do a lot of repeats and take an average of the distance the ruler fell. Use this average in your calculations.

distance fallen

7) Make sure it's a fair test — keep the variables you aren't testing the same every time, e.g. use the same ruler for each repeat and have the same person dropping it.

8) For an experiment like this, a typical reaction time is around 0.2-0.6 s.

9) A person's reaction time in a real situation (e.g. when driving) will be longer than that, though. Typically, an alert driver will have a reaction time of about 1 s.

## Stop right there — and learn this page...

Bad visibility also causes accidents — if it's foggy, it's harder to notice a hazard, so there's less room to stop.

Q1    Drivers on long journeys should take regular breaks. Explain why, in terms of stopping distance. [3 marks]

# Energy Stores

Energy stores are <u>different ways</u> of storing energy. Simple really...

## Energy is Transferred Between Energy Stores

<u>Energy</u> can be transferred between and held in different <u>energy stores</u>. There are eight you need to know:

1) <u>KINETIC</u>.............................. — anything <u>moving</u> has energy in its <u>kinetic energy store</u> (see below).
2) <u>THERMAL</u>............................. — <u>any object</u> — the <u>hotter</u> it is, the <u>more</u> energy it has in this <u>store</u>.
3) <u>CHEMICAL</u> ........................... — anything that can release energy by a <u>chemical reaction</u>, e.g. <u>food</u>, <u>fuels</u>.
4) <u>GRAVITATIONAL POTENTIAL</u>... — anything in a <u>gravitational field</u> (i.e. anything that can <u>fall</u>) (see below).
5) <u>ELASTIC POTENTIAL</u>.............. — anything stretched, like <u>springs</u>, <u>rubber bands</u>, etc. (p.206).
6) <u>ELECTROSTATIC</u>................... — e.g. two <u>charges</u> that attract or repel each other.
7) <u>MAGNETIC</u> .......................... — e.g. two <u>magnets</u> that attract or repel each other.
8) <u>NUCLEAR</u> ........................... — <u>atomic nuclei</u> release energy from this store in <u>nuclear reactions</u>.

## A Moving Object has Energy in its Kinetic Energy Store

1) When an object is <u>moving</u>, it has <u>energy</u> in its <u>kinetic energy store</u>.
2) Energy is transferred <u>to</u> this store if an object <u>speeds up</u> and <u>away</u> from this store if it <u>slows down</u>.
3) How much energy is in this store depends on both the object's <u>mass</u> and its <u>speed</u>.
4) The <u>greater its mass</u> and the <u>faster it's going</u>, the <u>more</u> energy it has in its kinetic energy store.
5) For example, a <u>high-speed train</u> will have <u>a lot more energy</u> in its kinetic energy store than you running.
6) You can find the energy in a <u>kinetic energy store</u> using:

$$\text{kinetic energy} = 0.5 \times \text{mass} \times (\text{speed})^2$$
$$\text{(J)} \qquad \text{(kg)} \quad \text{(m/s)}^2$$

or $KE = \frac{1}{2} \times m \times v^2$

7) If you <u>double the mass</u>, the energy in the kinetic energy store <u>doubles</u>.
   If you <u>double the speed</u>, though, the energy in the kinetic energy store <u>quadruples</u>
   (increases by a factor of <u>4</u>) — it's because of the '(speed)$^2$' in the formula.

**EXAMPLE:**

A car of mass 1450 kg is travelling at 28 m/s. Calculate the energy in its kinetic energy store, giving your answer to 2 s.f.

kinetic energy = 0.5 × mass × (speed)$^2$
= 0.5 × 1450 × 28$^2$ = 568 400 = 570 000 J (to 2 s.f.)

*Watch out for the (speed)$^2$ — that's where people tend to make mistakes and lose marks.*

## An Object at a Height has Energy in its Gravitational Potential Energy Store

1) When an object is at any <u>height</u> above the Earth's surface, it will have <u>energy</u> in its <u>gravitational potential energy store</u>.

2) You can <u>calculate</u> the <u>change in energy</u> in the gravitational potential energy store using the equation:

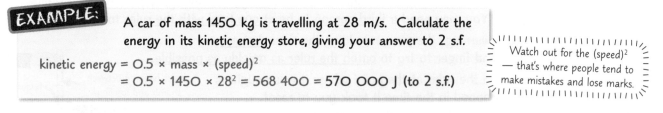

Change in gravitational potential energy (J)

$\Delta GPE = m \times g \times \Delta h$

Change in vertical height (m)

Mass (kg)  Gravitational field strength (N/kg)

*Δ just means 'change in'.*

## There's potential for a joke here somewhere...

Hopefully this page wasn't too hard — just don't forget that squared sign when you're working and remember that the energy in an object's kinetic energy store only changes if its speed is changing. Now have a crack at this...

Q1    A 2 kg object is dropped from a height of 10 m. Calculate the speed of the object
after it has fallen 5 m, assuming there is no air resistance. *g* = 10 N/kg.          [5 marks]

# Transferring Energy

Now you know about the different energy stores, it's time to find out how energy is transferred between them.

## Conservation of Energy Means Energy is Never Created or Destroyed

Energy can be stored, transferred between stores, and dissipated — but it can never be created or destroyed. The total energy of a closed system has no net change.

*See the next page for more on dissipation.*

A closed system is just a system (a collection of objects) that can be treated completely on its own, without any energy being exchanged to or from the surroundings. If you get a question where the energy of a system increases or decreases, then it's not closed. But you can make it into a closed system by increasing the number of things you treat as part of it. E.g. a pan of water heating on a hob isn't a closed system, but the pan, the gas and the oxygen that burn to heat it, and their surroundings are a closed system.

## Energy Transfers Show... well... the Transfer of Energy

Energy can be transferred between stores in four main ways:

1) Mechanically — a force acting on an object (and doing work, p.180), e.g. pushing, stretching, squashing.

2) Electrically — a charge doing work against resistance (p.185), e.g. charges moving round a circuit.

3) By heating — energy transferred from a hotter object to a colder object, e.g. heating a pan on a hob.

4) By radiation — energy transferred by waves, e.g. energy from the Sun reaching Earth by light.

Make sure you understand what's going on in these examples of energy transfers:

> **A BALL ROLLING UP A SLOPE:**
> The ball does work against the gravitational force, so energy is transferred mechanically from the kinetic energy store of the ball to its gravitational potential energy store.
>
> **A BAT HITTING A BALL:**
> The bat has energy in its kinetic energy store. Some of this is transferred mechanically to the ball's kinetic energy store. Some energy is also transferred mechanically to the thermal energy stores of the bat and the ball (and to the surroundings by heating). The rest is carried away by sound.
>
> **A ROCK DROPPED FROM A CLIFF:**
> Assuming there's no air resistance, gravity does work on the rock, so the rock constantly accelerates towards the ground. Energy is transferred mechanically from the rock's gravitational potential energy store to its kinetic energy store.
>
> **A CAR SLOWING DOWN (without braking):**
> Energy in the kinetic energy store of the car is transferred mechanically (due to friction between the tyres and road), and then by heating, to the thermal energy stores of the car and road.
>
> **A KETTLE BOILING WATER:**
> Energy is transferred electrically from the mains to the heating element of the kettle, and then by heating to the thermal energy store of the water.

## You can Draw Diagrams to Show Energy Transfers

*You may have to use or draw a diagram like this in the exam, so make sure you understand what it's showing.*

Diagrams can make it easier to see what's going on when energy is transferred. The diagram below shows the energy transferred when a ball is thrown upwards, taking air resistance into account. The boxes represent stores and the arrows show transfers:

| kinetic energy store of the ball | mechanically — work done against gravity → | gravitational potential energy store of the ball |
|---|---|---|
| | mechanically — work done against air resistance → | thermal energy store of the ball and the surroundings |

## *Energy can't be created or destroyed — only talked about a lot...*

This is important, so remember it. Energy can only be transferred to a different store, never destroyed.

Q1    Describe the energy transfers that occur when a piece of wood is burning.          [2 marks]

# Efficiency

So energy is transferred between different stores. But not all of the energy is transferred to useful stores.

## Most Energy Transfers Involve Some Losses, Often by Heating

1) You've already met the principle of conservation of energy on the previous page, but another important principle you need to know is:

> Energy is only useful when it is transferred from one store to a useful store.

2) Useful devices can transfer energy from one store to a useful store.

3) However, some of the input energy is always dissipated or wasted, often to thermal energy stores of the surroundings.

*Dissipated is a fancy way of saying the energy is spread out and so is 'lost'.*

4) Whenever work is done mechanically (see p.157), frictional forces have to be overcome, including things like moving parts rubbing together, and air resistance. The energy needed to overcome these frictional forces is transferred to the thermal energy stores of whatever's doing the work and the surroundings.

5) This energy usually isn't useful, and is quickly dissipated.

The diagram shows a motor lifting a load.
The motor transfers energy usefully from its kinetic energy store to the kinetic energy store and the gravitational potential energy store of the load, but it also transfers energy mechanically to the thermal energy stores of its moving parts, and electrically to the thermal energy stores of its circuits.
This energy is dissipated, heating the surroundings.

wasted energy heats the surroundings

MOTOR

energy is transferred to the motor electrically from the mains

LOAD

energy is transferred usefully from the kinetic energy store of the motor to the kinetic energy store and the gravitational potential energy store of the load

6) The conservation of energy principle means that:
total energy input = useful energy output + wasted energy.

7) The less energy that's wasted, the more efficient the device is said to be. The amount of energy that's wasted can often be reduced — see next page.

## You can Calculate the Efficiency of an Energy Transfer

The efficiency of any device is defined as:

$$\text{efficiency} = \frac{\text{useful energy transferred by device (J)}}{\text{total energy supplied to device (J)}}$$

*This will give the efficiency as a decimal. To give it as a percentage, you need to multiply the answer by 100.*

**EXAMPLE:**

A toaster transfers 216 000 J of energy electrically from the mains. 84 000 J of energy is transferred to the bread's thermal energy store. Calculate the efficiency of the toaster.

$$\text{efficiency} = \frac{\text{useful energy transferred by device}}{\text{total energy supplied to device}} = \frac{84\,000}{216\,000} = 0.388... = 0.39 \text{ (to 2 s.f.)}$$

*This could also be written as 39% (to 2 s.f.).*

All devices have an efficiency, but because some energy is always wasted, the efficiency can never be equal to or higher than 1 (or 100%).

## Make sure your revising efficiency is high...

One really important thing to take from here — devices that transfer energy from one store to other stores will always transfer energy to stores that aren't useful. And when I say always, I mean always. Always. (Always.)

Q1 An electrical device wastes 420 J of energy when it has an input energy of 500 J.
Calculate the efficiency of the device as a percentage.
[3 marks]

# Reducing Unwanted Energy Transfers

There are many ways you can <u>reduce</u> the amount of energy that is <u>wasted</u> during a process (and so <u>increase its efficiency</u>) — <u>lubrication</u> and <u>thermal insulation</u> are two of the main ones that you need to know about.

## You can Use Diagrams to Show Efficiency

<u>No device</u> is 100% efficient (see previous page), but some are <u>more efficient</u> than others. You can use diagrams like the one below to show the different <u>energy transfers</u> made by a device, and so how <u>efficient</u> it is:

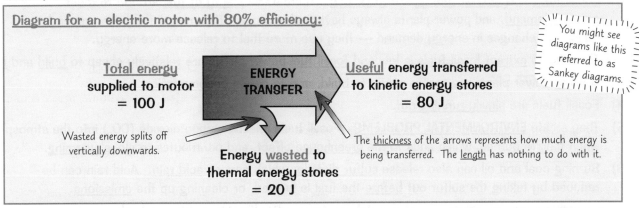

<u>Diagram for an electric motor with 80% efficiency:</u>

<u>Total energy</u> supplied to motor = 100 J

ENERGY TRANSFER

<u>Useful</u> energy transferred to kinetic energy stores = 80 J

Wasted energy splits off vertically downwards.

Energy <u>wasted</u> to thermal energy stores = 20 J

The <u>thickness</u> of the arrows represents how much energy is being transferred. The <u>length</u> has nothing to do with it.

You might see diagrams like this referred to as Sankey diagrams.

You can <u>reduce</u> the amount of energy that's <u>wasted</u> in various ways — including by <u>lubrication</u> and by <u>thermal insulation</u>. <u>Decreasing</u> the amount of <u>wasted energy</u> means that a <u>higher proportion</u> of the <u>supplied</u> energy is transferred to <u>useful</u> stores, so the <u>efficiency</u> of the process is <u>increased</u>.

## Lubrication Reduces Energy Transferred by Friction

1) Whenever something <u>moves</u>, there's usually at least one <u>frictional force</u> acting against it.

2) This <u>transfers</u> energy <u>mechanically</u> (<u>work</u> is done <u>against</u> friction) to the <u>thermal energy store</u> of the objects involved, which is then <u>dissipated</u> by heating to the surroundings. For example, <u>pushing</u> a <u>box</u> along the <u>ground</u> causes energy to be transferred mechanically to the thermal energy stores of the box and the ground. This energy is then <u>radiated away</u> to the thermal energy store of the surroundings.

3) For objects that are touching each other, <u>lubricants</u> can be used to reduce the friction between the objects' surfaces when they move. Lubricants are usually <u>liquids</u> (like <u>oil</u>), so they can <u>flow</u> easily between objects and <u>coat</u> them.

## Insulation Reduces the Rate of Energy Transfer by Heating

1) When one side of an object is <u>heated</u>, the particles in the <u>hotter</u> part <u>vibrate</u> more and <u>collide</u> with each other. This transfers energy from their <u>kinetic energy stores</u> to <u>other particles</u>, which then vibrate faster.

2) This process is called <u>conduction</u>. It <u>transfers energy</u> through the object.

3) All materials have a <u>thermal conductivity</u> — it describes how well a material transfers energy by conduction. For example, <u>metals</u> have a <u>high thermal conductivity</u> and <u>gases</u> (like <u>air</u>) have a <u>low thermal conductivity</u>.

4) In a <u>building</u>, the lower the thermal conductivity of its <u>walls</u>, the slower the rate of energy transfer through them (meaning the building will <u>cool more slowly</u>).

5) Some houses have <u>cavity walls</u>, made up of an inner and an outer wall with an <u>air gap</u> in the middle. The air gap reduces the amount of energy transferred by <u>conduction</u>, because air has a very low thermal conductivity.

6) <u>Thicker</u> walls help too — the thicker the wall, the slower the rate of energy transfer.

## Don't waste energy — turn the TV off while you revise...

Unwanted energy transfers can cost you a lot in energy bills — it's why so many people invest in home insulation.

Q1    Suggest one way to improve the efficiency of an electric motor.    [1 mark]

# Energy Resources

There are lots of <u>energy resources</u> available on Earth. They are either <u>renewable</u> or <u>non-renewable</u> resources.

## *Non-Renewable Energy Resources Will Run Out One Day*

<u>Non-renewable</u> energy resources are <u>fossil fuels</u> and <u>nuclear fuel</u> (uranium and plutonium). They currently provide most of the world's energy. <u>Fossil fuels</u> are natural resources that form <u>underground</u> over <u>millions</u> of years that are typically <u>burnt</u> to provide energy. The <u>three main</u> fossil fuels are <u>coal</u>, <u>oil</u> and <u>(natural) gas</u>.

1) <u>Fossil fuels</u> and <u>nuclear energy</u> are <u>RELIABLE</u>. There's still <u>plenty of fuel</u> around to meet <u>current demand</u>, and power plants always have fuel in stock. This means they can <u>respond quickly</u> to changes in energy demand — they use more fuel to release more energy.

2) The cost to <u>extract fossil fuels</u> is low and <u>fossil fuel</u> power plants are relatively cheap to <u>build</u> and <u>run</u>.

3) <u>Nuclear</u> power plants are pretty costly to build, and to <u>safely decommission</u>.

4) Fossil fuels are <u>slowly running out</u>.

5) They create <u>ENVIRONMENTAL PROBLEMS</u>. Fossil fuels release carbon dioxide ($CO_2$) into the atmosphere when they're burned, which adds to the <u>greenhouse effect</u>, and contributes to <u>global warming</u>.

6) Burning coal and oil can also release <u>sulfur dioxide</u>, which causes <u>acid rain</u>. Acid rain can be reduced by taking the sulfur out <u>before</u> the fuel is burned, or cleaning up the <u>emissions</u>.

7) <u>Oil spillages</u> cause <u>serious environmental problems</u>, affecting mammals and birds that live in and around the sea. We try to avoid them, but they'll always happen.

8) <u>Nuclear power</u> is <u>clean</u> but the <u>nuclear waste</u> is very <u>dangerous</u> and difficult to <u>dispose of</u>. And there's always the risk of a major <u>catastrophe</u> like the <u>Fukushima disaster</u> in Japan.

## *Renewable Energy Resources Will Never Run Out*

<u>Renewable</u> energy resources include:
1) Bio-fuels
2) Wind
3) The Sun (solar)
4) Hydro-electricity
5) Tides

- These will <u>never run out</u> — the energy can be 'renewed' as it is used.
- Most of them do <u>damage</u> the environment, but in <u>less nasty</u> ways than non-renewables.
- The trouble is they <u>don't</u> provide much <u>energy</u> and some of them are <u>unreliable</u> because they depend on the weather.

## *Bio-fuels are Made from Plants and Waste*

1) <u>Bio-fuels</u> are <u>renewable energy resources</u> created from either plant products or animal dung. They can be <u>solid</u>, <u>liquid</u> or <u>gas</u> and can be burnt to produce <u>electricity</u> or run <u>cars</u> in the same way as <u>fossil fuels</u>.

2) They are supposedly <u>carbon neutral</u>, although there is some <u>debate</u> about this as it's only really true if you keep growing plants (or raising animals) <u>at the rate</u> that you're burning things.

3) Bio-fuels are fairly <u>reliable</u>, as crops take a relatively <u>short time</u> to grow and different crops can be grown all year round. However, they cannot respond to <u>immediate energy demands</u>. To combat this, bio-fuels are continuously produced and <u>stored</u> for when they are needed.

4) The <u>cost</u> to refine <u>bio-fuels</u> is <u>very high</u> and some worry that growing crops specifically for bio-fuels will mean there isn't enough <u>space</u> or <u>water</u> to meet the demands for crops that are grown for <u>food</u>.

5) In some regions, large areas of <u>forest</u> have been <u>cleared</u> to make room to grow bio-fuels, resulting in lots of species losing their <u>natural habitats</u>. The <u>decay</u> or <u>burning</u> of this cleared vegetation also increases <u>methane</u> and $CO_2$ emissions.

## *Burning poo... lovely...*

Given our electricity-guzzling ways, it's pretty important we find ways to generate electricity without destroying the planet. Burning cow pats may not be the ultimate fix, but it's a start. See the next page for more ways.

Q1 State two renewable energy sources. [2 marks]

# More Energy Resources

Renewable energy resources, like <u>wind</u>, <u>solar</u>, <u>hydro-electricity</u> and <u>tides</u>, won't run out. They don't generate as much <u>electricity</u> as non-renewables though — if they did we'd all be using solar-powered toasters by now.

## Wind Power — Lots of Little Wind Turbines

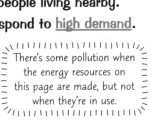

1) Each wind turbine has a <u>generator</u> inside it — wind rotates the <u>blades</u>, which turn the generator and produce <u>electricity</u>. So there's <u>no pollution</u>.

2) <u>Initial costs</u> are quite <u>high</u>, but <u>running</u> costs are <u>minimal</u>.

3) But <u>lots</u> of them are needed to produce as much <u>power</u> as, for example, a <u>coal</u> power plant. This means they can <u>spoil the view</u>. They can also be <u>noisy</u>, which can be annoying for people living nearby.

4) They <u>only</u> work when it's <u>windy</u>, so you can't always <u>supply</u> electricity, or respond to <u>high demand</u>.

## Solar Cells — Expensive but No Environmental Damage

There's some pollution when the energy resources on this page are made, but not when they're in use.

1) Solar cells are made from <u>materials</u> that use energy <u>transferred</u> by <u>light</u> to create an <u>electric current</u>.

2) Solar power is often used in <u>remote places</u> where there's not much choice (e.g. the Australian outback) and to power electric <u>road signs</u> and <u>satellites</u>.

3) There's <u>no pollution</u>. (Although they do use quite a lot of energy to make.)

4) <u>Initial costs</u> are <u>high</u>, but there are basically <u>no running costs</u>.

5) They're mainly used to generate electricity on a relatively <u>small scale</u>, e.g. in <u>homes</u>.

Time to recharge.

6) Solar power is most suitable for <u>sunny countries</u>, but it can be used in <u>cloudy countries</u> like Britain.

7) And of course, you <u>can't</u> make solar power at <u>night</u> or <u>increase production</u> when there's extra demand.

## Hydro-electricity — Building Dams and Flooding Valleys

1) <u>Producing hydro-electricity</u> usually involves <u>flooding</u> a <u>valley</u> by building a <u>big dam</u>. <u>Rainwater</u> is caught and allowed out <u>through turbines</u>. There is <u>no pollution</u> (as such).

2) There is a <u>big impact</u> on the <u>environment</u> due to the flooding of the valley and possible <u>loss of habitat</u> for some species.

3) A <u>big advantage</u> is it can <u>immediately respond</u> to increased electricity demand — <u>more</u> water can be let out through the turbines to generate more electricity.

4) <u>Initial costs are often high</u> but there are <u>minimal running costs</u> and it's generally a <u>reliable</u> energy source.

## Tidal Barrages — Using the Sun and Moon's Gravity

1) <u>Tidal barrages</u> are <u>big dams</u> built across <u>river estuaries</u> with <u>turbines</u> in them.

2) As the <u>tide comes in</u> it fills up the estuary. The water is then let out <u>through turbines</u> at a controlled speed to generate electricity.

None shall pass!

3) There is <u>no pollution</u> but they <u>affect boat access</u>, can <u>spoil the view</u> and they <u>alter the habitat</u> for wildlife, e.g. wading birds.

4) Tides are pretty <u>reliable</u> (they always happen twice a day). But the <u>height</u> of the tides is <u>variable</u> and barrages don't work when the water <u>level</u> is the <u>same either side</u>.

5) <u>Initial costs</u> are <u>moderately high</u>, but there are <u>no fuel costs</u> and <u>minimal running costs</u>.

## The hydro-electric power you're supplying — it's electrifying...

There are pros and cons to all energy resources. Make sure you know them for solar, wind and water.

Q1    The government is considering closing down a traditional coal-fired power station.
Explain the benefits and disadvantages of replacing the power station with a wind farm.    [4 marks]

# Trends in Energy Resource Use

Over time, the types of energy resources we use change. There are lots of reasons for this — breakthroughs in technology, understanding more about how they affect the environment or changes in cost are just a few.

## Currently We Still Depend on Fossil Fuels

1) Over the 20th century, the electricity use of the UK hugely increased as the population got bigger and people began to use electricity for more and more things.

2) Since the beginning of the 21st century, electricity use in the UK has been decreasing (slowly), as we get better at making appliances more efficient (p.158) and try to be more careful with energy use in our homes.

3) Most of our electricity is produced using fossil fuels (mostly coal and gas) and from nuclear power. But we do use renewable energy resources like wind power to generate some of our electricity.

4) Generating electricity isn't the only reason we burn fossil fuels — oil (diesel and petrol) is used to fuel cars, and gas is used to heat homes and cook food.

5) However, renewable energy resources can be used for these purposes as well. Bio-fuels can be used to exclusively power vehicles, and solar water heaters can be used to heat buildings.

6) We are trying to increase our use of renewable energy resources (the UK aims to use renewable resources to provide 15% of its total yearly energy by 2020). This move towards renewable energy resources has been triggered by many things...

## Energy Resources are Chosen for their Effect on the Environment

1) We now know that burning fossil fuels has a lot of negative effects on the environment (p.160). This has led to many people wanting to use more renewable energy resources that have less of an effect on the environment.

2) Pressure from other countries and the public has meant that governments have begun to introduce targets for using renewable resources. This in turn puts pressure on energy providers to build new power plants that use renewable resources to make sure they do not lose business and money.

3) Car companies have also been affected by this change in attitude towards the environment. Electric cars and hybrids (cars powered by two fuels, e.g. petrol and electricity) are already on the market and their popularity is increasing.

## The Use of Renewables is Usually Limited by Reliability and Money

1) Building new renewable power plants costs money, so some smaller energy providers are reluctant to do this — especially when fossil fuels are such a cost effective way of meeting demand.

2) Even if new power plants are built, there are a lot of arguments over where they should be. E.g. many people don't want to live next to a wind farm, which can lead to protests.

3) Some energy resources like wind power are not as reliable as traditional fossil fuels, whilst others cannot increase their power output on demand. This would mean either having to use a combination of different power plants (which would be expensive) or researching ways to improve reliability.

4) Research into improving the reliability and cost of renewable resources takes time and money. This means that, even with funding, it might be years before improvements are made. In the meantime, dependable, non-renewable power stations have to be used.

5) Making personal changes can also be quite expensive. Hybrid cars are generally more expensive than equivalent petrol cars and things like solar panels for your home are still quite pricey. The cost of these things is slowly going down, but they are still not an option for many people.

## Going green is on-trend this season...

So with more people wanting to help the environment, others not wanting to be inconvenienced and greener alternatives being expensive to set up, the energy resources we use are changing. Just not particularly quickly.

Q1     Give two reasons we currently do not use more renewable energy resources in the UK.          [2 marks]

# Revision Questions for Section 17

Wow, that was a whole lot of Physics in one place — time to see how much of it you can remember.

- Try these questions and <u>tick off each one</u> when you <u>get it right</u>.
- When you've done <u>all the questions</u> under a heading and are <u>completely happy</u>, tick it off.

## <u>Motion (p.145-148)</u> ☑

1) What is the difference between a scalar and a vector quantity? Give two examples of each. ☑
2) Give the equation relating distance, speed and time. ☑
3) Estimate typical speeds for a) walking, b) running, c) a car in a built-up area. ☑
4) Define acceleration in terms of velocity and time. ☑
5) What does the gradient represent for a) a distance/time graph? b) a velocity/time graph? ☑
6) How would you find the distance travelled by an object from its velocity/time graph? ☑

## <u>Newton's Laws, Forces and Momentum (p.149-154)</u> ☑

7) State Newton's First and Second Laws of Motion. ☑
8) Explain why cars have safety features to reduce the decelerations experienced by passengers. ☑
9) What is the formula for calculating the weight of an object? ☑
10) Explain why there must be a force acting to produce circular motion. What is the name of the force? ☑
11) Describe an experiment to investigate Newton's Second Law of Motion. ☑
12) What is inertia? ☑
13) What is Newton's Third Law of Motion? Give an example of it in action. ☑
14) State the formula used to calculate an object's momentum. ☑
15) Explain the link between Newton's Third Law and conservation of momentum. ☑

## <u>Stopping Distances and Reaction Times (p.155)</u> ☑

16) What is meant by a person's reaction time? Describe an experiment to measure reaction time. ☑
17) State two factors that can affect the thinking distance for a stopping car. ☑

## <u>Energy Stores, Transfers and Efficiency (p.156-159)</u> ☑

18) What is the equation for calculating the energy in a moving object's kinetic energy store? ☑
19) State the conservation of energy principle. ☑
20) What is meant by the 'dissipation' of energy? ☑
21) Describe the energy transfers when a ball is rolled up a slope. ☑
22) Describe the energy transfers when a hair dryer is switched on. ☑
23) Give the equation for the efficiency of a device. ☑
24) How can you reduce unwanted energy transfers in a machine with moving, touching components? ☑
25) How does the thermal conductivity of a wall affect its rate of energy transfer? ☑

## <u>Energy Resources and Trends in their Use (p.160-162)</u> ☐

26) What is the difference between renewable and non-renewable energy resources? ☑
27) What are bio-fuels made from? Explain the benefits and drawbacks of using bio-fuels. ☑
28) Give two benefits and two disadvantages of solar and wind power. ☑
29) Explain why the UK plans to use more renewable energy resources in the future. ☑

# Wave Basics

Waves transfer <u>energy</u> from one place to another without transferring any <u>matter</u> (stuff). Clever so and so's.

## Waves Transfer Energy and Information in the Direction they are Travelling

When waves travel through a medium, the <u>particles</u> of the medium <u>vibrate</u> and <u>transfer energy</u> and <u>information</u> between each other. BUT overall, the particles stay in the <u>same place</u>.

> For example, if you drop a twig into a calm pool of water, <u>ripples</u> form on, and <u>move</u> across, the water's surface. The ripples <u>don't</u> carry the <u>water</u> (or the twig) away with them though.
>
> Similarly, if you strum a <u>guitar string</u> and create a <u>sound wave</u>, the sound wave travels to your <u>ear</u> (so you can hear it) but it doesn't carry the <u>air</u> away from the guitar — if it did, it would create a <u>vacuum</u>.

1) The <u>amplitude</u> of a wave is the <u>displacement</u> from the <u>rest position</u> to a <u>crest</u> or <u>trough</u>.

2) The <u>wavelength</u> is the length of a <u>full cycle</u> of the wave (e.g. from <u>crest to crest</u>, or from <u>compression</u> to <u>compression</u> — see below).

3) <u>Frequency</u> is the <u>number of complete cycles</u> of the wave passing a certain point <u>per second</u>. Frequency is measured in <u>hertz</u> (<u>Hz</u>). 1 Hz is <u>1 wave per second</u>.

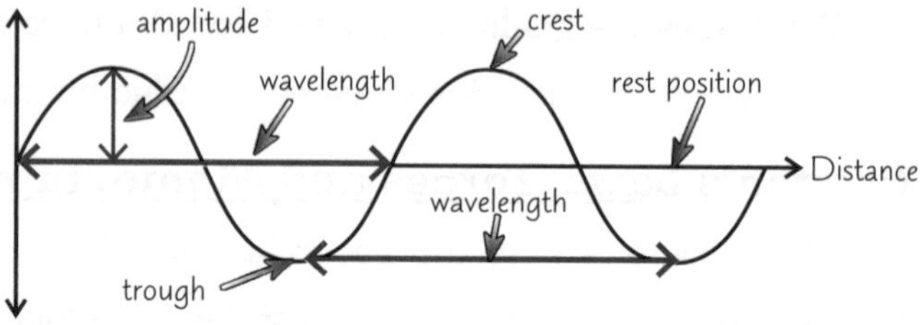

4) The <u>period</u> of a wave is the <u>number of seconds</u> it takes for <u>one full cycle</u>. <u>Period = 1 ÷ frequency</u>.

*Diagram labels: amplitude, wavelength, crest, rest position, Distance, wavelength, trough*

## Transverse Waves Have Sideways Vibrations

In <u>transverse waves</u>, the vibrations are <u>perpendicular</u> (at **90°**) to the <u>direction</u> the wave travels. <u>Most waves</u> are transverse, including:
   1)   <u>All electromagnetic waves</u>, e.g. light (p.168).
   2)   <u>S-waves</u> (a type of <u>seismic</u> wave).
   3)   <u>Ripples</u> and waves in <u>water</u> (see p.165).

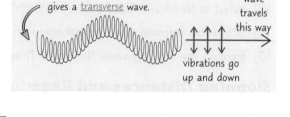
A spring wiggled <u>up and down</u> gives a <u>transverse</u> wave. wave travels this way / vibrations go up and down

## Longitudinal Waves Have Parallel Vibrations

1) In <u>longitudinal waves</u>, the vibrations are <u>parallel</u> to the <u>direction</u> the wave travels.

2) Examples are <u>sound waves</u> and <u>P-waves</u> (a <u>seismic</u> wave).

3) Longitudinal waves <u>squash up</u> and <u>stretch out</u> the arrangement of particles in the medium they pass through, making <u>compressions</u> (<u>high pressure</u>, lots of particles) and <u>rarefactions</u> (<u>low pressure</u>, fewer particles).

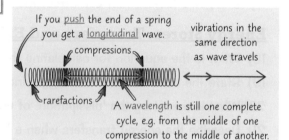
If you <u>push</u> the end of a spring you get a <u>longitudinal</u> wave. vibrations in the same direction as wave travels. compressions / rarefactions / A wavelength is still one complete cycle, e.g. from the middle of one compression to the middle of another.

## Wave Speed = Frequency × Wavelength

<u>Wave speed</u> is no different to any other speed — it tells you how <u>quickly</u> a <u>wave</u> moves through space.
There are two ways to calculate wave speed:

Wave speed (m/s) — $v = \dfrac{x}{t}$ — Distance (m) / Time (s)

This is called the wave equation.

Wave speed (m/s) — $v = f\lambda$ — Wavelength (m) / Frequency (Hz)

---

### What about Mexican waves...

You won't get far unless you understand these wave basics. Try a question to test your knowledge.

Q1     A wave has a speed of 0.15 m/s and a wavelength of 7.5 cm. Calculate its frequency.     [3 marks]

# Measuring Waves

The speeds, frequencies and wavelengths of waves can vary by huge amounts. So you have to use suitable equipment to measure waves in different materials, to make sure you get accurate and precise results.

## Use an Oscilloscope to Measure the Speed of Sound

By attaching a signal generator to a speaker you can generate sounds with a specific frequency.
You can use two microphones and an oscilloscope to find the wavelength of the sound waves generated.

1) Set up the oscilloscope so the detected waves at each microphone are shown as separate waves.

2) Start with both microphones next to the speaker, then slowly move one away until the two waves are aligned on the display, but have moved exactly one wavelength apart.

3) Measure the distance between the microphones to find one wavelength ($\lambda$).

4) You can then use the formula $v = f\lambda$ (p.164) to find the speed ($v$) of the sound waves passing through the air — the frequency ($f$) is whatever you set the signal generator to in the first place.

speaker attached to signal generator

oscilloscope

microphones

wavelength

waves line up

## Measure the Speed of Water Ripples Using a Strobe Light

1) Using a signal generator attached to the dipper of a ripple tank you can create water waves at a set frequency.

2) Dim the lights and turn on the strobe light — you'll see a wave pattern made by the shadows of the wave crests on the screen below the tank.

3) Alter the frequency of the strobe light until the wave pattern on the screen appears to 'freeze' and stop moving. This happens when the frequency of the waves and the strobe light are equal — the waves appear not to move because they are being lit at the same point in their cycle each time.

4) The distance between each shadow line is equal to one wavelength. Measure the distance between lines that are 10 wavelengths apart, then find the average wavelength.

5) Use $v = f\lambda$ to calculate the speed of the waves.

strobe light

dipper dips in and out of the water producing ripples

to signal generator

water

screen

shadows cast by ripples

You can find the frequency by using a regular light, so you can see the waves moving. Count how many waves pass a mark on the screen in a given time, then divide this by the time in seconds to find the frequency.

## Use Peak Frequency to find the Speed of Waves in Solids

You can find the speed of waves in a solid by measuring the frequency of the sound waves produced when you hit the object, e.g. a rod, with a hammer. Hitting the rod causes waves to be produced along the rod. These waves make the rod vibrate and produce sound waves in the air around the rod (this is how a percussion triangle works). These sound waves have the same frequencies as the waves in the rod.

1) Measure and record the length of a metal rod, e.g. a brass rod.

2) Set up the apparatus shown in the diagram, making sure to secure the rod at its centre.

3) Tap the rod with the hammer. Write down the peak frequency displayed by the computer.

4) Repeat this three times to get an average peak frequency.

5) Calculate the speed of the wave using $v = f\lambda$, where $\lambda$ is equal to twice the length of the rod.

Lots of waves at lots of different frequencies are created in the rod when it is hit. The peak (loudest) frequency is created by this wave in the rod:

wave

rod

rod length = half a wavelength

clamps

elastic bands

hammer

microphone

rod

to computer

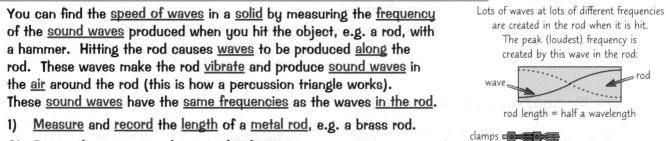

---

## My wave speed depends on how tired my arm is...

The sound and water waves experiments are really common, so make sure they're firmly stuck in your head.

Q1    Describe an experiment to measure the wavelength of a water wave.                    [4 marks]

# Wave Behaviour at Boundaries

When <u>waves</u> cross a boundary, they can be <u>absorbed</u>, <u>transmitted</u>, <u>reflected</u>, <u>refracted</u>... Read on for more.

## Waves Are Absorbed, Transmitted and Reflected at Boundaries

When a <u>wave</u> meets a <u>boundary</u> between two materials (a <u>material interface</u>), <u>three</u> things can happen:

1) The wave is <u>ABSORBED</u> by the second material — the wave <u>transfers energy</u> to the material's energy stores. Often, the energy is transferred to a <u>thermal</u> energy store, which leads to <u>heating</u> (this is how a <u>microwave</u> works, see page 170).

2) The wave is <u>TRANSMITTED</u> through the second material — the wave <u>carries on travelling</u> through the new material. This often leads to <u>refraction</u> (see below). This can be used in <u>communications</u> (p.170) as well as in the lenses of <u>glasses</u> and <u>cameras</u>.

3) The wave is <u>REFLECTED</u> — this is where the incoming ray is neither <u>absorbed</u> or <u>transmitted</u>, but instead is '<u>sent back</u>' away from the second material. This is how <u>echoes</u> are created.

What actually happens depends on the <u>wavelength</u> of the wave and the <u>properties</u> of the <u>materials</u> involved.

## Refraction — Waves Changing Direction at a Boundary

*You might see refraction of light talked about in terms of 'optical density'.*

1) Waves travel at <u>different speeds</u> in materials with <u>different densities</u>. So when a wave crosses a <u>boundary</u> between materials it <u>changes speed</u>.

2) If the wave hits the boundary at an <u>angle</u>, this change of <u>speed</u> causes a <u>change in direction</u> — <u>refraction</u>.

3) If the wave is travelling <u>along the normal</u> (see below) it will <u>change speed</u>, but it's <u>NOT refracted</u>.

4) The <u>greater</u> the <u>change</u> in speed, the <u>more</u> a wave <u>bends</u> (changes direction).

5) The wave bends <u>towards the normal</u> if it <u>slows down</u>. It bends <u>away</u> from the normal if it <u>speeds up</u>.

6) <u>Electromagnetic</u> (EM) waves (see p.168) like light usually travel more <u>slowly</u> in <u>denser</u> materials, so entering glass from air they would <u>bend towards</u> the normal if refracted.

7) How <u>much</u> a wave refracts depends on its <u>wavelength</u> (as the <u>frequency</u> of a wave doesn't change between boundaries, p.164). <u>EM waves</u> with <u>shorter</u> wavelengths <u>bend more</u>.

8) <u>Wavefront diagrams</u> can help to show refraction. When one part of the wavefront <u>crosses</u> a boundary into a <u>denser</u> material, that part travels <u>slower</u> than the rest of the wavefront.

9) So by the time the whole wavefront crosses the boundary, the <u>faster</u> part of the wavefront will have <u>travelled</u> <u>further</u> than the <u>slower</u> part of the wavefront.

10) This difference in <u>distance</u> travelled (caused by the difference in <u>speed</u>) by the wavefront causes the wave to <u>bend</u>. (Imagine a <u>toy car</u> rolling along — if one of its front wheels got caught in some <u>mud</u>, the car would <u>turn</u>.)

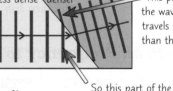

less dense \ denser — This part of the wavefront travels slower than the rest.

So this part of the wavefront will have travelled further by the time it crosses the boundary.

### The Normal is An Imaginary Line

<u>Ray diagrams</u> can be used to show the <u>path</u> that a <u>wave travels</u>. Rays are <u>straight lines</u> that are <u>perpendicular</u> to <u>wavefronts</u>. You need to understand the <u>following terms</u> for ray diagrams:

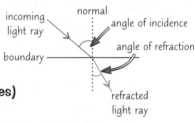

incoming light ray — normal — angle of incidence — boundary — angle of refraction — refracted light ray

1) The <u>normal</u> is an <u>imaginary line</u> that's <u>perpendicular</u> (at right angles) to the point where the incoming wave <u>hits</u> the boundary.

2) <u>The angle of incidence</u> is the angle between the <u>incoming</u> (<u>incident</u>) <u>ray</u> and the <u>normal</u>.

3) <u>The angle of refraction</u> is the angle between the <u>refracted ray</u> and the normal.

---

## Time to reflect on what you've read and really absorb it...

Refraction has loads of uses (e.g. in glasses, cameras and telescopes) so make sure you really understand it.

Q1    A light ray enters air from water. How does it bend relative to the normal?          [1 mark]

# Investigating Refraction PRACTICAL

Hurrah — it's time to whip out your ray box and get some refraction going on.

## You Need to Do This Experiment in a Dim Room

1) This experiment uses a ray of light, so it's best to do it in a dim room so you can clearly see the ray.

2) The ray of light must be thin, so you can easily see the middle
of the ray when tracing it and measuring angles from it.

3) To do this, you can use a ray box — an enclosed box that contains a light bulb. A thin slit is cut into
one of the sides — allowing a thin ray of light out of the box that you can use for your experiment.

## You Can Use Transparent Materials to Investigate Refraction

The boundaries between different substances refract light by different amounts. You can investigate
this by looking at how much light is refracted when it passes through transparent blocks.

1) Place a transparent rectangular block on a piece of paper
and trace around it. Use a ray box to shine a ray of light
at the middle of one side of the block.

2) Trace the incident ray and the emergent ray on the other
side of the block. Remove the block and, with a
straight line, join up the incident ray and the emergent
ray to show the path of the refracted ray through the block.

3) Draw the normal at the point where the light
ray entered the block. Use a protractor to
measure the angle between the incident ray
and the normal (the angle of incidence, *I*)
and the angle between the refracted ray
and the normal (the angle of refraction, *R*).

4) Do the same for the point where
the ray emerges from the block.

5) Repeat this three times, to get
an average for all the angles.

6) Then, repeat the experiment using rectangular blocks made from
different materials, keeping the initial incident angle the same throughout.

- You should see that the ray of light bends towards the normal as it enters the block (so the angle
of refraction is less than the angle of incidence). This is because air has one of the lowest optical
densities that there is (p.166) so the light ray will almost always slow down when it enters the block.

- You should then see the ray of light bends away from the normal as it leaves the block.
This is because the light ray speeds up as it leaves the block and travels through the air.

- You should also find that the angle of refraction changes for different materials
(as they all have different optical densities). E.g. a block of pure crown glass
bends a light ray more than a block of acrylic (plastic) glass does.

- It's important to remember that all electromagnetic waves can be refracted — this experiment uses
visible light so that you can actually see the ray being refracted as it travels through the block.

## Lights, camera, refraction...

This experiment isn't the trickiest, but you still have to be able to describe how to do it and what it shows.

Q1  a) Describe an experiment you could do to measure how much light is refracted
      when it enters blocks of different materials.                                    [4 marks]
    b) Explain why a thin beam of light should be used.                                 [1 mark]

# Electromagnetic Waves

You've learned a lot about light so far, but light's just one small part of the EM spectrum...

## There's a Continuous Spectrum of EM Waves

1) Electromagnetic (EM) waves are transverse waves (p.164).
2) They all travel at the same speed through a vacuum (space). But they travel at different speeds in different materials (which can lead to refraction, p.166).
3) EM waves vary in wavelength from around $10^{-15}$ m to more than $10^4$ m.
4) We group them based on their wavelength and frequency — there are seven basic types, but the different groups merge to form a continuous spectrum.
5) EM waves are generated by a variety of changes in atoms and their nuclei, giving a large range of frequencies. E.g. changes in the nucleus of an atom create gamma rays (p.174) and visible light is often produced by changes in an electron's energy level (p.173). This also explains why atoms can absorb a range of frequencies — each one causes a different change.
6) Our eyes can only detect a small part of this spectrum — visible light. Different colours of light have different wavelengths — from longest to shortest: red, orange, yellow, green, blue, indigo, violet.

*Electromagnetic waves aren't vibrations of particles, they're vibrations of electric and magnetic (p.195) fields. This means they can travel through a vacuum.*

| RADIO WAVES | MICRO WAVES | INFRA RED | VISIBLE LIGHT | ULTRA VIOLET | X-RAYS | GAMMA RAYS |
|---|---|---|---|---|---|---|
| 1 m – $10^4$ m | $10^{-2}$ m | $10^{-5}$ m | $10^{-7}$ m | $10^{-8}$ m | $10^{-10}$ m | $10^{-15}$ m |

wavelength →

long wavelength, low frequency → short wavelength, high frequency

7) All EM waves transfer energy from a source to an observer. For example, when you warm yourself by an electric heater, infrared waves transfer energy from the thermal energy store of the heater (the source) to your thermal energy store (the observer).
8) The higher the frequency of the EM wave, the more energy it transfers (and so the more dangerous it is for humans — see below).

## Different EM Waves Have Different Properties

*EM waves are sometimes called EM radiation.*

As you saw on p.166, when EM waves meet a boundary they can be absorbed, transmitted, refracted or reflected. What happens depends on the materials at the boundary and the wavelength of the EM wave — e.g. some materials absorb some wavelengths of light but reflect others. This is what causes things to be a certain colour.

Differences in how EM waves are transmitted, reflected and absorbed have implications for human health:

1) Radio waves are transmitted through the body without being absorbed.
2) Some wavelengths of microwaves can be absorbed, causing heating of cells, which may be dangerous.
3) Infrared (IR) and visible light are mostly reflected or absorbed by the skin, causing some heating too. IR can cause burns if the skin gets too hot.

*Most of the UV radiation produced by the Sun is absorbed by the Earth's atmosphere.*

4) Ultraviolet (UV) is also absorbed by the skin. But it has a higher frequency, so it is potentially more dangerous. It's a type of ionising radiation (p.173) and when absorbed it can cause damage to cells on the surface of your skin, which could lead to skin cancer. It can also damage your eyes and cause a variety of eye conditions or even blindness.
5) X-rays and gamma rays are also ionising, so they can cause mutations and damage cells too (which can lead to cancer). But they have even higher frequencies, so transfer even more energy, causing even more damage. They can also pass through the skin and be absorbed by deeper tissues.

## Learn about the EM spectrum and wave goodbye to exam woe...

Here's a handy mnemonic for the order of EM waves: 'Rock Music Is Very Useful for eXperiments with Goats'.

Q1 Explain why gamma rays are more dangerous to humans than visible light. [2 marks]

# EM Waves for Communication

Different EM waves have different properties, which make them useful to us in different ways.

## Radio Waves are Made by Oscillating Charges

1) EM waves are made up of oscillating electric and magnetic fields.

2) Alternating currents (a.c.) (p.192) are made up of oscillating charges. As the charges oscillate, they produce oscillating electric and magnetic fields, i.e. electromagnetic waves.

3) The frequency of the waves produced will be equal to the frequency of the alternating current.

4) You can produce radio waves using an alternating current in an electrical circuit. The object in which charges (electrons) oscillate to create the radio waves is called a transmitter.

5) When transmitted radio waves reach a receiver, the radio waves are absorbed.

6) The energy carried by the waves is transferred to the electrons in the material of the receiver.

7) This energy causes the electrons to oscillate and, if the receiver is part of a complete electrical circuit, it generates an alternating current.

8) This current has the same frequency as the radio wave that generated it.

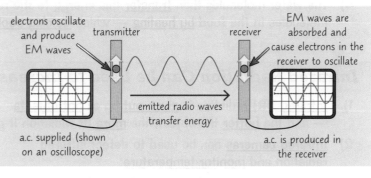

electrons oscillate and produce EM waves — transmitter
a.c. supplied (shown on an oscilloscope)
emitted radio waves transfer energy
receiver
EM waves are absorbed and cause electrons in the receiver to oscillate
a.c. is produced in the receiver

## Radio Waves are Used Mainly for Communication and Broadcasting

1) Long-wave radio (wavelengths of 1 – 10 km) can be received halfway round the world from where they started, because long wavelengths bend around the curved surface of the Earth. This makes it possible for radio signals to be received even if the receiver isn't in line of the sight of the transmitter.

2) Short-wave radio signals (wavelengths of about 10 m – 100 m) can, like long-wave, be received at long distances from the transmitter. That's because they are reflected by the Earth's atmosphere.

3) Bluetooth® uses short-wave radio waves to send data over short distances between devices without wires (e.g. wireless headsets so you can use your phone while driving a car).

4) The radio waves used for TV and FM radio transmissions have very short wavelengths. To get reception, you must be in direct sight of the transmitter — the signal doesn't bend or travel far through buildings.

## Microwaves and Radio Waves are Used by Satellites

1) Communication to and from satellites (including satellite TV signals and satellite phones) uses EM waves which can pass easily through the Earth's watery atmosphere.

2) These waves are usually microwaves, but can sometimes be relatively high frequency radio waves.

3) For satellite TV, the signal from a transmitter is transmitted into space and picked up by the satellite receiver dish orbiting thousands of kilometres above the Earth.

4) The satellite transmits the signal back to Earth in a different direction, where it's received by a satellite dish on the ground.

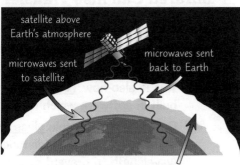

satellite above Earth's atmosphere
microwaves sent to satellite
microwaves sent back to Earth
cloud and water vapour

## Size matters — and my wave's longer than yours...

Producing radio waves — who knew it was so tricky? It's worth it though — they're just so darn useful.

Q1    Explain why signals between satellites are usually transmitted as microwaves.                [1 mark]

# Microwaves and Infrared

Haven't had enough <u>uses of EM waves</u>? Good, because here are just a few more uses of those incredibly handy waves — complete with the all-important <u>reasons</u> for why they have been used. Get learning.

## *Microwave Ovens Use a Different Wavelength from Satellites*

1) In <u>communications</u>, the microwaves used need to <u>pass through</u> the Earth's watery atmosphere.

2) In <u>microwave ovens</u>, the microwaves need to be <u>absorbed</u> by <u>water molecules</u> in food — so they use a <u>different</u> wavelength to those used in satellite communications.

3) The microwaves penetrate up to a few centimetres into the food before being <u>absorbed</u> and <u>transferring</u> the energy they are carrying to the <u>water molecules</u> in the food, causing the water to <u>heat up</u>.

4) The water molecules then <u>transfer</u> this energy to the rest of the molecules in the food <u>by heating</u> — which <u>quickly cooks</u> the food.

## *Infrared Radiation Can be Used to Increase or Monitor Temperature*

1) <u>Infrared</u> (IR) radiation is <u>given out</u> by all <u>hot objects</u> — and the <u>hotter</u> the object, the <u>more</u> IR radiation it gives out.

2) <u>Infrared cameras</u> can be used to detect infrared radiation and <u>monitor temperature</u>.

3) The camera detects the IR radiation and turns it into an <u>electrical signal</u>, which is <u>displayed on a screen</u> as a picture. This is called <u>thermal imaging</u>.

4) <u>Thermal imaging</u> is used by police to see suspects that are trying to <u>escape or hide in the dark</u>.

Different colours represent different amounts of IR radiation being detected. Here, the redder the colour, the more infrared radiation is being detected.

5) <u>Infrared sensors</u> can be used in <u>security systems</u>. If infrared radiation is detected, an <u>alarm</u> sounds or a <u>security light</u> turns on.

6) <u>Absorbing</u> IR radiation causes objects to get <u>hotter</u>. <u>Food</u> can be <u>cooked</u> using IR radiation — the <u>temperature</u> of the food increases when it <u>absorbs</u> IR radiation, e.g. from a toaster's heating element.

7) <u>Electric heaters</u> heat a room in the same way. Electric heaters contain a <u>long piece of wire</u> that <u>heats up</u> when a current flows through it. This wire then <u>emits</u> lots of <u>infrared radiation</u> (and a little <u>visible light</u> — the wire <u>glows</u>). The emitted IR radiation is <u>absorbed</u> by objects and the air in the room — energy is transferred <u>by the IR waves</u> to the <u>thermal energy stores</u> of the objects, causing their <u>temperature</u> to <u>increase</u>.

### *Infrared Can Also Transfer Information*

1) <u>Infrared</u> radiation can also be used to <u>transfer information</u>.

2) For example, it can be used to <u>send files</u> between <u>mobile phones</u> or <u>laptops</u>. The <u>distances</u> must be fairly <u>small</u> and the receiver must be in the <u>line of sight</u> of the emitter.

3) This is also how <u>TV remote controls</u> work. In fact, some <u>mobile phones</u> now have built in <u>software</u> which means that you can use your phone as a TV remote.

4) <u>Optical fibres</u> are thin <u>glass or plastic fibres</u> that can <u>carry data</u> (e.g. from telephones or computers) over long distances as <u>pulses</u> of <u>infrared</u> radiation. They usually use a <u>single</u> wavelength to prevent <u>dispersion</u>, which can otherwise cause some information to be <u>lost</u>.

5) They use <u>total internal reflection</u> to send lots of data over <u>long distances</u>.

## *Revision time — adjust depending on brain wattage...*

The next time you're feeling hungry and zap some food in the microwave, think of it as doing revision.

Q1    Give three uses of infrared radiation.    [3 marks]

# More Uses of EM Waves

And we're still not finished with <u>uses</u> of <u>waves</u> — is there no end to their talents...

## Photography Uses Visible Light

1) <u>Visible light</u> is the light that we can <u>see</u>. So it's only natural that we use it for <u>illuminating</u> things so that we can see them.

2) <u>Photographic film</u> reacts to light to form an image. This is how traditional <u>cameras</u> create <u>photographs</u>.

3) <u>Digital cameras</u> contain <u>image sensors</u>, which detect <u>visible light</u> and generate an electrical signal. This signal is then <u>converted</u> into an image that can be stored digitally or <u>printed</u>.

## Ultraviolet is Used in Fluorescent Lamps

1) <u>Fluorescence</u> is a property of certain chemicals, where <u>ultraviolet</u> (<u>UV</u>) radiation is <u>absorbed</u> and then <u>visible light</u> is <u>emitted</u>. That's why fluorescent colours look so <u>bright</u> — they actually <u>emit light</u>.

2) <u>Fluorescent lights</u> use UV to <u>emit</u> visible light. They're <u>energy-efficient</u> (p.158) so they're good to use when light is needed for <u>long periods</u> (like in your <u>classroom</u>).

3) <u>Security pens</u> can be used to <u>mark</u> property (e.g. laptops). Under <u>UV light</u> the ink will <u>glow</u>, but it's <u>invisible</u> otherwise, helping to <u>identify</u> stolen property.

4) <u>Bank notes</u> and <u>passports</u> use a similar technique to detect <u>forgeries</u> — genuine notes and passports have <u>special markings</u> that only show up under UV light.

5) Ultraviolet radiation is sometimes used to <u>sterilise water</u>. It <u>kills bacteria</u> in the water, making it <u>safe</u> to drink. (Gamma rays are used in a similar way, see below.)

## X-rays Let Us See Inside Things

1) <u>X-rays</u> can be used to view the <u>internal structure</u> of <u>objects</u> and <u>materials</u>, including our <u>bodies</u>.

2) They affect <u>photographic</u> film in the same way as <u>light</u>, meaning you can take <u>X-ray photographs</u>. But X-ray images are usually formed <u>electronically</u> these days.

3) <u>Radiographers</u> in <u>hospitals</u> take <u>X-ray images</u> to help doctors diagnose <u>broken bones</u> — X-rays are <u>transmitted by flesh</u> but are <u>absorbed</u> by <u>denser material</u> like <u>bones</u> or metal.

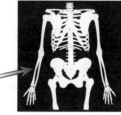

4) To produce an <u>X-ray image</u>, X-ray radiation is directed <u>through the object</u> or <u>body</u> onto a <u>detector plate</u>. The <u>brighter bits</u> of the image are where <u>fewer</u> <u>X-rays</u> get through, producing a <u>negative image</u> (the plate starts off <u>all white</u>).

5) X-rays are also used in <u>airport security scanners</u> to detect hidden objects that can't be detected with <u>metal detectors</u>.

## Gamma Rays are Used for Sterilising Things

1) <u>Gamma rays</u> are used to <u>sterilise</u> medical instruments — they <u>kill</u> microbes (e.g. bacteria).

2) <u>Food</u> can be <u>sterilised</u> in the same way — again <u>killing microbes</u>. This keeps the food <u>fresh for longer</u>, without having to freeze it, cook it or preserve it some other way, and it's <u>perfectly safe</u> to eat.

3) Some <u>medical imaging</u> techniques such as <u>tracers</u> use gamma rays to <u>detect cancer</u>.

4) Gamma radiation is also used in <u>cancer treatments</u> — radiation is targeted at cancer cells to <u>kill them</u>. Doctors have to be careful to <u>minimise</u> the damage to <u>healthy cells</u> when treating cancer like this.

---

## Don't lie to an X-ray — they can see right through you...

I hate to say it, but go back to page 169 and re-read all of the uses for electromagnetic waves to really learn them.

Q1     State two uses of ultraviolet radiation.                                [2 marks]

Q2     Suggest one advantage of sterilising food with gamma rays.          [1 mark]

# The Model of the Atom

We used to think <u>atoms</u> were tiny solid spheres (like ball-bearings), but they're <u>much more complex</u> than that...

## The Theory of Atomic Structure Has Changed Over Time

1) In 1897 <u>J. J. Thomson</u> discovered that <u>electrons</u> could be <u>removed</u> from atoms, so atoms must be made up of smaller bits. He suggested the <u>'plum-pudding' model</u> — that atoms were <u>spheres of positive charge</u> with tiny negative electrons <u>stuck in them</u> like fruit in a plum pudding.

2) That "plum pudding" theory didn't last very long though. In 1909, <u>Rutherford</u> and <u>Marsden</u> tried firing a beam of <u>alpha particles</u> (see p.174) at <u>thin gold foil</u>. From the plum-pudding model, they expected the particles to <u>pass straight through</u> the gold sheet, or only be <u>slightly deflected</u>.

3) But although most of the particles did go <u>straight through</u> the sheet, some were deflected more than they had expected, and a few were <u>deflected back</u> the way they had come — something the plum-pudding model <u>couldn't explain</u>.

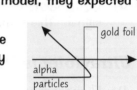

4) Being a pretty clued-up guy, Rutherford realised this meant that <u>most of the mass</u> of the atom was concentrated at the <u>centre</u> in a <u>tiny nucleus</u>.

5) He also realised that most of an atom is just <u>empty space</u>, and that the nucleus must have a <u>positive charge</u>, since it repelled the positive alpha particles.

6) This led to the creation of the <u>nuclear model</u> of the atom.

7) <u>Niels Bohr</u> tweaked Rutherford's idea a few years later by proposing a model where the electrons were in <u>fixed orbits</u> at <u>set distances</u> from the nucleus. These distances were called <u>energy levels</u> (p.173).

8) He suggested that electrons can <u>only</u> exist in these fixed orbits (or <u>shells</u>), and not anywhere inbetween.

9) This model is known as the <u>Bohr model</u> and is <u>pretty close</u> to our currently accepted model of the atom.

## The Current Model of the Atom — Protons, Neutrons and Electrons

The quantities to do with atoms are <u>really tiny</u>, so they're written in <u>standard form</u>:

$$A \times 10^n$$

where A is a number between 1 and 10 and n is the number of places the decimal point would move if you wrote the number out in decimal form.

According to our current model of the atom:

1) An atom is a <u>positively-charged nucleus</u> surrounded by <u>negatively-charged electrons</u>.

2) Virtually all the <u>mass</u> of the atom is in the <u>nucleus</u>. The nucleus is <u>tiny</u> — about <u>10 000</u> times <u>smaller</u> than the whole atom. It contains <u>protons</u> (which are <u>positively charged</u>) and <u>neutrons</u> (which are <u>neutral</u>). The rest of the atom is mostly <u>empty space</u>.

3) The <u>negative electrons</u> whizz round outside the nucleus in <u>fixed orbits</u> called <u>energy levels</u> or <u>shells</u>. They give the atom its <u>overall size</u> of around $1 \times 10^{-10}$ m.

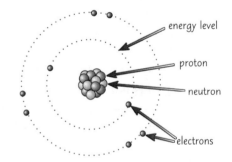

4) Atoms are <u>neutral</u>, so <u>the number of protons = the number of electrons</u>. This is because <u>protons</u> and <u>electrons</u> have an <u>equal</u> but <u>opposite relative charge</u>.

5) If an atom <u>loses an electron</u> it becomes a <u>positive ion</u>. If it <u>gains</u> an electron it becomes a <u>negative ion</u> (p.173).

6) Atoms can <u>join together</u> to form <u>molecules</u> — e.g. molecules of <u>oxygen</u> gas are made up of two oxygen atoms bonded together. <u>Small molecules</u> like this have a typical size of $10^{-10}$ m — the <u>same sort of scale</u> as the size of an atom.

| Particle | Relative Mass | Relative Charge |
|----------|---------------|-----------------|
| Proton | 1 | +1 |
| Neutron | 1 | 0 |
| Electron | 0.0005 | −1 |

---

## *These models don't have anything on my miniature trains...*

That's a whole lot of history, considering this is a book about physics. It's all good, educational fun though.

Q1    a) Describe the current model of the atom.           [4 marks]

        b) Describe how the radius of an atom compares to the size of its nucleus.    [1 mark]

# Electron Energy Levels

There's some quirky stuff on this page — and the best part is that you can tell everyone you've been doing a little quantum physics today. Honestly. And if you study physics to a higher level, things get even quirkier.

## Electrons Can be Excited to Higher Energy Levels

1) Electrons in an atom sit in different energy levels or shells.

2) Each energy level is a different distance from the nucleus.

3) An inner electron can move up to a higher energy level if it absorbs electromagnetic (EM) radiation with the right amount of energy.

4) When it does move up, it moves to an empty or partially filled shell and is said to be 'excited'.

5) The electron will then quickly fall back to its original energy level, and in doing so will emit (lose) the same amount of energy it absorbed. The energy is carried away by EM radiation.

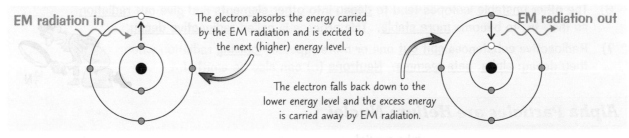

EM radiation in

The electron absorbs the energy carried by the EM radiation and is excited to the next (higher) energy level.

The electron falls back down to the lower energy level and the excess energy is carried away by EM radiation.

EM radiation out

6) The part of the EM spectrum the radiation emitted from the atom is from depends on its energy. This depends on the energy levels the electron moves between. A higher energy means a higher frequency of EM radiation — p.168. Often, visible light is released when electrons move between energy levels.

7) As you move further out from the nucleus, the energy levels get closer together (so the difference in energy between two levels next to each other gets smaller).

8) This means that an excited electron falling from the third energy level to the second would release less energy than an excited electron falling from the second energy level to the first. So the frequency of the generated radiation decreases as you get further from the nucleus.

9) Changes within the nucleus itself lead to the production of high energy, high frequency gamma rays (p.174).

## An Atom is Ionised if it Loses an Electron

I can't see anything — are you positive you've lost one?

1) If an outer electron absorbs radiation with enough energy, it can move so far that it leaves the atom.

2) It is now a free electron and the atom is said to have been ionised.

3) The atom is now a positive ion. It's positive because there are now more protons than electrons.

4) An atom can lose more than one electron. The more electrons it loses, the greater its positive charge.

## Nuclear Radiation Ionises Atoms

1) Ionising radiation is any radiation that can knock electrons from atoms.

2) How likely it is that each type of radiation will ionise an atom varies. You can see more about the different types of ionising nuclear radiation on the next page.

## Ionising radiation — good for getting creases out of your clothes...

So, an electron absorbs EM radiation and moves up one or more energy levels, then falls back to its original energy level and loses the same amount of energy it absorbed, which is carried away by EM radiation. Simple...

Q1    What is a positive ion and how is one formed?    [2 marks]

# Isotopes and Nuclear Radiation

Isotopes and ionisation. They sound similar, but they're totally different, so read this page carefully.

## Isotopes are Different Forms of the Same Element

1) Each element has a set number of protons (so each nucleus has a given positive charge). The number of protons in an atom is called its atomic number or its proton number.

2) The mass (nucleon) number of an atom (the mass of the nucleus) is the number of protons + the number of neutrons in its nucleus.

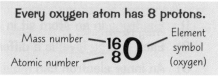

Every oxygen atom has 8 protons.

Mass number $\longrightarrow$ $^{16}_{8}O$ $\longleftarrow$ Element symbol (oxygen)

Atomic number $\longrightarrow$

3) Elements (usually isotopes) can be written as, e.g. carbon-14. This means that the mass number is 14.

4) Isotopes of an element are atoms with the same number of protons (the same atomic number) but a different number of neutrons (a different mass number). E.g. $^{18}_{8}O$ and $^{16}_{8}O$ are two isotopes of oxygen.

5) All elements have different isotopes, but there are usually only one or two stable ones.

6) The other unstable isotopes tend to decay into other elements and give out radiation as they try to become more stable. This process is called radioactive decay.

7) Radioactive substances spit out one or more types of ionising radiation when they decay: alpha, beta, gamma. Neutrons (n) can also be emitted.

$^{14}_{7}N$

## Alpha Particles are Helium Nuclei

1) Alpha radiation is when an alpha particle ($\alpha$) is emitted from the nucleus. An $\alpha$-particle is two neutrons and two protons (like a helium nucleus).

2) They don't penetrate very far into materials and are stopped quickly — they can only travel a few cm in air and are absorbed by a thin sheet of paper.

3) Because of their size they are strongly ionising.

## Beta Particles can be Electrons or Positrons

1) A beta-minus particle ($\beta^-$) is simply a fast-moving electron released by the nucleus. Beta-minus particles have virtually no mass and a relative charge of –1.

2) A beta-plus particle ($\beta^+$) is a fast-moving positron. The positron is the antiparticle of the electron. This just means it has exactly the same mass as the electron, but a positive (+1) charge.

3) They are both moderately ionising. Beta-minus particles have a range in air of a few metres and are absorbed by a sheet of aluminium (around 5 mm thick).

4) Positrons have a smaller range, because when they hit an electron the two destroy each other and produce gamma rays — this is called annihilation and it's used in medical imaging.

## Gamma Rays are EM Waves with a Short Wavelength

1) After a nucleus has decayed, it often undergoes nuclear rearrangement and releases some energy. Gamma rays ($\gamma$) are waves of EM radiation (p.168) released by the nucleus that carry away this energy.

2) They penetrate far into materials without being stopped and will travel a long distance through air.

3) This means they are weakly ionising because they tend to pass through rather than collide with atoms. Eventually they hit something and do damage.

4) They can be absorbed by thick sheets of lead or metres of concrete.

---

## Isotopes of an outfit — same dress, different accessories...

Knowing different kinds of radiation and what can absorb them could bag you a few easy marks in an exam.

Q1     For each of alpha, beta-minus and gamma radiations, give an example of a material that could be used to absorb it. Refer to the material's thickness in your answer.          [3 marks]

# Nuclear Equations

Nuclear equations show radioactive decay and once you get the hang of them they're dead easy. Get going.

## Mass and Atomic Numbers Have to Balance

1) Nuclear equations are a way of showing radioactive decay by using element symbols (p.174).
2) They're written in the form: atom before decay → atom after decay + radiation emitted.
3) There is one golden rule to remember: the total mass and atomic numbers must be equal on both sides.

## Alpha Decay Decreases the Charge and Mass of the Nucleus

When a nucleus emits an alpha particle, it loses two protons and two neutrons, so:
- the mass number decreases by 4.
- the atomic number decreases by 2.

$$^{226}_{88}\text{Ra} \rightarrow \ ^{222}_{86}\text{Rn} + \ ^{4}_{2}\alpha$$

| mass number: | 226 | → | 222 | + | 4 | (= 226) |
| atomic number: | 88 | → | 86 | + | 2 | (= 88) |

In both alpha and beta emissions, a new element will be formed, as the number of protons (atomic number) changes.

## Beta-minus Decay Increases the Charge of the Nucleus

In a beta-minus decay, a neutron changes into a proton and an electron, so:
- the mass number doesn't change — as it has lost a neutron but gained a proton.
- the atomic number increases by 1 — because it has one more proton.

$$^{14}_{6}\text{C} \rightarrow \ ^{14}_{7}\text{N} + \ ^{0}_{-1}\beta$$

| mass number: | 14 | → | 14 | + | 0 | (= 14) |
| atomic number: | 6 | → | 7 | + | (–1) | (= 6) |

## Positron Emission Decreases the Charge of the Nucleus

In beta-plus decay, a proton changes into a neutron and a positron, so:
- the mass number doesn't change — as it has lost a proton but gained a neutron.
- the atomic number decreases by 1 — because it has one less proton.

$$^{18}_{9}\text{F} \rightarrow \ ^{18}_{8}\text{O} + \ ^{0}_{1}\beta$$

| mass number: | 18 | → | 18 | + | 0 | (= 18) |
| atomic number: | 9 | → | 8 | + | 1 | (= 9) |

## Neutron Emission Decreases the Mass of the Nucleus

When a nucleus emits a neutron:
- the mass number decreases by 1 — as it has lost a neutron.
- the atomic number stays the same.

$$^{13}_{4}\text{Be} \rightarrow \ ^{12}_{4}\text{Be} + \ ^{1}_{0}\text{n}$$

| mass number: | 13 | → | 12 | + | 1 | (= 13) |
| atomic number: | 4 | → | 4 | + | 0 | (= 4) |

## Gamma Rays Don't Change the Charge or Mass of the Nucleus

1) Gamma rays are a way of getting rid of excess energy from an atom.
   The nucleus goes from an excited state to a more stable state by emitting a gamma ray.
2) The mass and atomic numbers stay the same after a gamma ray has been emitted.

## Keep balanced during revision and practise nuclear equations...

Nuclear equations are simple, but that doesn't mean you shouldn't practise them. Try these questions on for size.

Q1     What type of radiation is given off in this decay? $^{8}_{3}\text{Li} \rightarrow \ ^{8}_{4}\text{Be} + \text{radiation}$.     [1 mark]

Q2     Write the nuclear equation for $^{219}_{86}\text{Rn}$ decaying to polonium (Po) by emitting an alpha particle.     [3 marks]

# Half-Life

How quickly unstable nuclei decay is measured using activity and half-life — two very important terms.

## Radioactivity is a Totally Random Process

1) Radioactive sources contain radioactive isotopes that give out radiation from the nuclei of their atoms.

2) This process is entirely random. This means that if you have 1000 unstable nuclei, you can't say when any one of them is going to decay, or which one will decay next.

3) If there are lots of nuclei though, you can predict how many will have decayed in a given time based on the half-life of the source (see below). The rate at which a source decays is called its ACTIVITY. Activity is measured in becquerels, Bq. 1 Bq is 1 decay per second.

4) Activity can be measured with a Geiger-Müller tube, which clicks each time it detects radiation. The tube can be attached to a counter, which displays the number of clicks per second (the count-rate).

5) You can also detect radiation using photographic film. The more radiation the film's exposed to, the darker it becomes (just like when you expose it to light).

## The Radioactivity of a Source Decreases Over Time

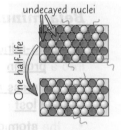

undecayed nuclei
One half-life

1) Each time a radioactive nucleus decays, one more radioactive nucleus disappears. As the unstable nuclei all steadily disappear, the activity as a whole will decrease.

2) For some isotopes it takes just a few hours before nearly all the unstable nuclei have decayed, whilst others last for millions of years.

3) The problem with trying to measure this is that the activity never reaches zero, so we have to use the idea of half-life to measure how quickly the activity drops off.

> The half-life is the average time taken for the number of radioactive nuclei in an isotope to halve.

4) A short half-life means the activity falls quickly, because the nuclei are very unstable and rapidly decay. Sources with a short half-life are dangerous because of the high amount of radiation they emit at the start, but they quickly become safe. (Half-life can also be described as the time taken for the activity to halve.)

5) A long half-life means the activity falls more slowly because most of the nuclei don't decay for a long time — the source just sits there, releasing small amounts of radiation for a long time. This can be dangerous because nearby areas are exposed to radiation for (millions of) years.

**EXAMPLE:** The activity of a radioactive sample is measured as 640 Bq. Two hours later it has fallen to 40 Bq. Find its half-life.

1) Count how many half-lives it took to fall to 40 Bq.

| Initial activity: | | after 1 half-life: | | after 2 half-lives: | | after 3 half-lives: | | after 4 half-lives: |
|---|---|---|---|---|---|---|---|---|
| 640 | ($\div 2$) $\rightarrow$ | 320 | ($\div 2$) $\rightarrow$ | 160 | ($\div 2$) $\rightarrow$ | 80 | ($\div 2$) $\rightarrow$ | 40 |

2) Calculate the half-life of the sample. Two hours is four half-lives — so the half-life is 2 hours $\div$ 4 = **30 min**

## You Can Measure Half-Life Using a Graph

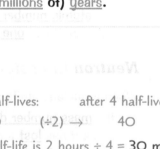

Activity (Bq)

Each of these sections is one half-life. So the half-life is 2 seconds.

1) If you plot a graph of activity against time (taking into account background radiation, p.177), it will always be shaped like the one to the right.

2) The half-life is found from the graph by finding the time interval on the bottom axis corresponding to a halving of the activity on the vertical axis. Easy.

---

## The half-life of a box of chocolates is about five minutes...

Half-life — the average time for the number of radioactive nuclei or the activity to halve. Simple.

Q1 A radioactive source has a half-life of 60 h and an activity of 480 Bq. Find its activity after 240 h. [2 marks]

---

# Background Radiation and Contamination

Forget love — radiation is all around. Don't panic too much though, it's usually a pretty small amount.

## Background Radiation Comes From Many Sources

Background radiation is the low-level radiation that's around us all the time. It comes from:

1) Radioactivity of naturally occurring unstable isotopes which are all around us — in the air, in some foods, building materials and some of the rocks under our feet.

2) Radiation from space, which is known as cosmic rays. These come mostly from the Sun. Luckily, the Earth's atmosphere protects us from much of this radiation.

3) Radiation due to human activity, e.g. fallout from nuclear explosions or nuclear waste. But this represents a tiny proportion of the total background radiation.

The amount of radiation you're exposed to (and so the amount of energy your body absorbs) is called the absorbed radiation dose. This varies depending on where you live or if you have a job that involves radiation.

## Exposure to Radiation is called Irradiation

1) Objects near a radioactive source are irradiated by it. This simply means they're exposed to it (we're always being irradiated by background radiation sources).

2) Irradiating something does not make it radioactive (and won't turn you into a superhero).

3) Keeping sources in lead-lined boxes, standing behind barriers or being in a different room and using remote-controlled arms are all ways of reducing the effects of irradiation. Medical staff who work with radiation also wear photographic film badges to monitor their exposure.

## Contamination is Radioactive Particles Getting onto Objects

1) If unwanted radioactive atoms get onto an object, the object is said to be contaminated. E.g. if you touch a radioactive source without wearing gloves, your hands would be contaminated.

2) These contaminating atoms might then decay, releasing radiation which could cause you harm.

3) Contamination is especially dangerous because radioactive particles could get inside your body.

4) Gloves and tongs should be used when handling sources, to avoid particles getting stuck to your skin or under your nails. Some industrial workers wear protective suits to stop them breathing in particles.

## Radiation Damages Cells by Ionisation

1) Radiation can enter living cells and ionise atoms and molecules within them. This can lead to tissue damage.

2) Lower doses tend to cause minor damage without killing the cells. This can give rise to mutant cells which divide uncontrollably. This is cancer.

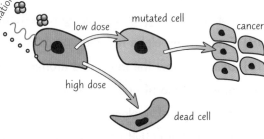

3) Higher doses tend to kill cells completely, causing radiation sickness (leading to vomiting, tiredness and hair loss) if a lot of cells all get blatted at once.

4) This is why places like hospitals try to limit staff and patients' exposure to radiation. E.g. shielding is used to protect staff and untreated body parts of patients, and tracers (p.171) with short half-lives are used.

5) Outside the body, beta and gamma radiation are the most dangerous, because they can penetrate the body and get to the delicate organs. Alpha is less dangerous, because it can't penetrate the skin.

6) Inside the body, alpha sources are the most dangerous. Alpha particles are strongly ionising, so they do all their damage in a very localised area. That means contamination, rather than irradiation, is the major concern when working with alpha sources.

## Background radiation — the ugly wallpaper of the Universe...

Make sure you can describe how to prevent irradiation and contamination, and why it's so important that you do.

Q1      Give three sources of background radiation.          [3 marks]

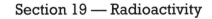

Section 19 — Radioactivity

# Revision Questions for Sections 18 and 19

And that's <u>Section 19</u> over and done with — time to celebrate with some fun revision questions (woo...).

- Try these questions and <u>tick off each one</u> when you <u>get it right</u>.
- When you've done <u>all the questions</u> for a topic and are <u>completely happy</u> with it, tick off the topic.

## <u>Wave Properties (p.164-167)</u> ☑

1) What is the amplitude, wavelength, frequency and period of a wave? ☑
2) Describe the difference between transverse and longitudinal waves and give an example of each kind. ☑
3) Describe experiments you could do to measure the speed of sound and the speed of ripples in water. ☑
4) Explain why you need to conduct experiments to investigate refraction in a dim room. ☑

## <u>Uses and Dangers of Electromagnetic Waves (p.168-171)</u> ☑

5) True or false? All electromagnetic waves are transverse. ☑
6) Give one potential danger of:   a) ultraviolet radiation        b) X-rays and gamma rays. ☑
7) What kind of current is used to generate radio waves in an antenna? ☑
8) What type of radiation is used in thermal imaging cameras? ☑
9) Give two uses of gamma rays. ☑

## <u>Atoms (p.172-173)</u> ☐

10) Briefly explain how the model of the atom has changed over time. ☑
11) True or false? Atoms are neutral. ☑
12) What happens to an electron in an atom if it releases EM radiation? ☑
13) True or false? The frequency of generated radiation increases as the site of generation gets closer to the nucleus. ☑

## <u>Radioactivity (p.174-177)</u> ☑

14) What is the atomic number of an atom? ☑
15) What is an isotope? Are they usually stable? ☑
16) Name four things that may be emitted during radioactive decay. ☑
17) For the four types of ionising radiation, give: a) their ionising power,    b) their range in air. ☑
18) Explain why alpha radiation could not be used to check the thickness of metal sheets. ☑
19) Describe how the mass and atomic numbers of an atom change if it emits an alpha particle. ☑
20) In what type of nuclear decay does a neutron change into a proton within the nucleus? ☑
21) What type of nuclear decay doesn't change the mass or charge of the nucleus? ☑
22) What is the activity of a radioactive source? What are its units? ☑
23) Define half-life. ☑
24) True or false? A short half-life means a small proportion of the atoms are decaying per second. ☑
25) What is background radiation? ☑

# Energy Transfers and Systems

Re-read pages 156 and 157 — energy is never used up, but it can always be talked about more...

## Energy is Transferred Between Stores

First things first, here's a quick recap of the different energy stores that you need to know:

1) Kinetic energy stores (KE = ½mv², p.156)
2) Thermal energy stores
3) Chemical energy stores
4) Gravitational potential energy stores (ΔGPE = mgΔh, p.156)

5) Elastic potential energy stores
6) Electrostatic energy stores
7) Magnetic energy stores
8) Nuclear energy stores

Energy can be transferred between stores mechanically (by a force doing work — see next page), electrically (by a moving charge doing work), by heating or by radiation (e.g. light or sound).

## When a System Changes, Energy is Transferred

1) A system is just a fancy word for a single object (e.g. the air in a piston) or a group of objects (e.g. two colliding vehicles) that you're interested in. You can define your system to be anything you like.

2) When a system changes, energy is transferred (p.157). It can be transferred into or away from the system, between different objects in the system or between different types of energy stores.

3) Whenever a system changes, some energy is dissipated and stored in less useful ways (p.158).

4) How you define your system changes how you describe the energy transfers that take place (see below). A closed system is one that's defined so that the net change in energy is zero (p.157).

### Energy can be Transferred by Heating...

1) A pan of water is heated on a gas camping stove.

2) When the system is the pan of water, energy is transferred into the system by heating to the thermal energy stores of the pan and the water, which increases their temperature.

3) When the system is the camping stove and the pan, energy is transferred from the chemical energy store of the gas to the thermal energy stores of the pan and the water, increasing their temperature.

### ...by Forces Doing Work...

1) A box is lifted up off of the floor. The box is the system.

2) As the box is lifted, work is done (see next page) against gravity.

3) This causes energy to be transferred to the box's kinetic and gravitational potential energy stores.

> If the box was dropped, the gravitational force would do work to transfer energy from the box's GPE store to its kinetic energy store.

### ...or by Electrical Equipment

1) Electrical devices work by transferring energy between different energy stores.

2) For example, electric irons transfer energy electrically from the mains power supply to the thermal energy store of their metal plates.

> You can show energy transfers using diagrams — see p.157.

1) An electric toothbrush is a system. It transfers energy electrically from the chemical energy store of its battery to the kinetic energy store of its bristles.

2) Some of this energy is transferred out of the system to the surroundings by sound and by heating.

1) A hair dryer is a system. It transfers energy into the system electrically from the mains supply to the kinetic energy store of the fan inside of it.

2) It also transfers energy electrically to the thermal energy store of the heating element and some energy is transferred away by sound.

## All this work, I can feel my energy stores being drained...

Make sure you understand exactly what a system contains before you describe any energy transfers.

Q1 Describe the energy transfers that occur when the wind causes a windmill to spin. [2 marks]

# Work Done and Power

I'm sure you're no stranger to doing work, but in physics it's all to do with forces and energy.

## If A Force Moves An Object, Work is Done

1) To make something move, some sort of force needs to act on it. The thing applying the force needs a source of energy (like fuel or food).

> When a force moves an object through a distance, WORK IS DONE on the object and ENERGY IS TRANSFERRED.

2) The force does 'work' to move the object and energy is transferred mechanically from one store to another (p.157).

3) Whether energy is transferred 'usefully' (e.g. lifting a load) or is 'wasted' (p.158) you can still say that 'work is done'. Just like Batman and Bruce Wayne, 'work done' and 'energy transferred' are indeed 'one and the same'.

4) You can find out how much work has been done using:

5) One joule of work is done when a force of one newton causes an object to move a distance of one metre. You can also write this as 1 J = 1 Nm (newton metre).

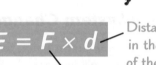

$$E = F \times d$$

Work done (J)  Force (N)

Distance moved in the direction of the force (m)

> **EXAMPLE:** Find the energy transferred when a tyre weighing 70 N is lifted 1.2 m into the air.
> work done = force × distance = 70 × 1.2 = 84 J

*Here, work is being done against gravity. Energy is being transferred to the tyre's gravitational potential energy store.*

6) A force doing work often causes a rise in temperature as energy is dissipated to the thermal energy stores of the moving object and its surroundings. This means that the process is wasteful and the efficiency of the process is reduced. Remember, efficiency = $\dfrac{\text{useful energy transferred by device}}{\text{total energy supplied to device}}$ (p.158).

> When you push something along a rough surface you are doing work against frictional forces. Energy is being transferred to the kinetic energy store of the object because it starts moving, but some is also being transferred to thermal energy stores due to the friction. This causes the overall temperature of the object to increase. (Like rubbing your hands together to warm them up.)

*Lubrication (p.159) reduces friction and unwanted energy transfers.*

## Power is How Much Work is Done per Second

1) Power is the RATE OF ENERGY TRANSFER. The unit of power is the watt (W). 1 W = 1 J/s. Another way of describing power is how much work is being done every second.

2) This is the very easy formula for power:

3) The larger the power of an object, the more work it does per second. E.g. if an electric heater has a power of 600 W this means it transfers 600 J of energy every second. A 1200 W heater would transfer twice as much energy per second and so would heat a room quicker than the 600 W heater.

$$\text{power (W)} = \frac{\text{work done (J)}}{\text{time taken (s)}} \quad \text{or} \quad P = \frac{E}{t}$$

> **EXAMPLE:** A motor does 4.8 kJ of work in 2 minutes. Find its power output.
> 1) Convert the values to the correct units first (see p.8).   4.8 kJ = 4800 J and 2 mins = 120 s
> 2) Substitute the values into the power equation.   $P = E \div t = 4800 \div 120 = 40$ W

## Watt's power? Power's watts...

Make sure you're happy using the equations on this page before you move on.

Q1   A constant force of 20 N pushes an object 20 cm. Calculate the work done on the object.   [2 marks]

Q2   An appliance transfers 6000 J of energy in 30 seconds. Calculate its power.   [2 marks]

# Forces

Force is a <u>vector</u> — it has both a <u>size</u> and a <u>direction</u> (unlike <u>scalar</u> quantities which only have a <u>size</u> — p.145). This means you can use <u>arrows</u> to represent the forces acting on an object or a system.

## Interactions Between Objects Cause Forces

1) A <u>force</u> is a <u>push</u> or a <u>pull</u> on an object that is caused by it <u>interacting</u> with something.

2) Sometimes, objects need to be <u>touching</u> for a force to act. E.g. the <u>normal contact force</u> that acts between <u>all</u> touching objects, or <u>friction</u> between a car's <u>tyre</u> and the <u>road</u>. These are <u>contact forces</u>.

3) Other forces can act between objects that <u>aren't touching</u> (<u>non-contact forces</u>). They're usually caused by <u>interacting fields</u>. E.g. the <u>gravitational attraction</u> between objects (like the <u>Earth</u> and the <u>Sun</u>) is caused by their <u>gravitational fields</u> interacting.

4) <u>Interacting magnetic fields</u> (p.195) cause <u>attraction</u> or <u>repulsion</u> between <u>magnetic objects</u>, and the electrostatic force causing <u>attraction</u> and <u>repulsion</u> between <u>electrical charges</u> is due to interactions between their <u>electric fields</u>.

5) Whenever two objects <u>interact</u>, both objects feel an equal but opposite <u>force</u> (Newton's 3rd Law). This pair of forces is called an <u>interaction pair</u>. You can represent an interaction pair with a pair of <u>vectors</u> (<u>arrows</u>).

> A <u>chair</u> exerts a force on the <u>ground</u>, whilst the ground pushes back at the chair with the <u>same</u> force (the <u>normal contact</u> force). <u>Equal</u> but <u>opposite</u> forces are felt by <u>both</u> the chair and the ground.
>
> This is <u>NOT</u> a free body force diagram below) — the forces are acting on <u>different objects</u>.
>
> Ground pushes on chair
> Chair pushes on ground

## Free Body Force Diagrams Show All the Forces Acting on Objects

1) A <u>free body force diagram</u> shows an <u>isolated body</u> (an object or system on its own), and <u>all</u> the <u>forces</u> acting on it.

2) It should include <u>every</u> force acting <u>on the body</u>, but <u>none</u> of the forces it <u>exerts</u> on the rest of the world.

3) The <u>sizes</u> of the arrows show the <u>relative magnitudes</u> of the forces and the <u>directions</u> show the directions of the forces.

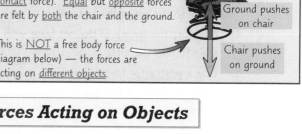

normal contact force

friction · push

weight

drag

weight

## A Resultant Force is the Overall Force on a Point or Object

1) In most <u>real</u> situations there are at least <u>two forces</u> acting on an object along any direction.

2) If you have a <u>number of forces</u> acting at a single point, you can replace them with a <u>single force</u> (so long as the single force has the <u>same effect</u> as all the original forces together).

3) This single force is called the <u>resultant force</u> (or sometimes the <u>net force</u> on an object).

4) If the forces all act along the <u>same line</u> (they're all parallel), the <u>overall effect</u> is found by <u>adding</u> those going in the <u>same</u> direction and <u>subtracting</u> any going in the opposite direction.

5) Objects in <u>equilibrium</u> have a resultant force of <u>zero</u> — see the next page. Objects in equilibrium are either <u>stationary</u>, or moving at a <u>steady speed</u> (this is Newton's 1st Law — p.149).

---

- The <u>normal contact force</u> felt by the van is <u>equal</u> to its weight. These forces act in <u>opposite directions</u>, so there is <u>no resultant force</u> in the <u>vertical</u> direction (1500 N – 1500 N = 0 N).

- The <u>frictional</u> force acting on the van is <u>smaller</u> than the <u>driving</u> force pushing it forward, so there <u>is</u> a <u>resultant force</u> in the <u>horizontal</u> direction.

- 1200 N – 1000 N = 200 N. So the resultant force is <u>200 N (to the left)</u>.

1500 N
1200 N ← →1000 N
1500 N

---

## *Consolidate all your forces into one easy-to-manage force...*

Free body force diagrams make most force questions easier, so if you can, always sketch one. Then get to work.

Q1    A car has a driving force of 2000 N and a weight of 1600 N. There is a total resistive force of 1200 N acting against the driving force. Draw the free body force diagram for the car.    **[2 marks]**

# Forces and Vector Diagrams

Scale drawings are useful things — they can help you <u>resolve</u> forces or <u>work out</u> the <u>resultant force</u>.

## Use Scale Drawings to Find Resultant Forces

1) Draw all the <u>forces</u> acting on an object, to scale, '<u>tip-to-tail</u>'.

2) Then draw a <u>straight line</u> from the start of the <u>first force</u> to the <u>end</u> of the <u>last force</u> — this is the <u>resultant</u> (or <u>net</u>) <u>force</u>.

3) Measure the <u>length</u> of the <u>resultant force</u> on the diagram to find the <u>magnitude</u> of the force and the <u>angle</u> to find its <u>direction</u>.

*Make sure the scale you use is sensible. You want large, clear diagrams that make your calculations easier to do.*

**EXAMPLE:** A man is on an electric bicycle that has a driving force of 4 N north. However, the wind produces a force of 3 N east. Find the net force acting on the man.

1) Start by drawing a <u>scale drawing</u> of the forces acting.

2) Make sure you choose a <u>sensible scale</u> (e.g. 1 cm = 1 N).

3) Draw the <u>net force</u> from the tail of the first arrow to the tip of the last arrow.

4) Measure the <u>length</u> of the net force with a <u>ruler</u> and use the <u>scale</u> to find the force in N.

*A bearing is an angle measured clockwise from north, given as a 3 digit number, e.g. 10° = 010°.*

5) Use a <u>protractor</u> to measure the direction as a <u>bearing</u>.

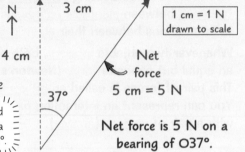

1 cm = 1 N drawn to scale

Net force is 5 N on a bearing of 037°.

## An Object is in Equilibrium if the Forces on it are Balanced

1) If <u>all</u> of the forces acting on an object <u>combine</u> to give a resultant force of <u>zero</u>, the object is in <u>equilibrium</u>.

2) On a <u>scale diagram</u>, this means that the <u>tip</u> of the <u>last</u> force you draw should end where the <u>tail</u> of the first <u>force</u> you drew begins. E.g. for <u>three</u> forces, the scale diagram will form a <u>triangle</u>.

3) You might be <u>given</u> forces acting on an <u>object</u> and told to find a <u>MISSING force</u>, given that the object is in <u>equilibrium</u>.

4) To do this, draw out the forces you <u>do</u> know (to <u>scale</u> and <u>tip-to-tail</u>), then <u>join</u> the <u>END</u> of the <u>LAST force</u> to the <u>START</u> of the <u>FIRST force</u>. Make sure you draw this last force in the <u>right direction</u> — it's in the <u>opposite</u> direction to how you'd draw a <u>resultant</u> force.

5) This line is the <u>missing force</u> so you can measure its <u>size</u> and <u>direction</u>.

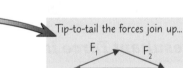

object in equilibrium

Tip-to-tail the forces join up...

...so the resultant force is zero.

## You Can Split a Force into Components

1) Not <u>all</u> forces act <u>horizontally</u> or <u>vertically</u> — some act at <u>awkward angles</u>.

2) To make these <u>easier</u> to deal with, they can be <u>split</u> into two <u>components</u> at <u>right angles</u> to each other (usually horizontal and vertical).

3) Acting <u>together</u>, these components have the <u>same effect</u> as the single force.

4) You can <u>resolve</u> a force (split it into components) by drawing it on a <u>scale grid</u>. Draw the force <u>to scale</u>, and then add the <u>horizontal</u> and <u>vertical</u> components along the <u>gridlines</u>. Then you can just <u>measure</u> them.

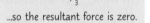

*F*

vertical component

horizontal component

## Don't blow things out of proportion — it's only scale drawings...

Keep those pencils sharp and those scale drawings accurate — or you'll end up with the wrong answer.

Q1 A remote-controlled boat crosses a stream. The motor provides a 12 N driving force to the west. The river's current causes a force of 5 N north to act on the boat. Find the size of the net force. [2 marks]

# Revision Questions for Section 20

Well, that's that for <u>Section 20</u> — have a go at these questions, then reward yourself with a nice cup of tea.

- Try these questions and <u>tick off each one</u> when you <u>get it right</u>.
- When you've done <u>all the questions</u> for a topic and are <u>completely happy</u> with it, tick off the topic.

## Energy, Work Done and Power (p.179-180) ☑

1) What is a system? ☑
2) Give three ways that the energy of a system can be changed. ☑
3) Give the formula for calculating the work done by a force. ☑
4) Describe how to convert between joules (J) and newton-metres (Nm). ☑
5) True or false? A mechanical process becomes wasteful when it causes an increase in temperature. ☑
6) Define power. State the equation relating power, work done and time. ☑
7) What unit is power measured in? ☑

## Forces (p.181-182) ☑

8) True or false? Friction is a non-contact force. ☑
9) What force causes the repulsion of two like electrical charges? What causes this force? ☑
10) What is an interaction pair? ☑
11) What is a free body force diagram? ☑
12) What is meant by the resultant force acting on an object? ☑
13) A parachuter has a weight of 900 N. At one point during his fall, the air resistance acting on him is 500 N. In what direction is his resultant force at this point? ☑
14) What is the resultant force on an object in equilibrium? ☑
15) Describe how you would use a scale diagram to work out the resultant force on an object. ☑
16) True or false? The arrows on a scale diagram for the forces on an object in equilibrium join up to create a closed shape. ☑
17) Describe how you would resolve a force into horizontal and vertical components using a scale drawing. ☑

# Current and Circuits

It's pretty bad news if the word <u>current</u> makes you think of delicious cakes instead of physics. Learn what it means, as well as some handy <u>symbols</u> to show items like <u>batteries</u> and <u>switches</u> in a circuit.

## *Current is the Flow of Electrical Charge*

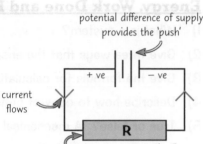

potential difference of supply provides the 'push'

1) <u>Current</u> is the <u>flow</u> of electric charge (e.g. electrons, p.172) around the circuit. Current will <u>only flow</u> through an electrical component if there is a <u>potential difference</u> across that component, and if the circuit is <u>complete</u> (closed). Unit: <u>ampere</u>, **A**.

2) <u>Potential difference</u> (or voltage) is the <u>driving force</u> that <u>pushes</u> the charge round. Unit: <u>volt</u>, **V**.

3) <u>Resistance</u> is anything that <u>slows the flow</u> down. Unit: <u>ohm</u>, Ω.

4) The current flowing <u>through a component</u> depends on the <u>potential difference</u> across it and the <u>resistance</u> of the component (p.185).

current flows

resistance opposes the flow

Generally speaking, the <u>higher the potential difference</u> across a given component, the <u>higher the current</u> will be. And the <u>greater the resistance</u> of a component, the <u>smaller the current</u> that flows (for a given potential difference across the component). There's more on resistance on p.185.

## *Total Charge Through a Circuit Depends on Current and Time*

1) <u>Current</u> is the <u>rate of flow</u> of <u>charge</u>. In <u>metals</u>, the current is caused by a flow of <u>electrons</u>.

2) If a <u>current</u> (*I*) flows past a point in a circuit for a length of <u>time</u> (*t*), then the <u>charge</u> (*Q*) that has passed this point is given by this formula:

$$\text{charge} = \text{current} \times \text{time}$$

More charge passes around the circuit in a given time when a greater current flows.

3) To use this formula, you need <u>current</u> in <u>amperes</u>, **A**, <u>charge</u> in <u>coulombs</u>, **C**, and <u>time</u> in <u>seconds</u>, **s**.

### EXAMPLE:

A battery passes a current of 0.25 A through a light bulb over a period of 4 hours. How much charge does the battery transfer through the bulb altogether?

charge = current × time = 0.25 × (4 × 60 × 60) = **3600 C**

Watch out for units — your time needs to be in seconds if you're calculating charge.

## *Circuit Symbols You Should Know*

There's more about a.c. and d.c. on p.192.

You need to be able to use these symbols to <u>interpret</u> and <u>draw circuit diagrams</u>.

| cell | battery | open switch | closed switch | filament lamp | fuse | LED | power supply |
|------|---------|-------------|---------------|---------------|------|-----|--------------|
| | | | | | | | d.c. / a.c. |
| resistor | variable resistor | ammeter | voltmeter | diode | LDR | thermistor | motor |
| | | A | V | | | | M |

## *I think it's about time you took charge...*

Electrons in circuits actually move from –ve to +ve, but it's conventional to draw current as though it's flowing from +ve to –ve. It's what early physicists thought (before they found out about the electrons), and it's stuck.

Q1    Calculate how long it takes a current of 2.5 A to transfer a charge of 120 C.      [2 marks]

# Potential Difference and Resistance

As current flows round a circuit, the charges transfer energy as they struggle against resistance.

## Potential Difference *is the Energy Transferred Per Unit Charge*

1) The potential difference is the energy transferred per coulomb of charge that passes between two points in an electrical circuit.

2) You can calculate energy transferred, in joules, J, from charge moved, in C, and potential difference, in V, using this formula:

| energy transferred = charge moved × potential difference | $E = Q \times V$ |

3) So, the potential difference (p.d.) across an electrical component is the amount of energy transferred by that electrical component (e.g. the amount of energy transferred by a motor to its kinetic energy store) per unit charge passed. One volt is one joule per coulomb.

4) Potential difference is sometimes called voltage. They're the same thing.

## Resistance, Potential Difference *and Current:* $V = I \times R$

For potential difference (*V*) in volts, V, current (*I*) in amps, A, and resistance (*R*) in ohms, Ω:

| potential difference = current × resistance |

As a formula triangle:

If you rearrange this equation, you can use it to calculate the resistance of a component from measurements of potential difference and current (e.g. from the experiment on the next page).

> **EXAMPLE:**
>
> A 4.0 Ω resistor in a circuit has a potential difference of 6.0 V across it. What is the current through the resistor?
>
> Rearrange $V = IR$ to give $I = V \div R$, then substitute in the values you have.　　$I = 6.0 \div 4.0 = 1.5$ A

## Resistance Increases *with Temperature (Usually)*

1) When an electrical charge flows through a component, it has to do work against resistance.

2) This causes an electrical transfer of energy (work done = energy transferred, p.180).

3) Some of this energy is transferred usefully (p.158) but some of it is dissipated to the thermal energy stores of the component and the surroundings.

4) So when a current flows through a resistor, the resistor heats up.

5) This happens because the electrons collide with the ions in the lattice that make up the resistor as they flow through it. This gives the ions energy, which causes them to vibrate and heat up.

> Low resistance wires (p.199) reduce the energy dissipated to thermal stores as the current flows between components.

6) The more the ions vibrate, the harder it is for electrons to get through the resistor (because there are more collisions). This means that for a given p.d. the current decreases as the resistor heats up.

7) If the resistor gets too hot, no current will be able to flow. There is one exception to this — the resistance of a thermistor decreases with an increase in temperature (p.187).

## In the end you'll have to learn this — resistance is futile...

$V = IR$ is one of the most useful equations in electricity — it crops up in a bunch of different places. So make sure you can bring it to mind super quickly and use it without trouble. Have a quick practise before moving on.

Q1　A current flowing through a resistor transfers 360 J of energy when 75 C of charge are passed through it. Calculate the potential difference across the resistor.　[2 marks]

Q2　A potential difference of 4.25 V is applied across a resistor, causing a current of 0.25 A to flow. Calculate the resistance, in ohms, of the resistor.　[2 marks]

# Investigating Components

Ooh experiments, you've gotta love 'em.  Here's a <u>simple experiment</u> for investigating different components.

## The Standard Test Circuit

You can use this circuit to investigate the <u>relationship</u> between <u>current</u> (*I*) <u>p.d.</u> (*V*) and <u>resistance</u> for a range of components, such as a <u>filament bulb</u> or a <u>fixed resistor</u>.  This relationship can be easily shown with an <u>*I-V* graph</u> — just like the ones over on the next page.

The standard test circuit contains:

variable d.c. source

replace this resistor with the component you're investigating

*   <u>Ammeter</u> — this measures the <u>current</u> (in amps) flowing through the component.  It can be put <u>anywhere</u> in the <u>main circuit</u> — but it must be placed <u>in series</u> (p.188) with the component, <u>never</u> in <u>parallel</u>.

*   <u>Voltmeter</u> — this measures the <u>potential difference</u> across the component.  It must be placed <u>in parallel</u> (p.188) with the <u>component</u> under test.

PRACTICAL

To use the circuit above to investigate a component, e.g. a <u>fixed resistor</u> or a <u>filament lamp</u>:

1)  Connect the circuit as shown above.  The <u>component</u> and the <u>ammeter</u> are in <u>series</u>, which means they can be put in <u>any order</u> in the main circuit.  (Remember the <u>voltmeter</u> must be <u>in parallel</u> around the <u>component under test</u>.)

2)  Change the <u>output potential difference</u> of the <u>power supply</u>.  This alters the <u>current</u> flowing through the circuit and the <u>potential difference</u> across the <u>component</u>.

3)  Take several <u>pairs of readings</u> from the <u>ammeter</u> and <u>voltmeter</u> to see how the <u>current through</u> the component varies as the <u>potential difference</u> across it is changed.

4)  <u>Plot</u> the <u>current</u> against the <u>potential difference</u> to get *I-V* graphs like the ones on p.187.

5)  You can use this data to work out the <u>resistance</u> for <u>each measurement</u> of *I* and *V*, using the formula on p.185, so you can see if the resistance of the component <u>changes</u> as *I* and *V* change.

6)  Make sure the circuit doesn't get <u>too hot</u> over the course of your experiment, as this will mess up your results (p.185).  If the circuit starts to warm up, <u>disconnect</u> it for a while between readings so it can cool down.  And, like any experiment, you should do repeats and <u>calculate means</u>.

Have a look at page 6 for more about calculating averages and interpreting your results.

## You Can Investigate Diodes, LDRs and Thermistors

You can also create <u>*I-V* graphs</u> for <u>diodes</u>, <u>thermistors</u> and <u>LDRs</u> using the method above (there's more about thermistors and LDRs on the next page).  However, the <u>resistance</u> of these components (and so their <u>potential difference</u>) can depend on <u>other factors</u> besides current.

1)  <u>Diodes</u> — after you've finished taking measurements for a range of currents, remove the diode and <u>swap its direction</u>.  You should find that <u>current cannot flow</u> through the diode anymore (see p.187).

2)  <u>Thermistors</u> — keeping the supply potential difference <u>constant</u>, gradually <u>heat</u> the thermistor.  (You can do this by placing the thermistor against a beaker of hot water.)  You should find that as the <u>temperature increases</u>, the <u>current</u> through the thermistor <u>increases</u> as the <u>resistance decreases</u>.

3)  <u>LDRs</u> — conduct your experiment in a <u>dim room</u>.  Again keep the supply p.d. <u>constant</u> and slowly adjust the light level near to the LDR (e.g. by using a lamp connected to a dimmer switch).  You should find as the light level gets <u>brighter</u>, the <u>current</u> through the LDR <u>increases</u> as the <u>resistance decreases</u>.

## Measure gymnastics — use a vaultmeter...

Make sure you can describe the experiment above — remember, ammeters in series, voltmeters in parallel.

Q1    Draw a circuit you could use to create an *I-V* graph for a filament lamp.                    [3 marks]

# Circuit Devices

With your current and your potential difference measured, you can now make some <u>sweet</u> graphs...

## Three Important Current-Potential Difference Graphs

*I-V* graphs show how the <u>current</u> varies as you <u>change</u> the <u>potential difference</u> (p.d.). Here are three examples, plotted from the experiment on the previous page:

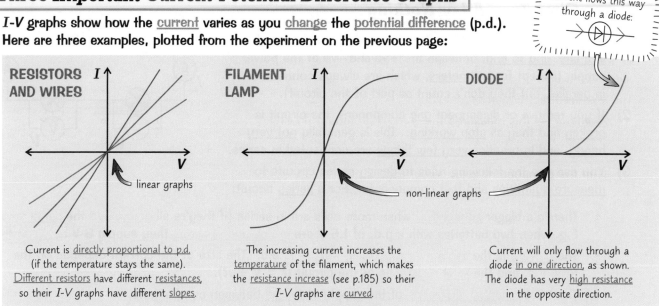

current flows this way through a diode:

**RESISTORS AND WIRES** — linear graphs

Current is <u>directly proportional to p.d.</u> (if the temperature stays the same). <u>Different resistors</u> have different <u>resistances</u>, so their *I-V* graphs have different <u>slopes</u>.

**FILAMENT LAMP** — non-linear graphs

The increasing current increases the <u>temperature</u> of the filament, which makes the <u>resistance increase</u> (see p.185) so their *I-V* graphs are <u>curved</u>.

**DIODE**

Current will only flow through a diode <u>in one direction</u>, as shown. The diode has very <u>high resistance</u> in the opposite direction.

1) <u>Linear</u> components have an *I-V* graph that's a <u>straight line</u> (e.g. a fixed resistor). <u>Non-linear</u> components have a <u>curved</u> *I-V* graph (e.g. a filament lamp or a diode).

2) For <u>linear</u> components, if the line goes through <u>(0,0)</u>, the resistance of the component equals the <u>inverse</u> of the <u>gradient</u> of the line, or "<u>1/gradient</u>". The <u>steeper</u> the graph, the <u>lower</u> the resistance.

3) You can find the <u>resistance</u> for <u>any point</u> on any *I-V* graph by reading the <u>p.d.</u> and <u>current</u> at that point and sticking them into **V = IR**, p.185.

## LDR is Short for Light Dependent Resistor

1) An LDR is a resistor that is <u>dependent</u> on the <u>intensity</u> of <u>light</u>. Simple really.

2) In <u>bright light</u>, the resistance <u>falls</u>.

3) In <u>darkness</u>, the resistance is <u>highest</u>.

4) They have lots of applications including <u>automatic night lights</u>, outdoor lighting and <u>burglar detectors</u>.

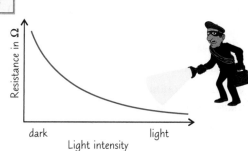

## The Resistance of a Thermistor Decreases as Temperature Increases

1) A <u>thermistor</u> is a <u>temperature dependent</u> resistor.

2) In <u>hot</u> conditions, the resistance <u>drops</u>.

3) In <u>cool</u> conditions, the resistance goes <u>up</u>.

4) Thermistors make useful <u>temperature detectors</u>, e.g. <u>car engine</u> temperature sensors and electronic <u>thermostats</u>.

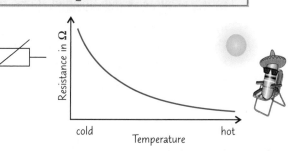

## LDRs — Light Dependent Rabbits...

You may get given an *I-V* graph in your exam that you haven't seen before. Make sure you understand why these graphs have the shape they do, and you'll be ready for anything they throw at you.

Q1    Describe one everyday use for:  a) an LDR        b) a thermistor        [2 marks]

# Series and Parallel Circuits

Make sure you know the <u>rules</u> about what happens to <u>current</u> and <u>p.d.</u> in series and parallel circuits.
You can find out how and why the <u>resistance</u> changes for <u>both</u> of these circuits over on the next page.

## Series Circuits — All or Nothing

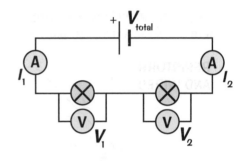

1) In <u>series circuits</u>, the different components are connected <u>in a line</u>, <u>end to end</u>, between the +ve and −ve of the power supply (except for <u>voltmeters</u>, which are always connected <u>in parallel</u>, but they don't count as part of the circuit).

2) If you remove or disconnect <u>one</u> component, the circuit is <u>broken</u> and they all <u>stop working</u>. This is generally <u>not very handy</u>, and in practice <u>very few things</u> are connected in series.

3) You can use the following rules to <u>design</u> series circuits to <u>measure quantities</u> and test components. For a <u>series</u> circuit:

- There's a bigger <u>supply p.d.</u> when more cells are in series (if they're all <u>connected</u> the <u>same way</u>). E.g. when two batteries with a p.d. of 1.5 V are <u>connected in series</u> they supply 3 V <u>between them</u>.

- The <u>current</u> is the <u>same everywhere</u>. $I_1 = I_2 = I_3$ etc. The size of the current depends on the <u>total p.d.</u> and the <u>total resistance</u> of the circuit ($I = V \div R$).

- The total <u>potential difference</u> of the supply is <u>shared</u> between components. The p.d. for each component depends on its <u>resistance</u>.

- The <u>total resistance</u> of the circuit <u>increases</u> as you <u>add</u> resistors (see next page).

## Parallel Circuits — Everything is Independent

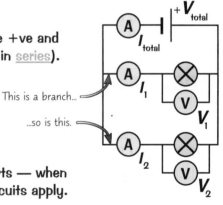

1) In <u>parallel circuits</u>, each component is <u>separately</u> connected to the +ve and −ve of the <u>supply</u> (except ammeters, which are <u>always</u> connected in <u>series</u>).

2) If you remove or disconnect <u>one</u> of them, it will <u>hardly affect</u> the others at all.

3) This is <u>obviously</u> how <u>most</u> things must be connected, for example in <u>cars</u> and in <u>household electrics</u>. You have to be able to switch everything on and off <u>separately</u>.

This is a branch...

...so is this.

4) Everyday circuits often contain a <u>mixture</u> of series and parallel parts — when looking at components on the <u>same branch</u> the rules for <u>series</u> circuits apply.

5) For a <u>parallel</u> circuit:

- The <u>potential difference</u> is the <u>same</u> across all components. $V_1 = V_2 = V_3$ etc.

- <u>Current</u> is <u>shared</u> between <u>branches</u>. The <u>total current</u> flowing around the circuit is equal to the <u>total</u> of all the currents through the <u>separate components</u>. $I_{total} = I_1 + I_2$ etc.

- In a parallel circuit, there are <u>junctions</u> where the current either <u>splits</u> or <u>rejoins</u>. The total current going <u>into</u> a junction has to equal the total current <u>leaving</u>. (If two <u>identical</u> <u>components</u> are connected in parallel then the <u>same current</u> will flow through each component.)

- The <u>total resistance</u> of the circuit <u>decreases</u> if you add a second resistor in parallel (see p.189).

## Series circuits — they're no laughing matter...

Get those rules straightened out in your head, then have a go at these questions to test what you can remember.

Q1    A filament lamp and a resistor are connected in series. A current of 0.5 A flows through the lamp. State the current flowing through the resistor. [1 mark]

Q2    Draw a circuit diagram for two filament lamps connected in parallel to a battery. Both of the lamps can be switched on and off without affecting each other. [3 marks]

# More on Series and Parallel Circuits

Time for a bit more about <u>series</u> and <u>parallel</u> circuits, including a quick <u>experiment</u>.  Fun, fun, fun...

## Adding Resistors in Series Increases Total Resistance

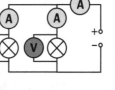

2 Ω   3 Ω

Total resistance = 5 Ω

1) In series circuits the <u>total resistance</u> of two components is just the <u>sum</u> of their resistances.

2) This is because by <u>adding a resistor</u> in series, the two resistors have to <u>share</u> the total p.d.

3) The potential difference across each resistor is <u>lower</u>, so the <u>current</u> through each resistor is also lower.  In a series circuit, the current is the <u>same everywhere</u> so the total current in the circuit is <u>reduced</u> when a resistor is added.  This means the total <u>resistance</u> of the circuit <u>increases</u>.

4) The <u>bigger</u> a component's <u>resistance</u>, the bigger its <u>share</u> of the <u>total potential difference</u>.

## Adding a Resistor in Parallel Reduces the Total Resistance

1) If you have <u>two resistors in parallel</u>, their <u>total resistance</u> is <u>less than</u> the resistance of the <u>smallest</u> of the two resistors.

2) This can be tough to get your head around, but think about it like this:

- In <u>parallel</u>, both resistors have the <u>same potential difference</u> across them as the source.
- This means the '<u>pushing force</u>' making the current flow is the <u>same</u> as the <u>source p.d.</u> for each resistor that you add.
- But by adding another loop, the <u>current</u> has <u>more</u> than one direction to go in.
- This increases the <u>total current</u> that can flow around the circuit.  Using $V = IR$, an <u>increase in current</u> means a <u>decrease</u> in the <u>total resistance</u> of the circuit.

## Use a Circuit to Investigate these Properties

PRACTICAL

1) Set out the <u>circuit</u> shown in the diagram on the right.

2) <u>Vary</u> the <u>output potential difference</u> from the power supply.  Record the readings from the <u>ammeter</u> and <u>voltmeter</u> for each change.

3) <u>Replace</u> the <u>resistor</u> with a <u>filament lamp</u> and <u>repeat</u> step 2.

4) Now, connect a <u>second filament lamp</u> to the circuit, <u>in parallel</u> to the first.  Connect <u>ammeters</u> and a second <u>voltmeter</u>, so you have:

5) Again, <u>vary</u> the output <u>potential difference</u> of the supply.

6) Write down the <u>current</u> through each ammeter and the <u>p.d.</u> across each <u>component</u>.

> You can also add more resistors to this circuit to see how potential difference is shared across components in series and how the increased resistance affects the current through the circuit.

For the <u>series circuit</u>, you should find that as the <u>potential difference increases</u>, the <u>current</u> through the resistor <u>increases</u>.  (Using $V = IR$ from page 185 — $R$ for a fixed resistor is <u>constant</u>, so an increase in $V$ causes an <u>increase</u> in $I$.)  You should find a <u>similar</u>, but <u>non-linear</u> relationship between p.d. and current for a filament bulb (see p.187).

For the <u>parallel</u> circuit, you should find that as <u>p.d. increases</u>, so does the <u>current</u> through each bulb (again, this is a <u>non-linear</u> relationship).  The <u>p.d.</u> across each bulb is the <u>same</u> as the p.d. of the <u>power supply</u>.  You should also notice that the <u>total current</u> through the circuit is the <u>sum</u> of the current through the two <u>branches</u> and that this is <u>larger than</u> the total current through the series circuit with one filament bulb (the <u>overall resistance</u> of the parallel circuit is <u>lower</u>, see above — $V = IR$, so a lower value of $R$ causes a higher value of $I$).

## A current shared (between identical components) — is a current halved...

Parallel circuits are more complicated than series circuits but you need to learn about both I'm afraid.

Q1    A 12 V cell is connected in series with a 2 Ω resistor, a 3 Ω resistor and a 7 Ω resistor.  Calculate the current through the circuit.    [3 marks]

# Energy in Circuits

Electrical devices are built to transfer energy. But nothing is perfect and some of this transferred energy ends up in thermal stores. This isn't always a bad thing though — devices like toasters and heaters make use of it.

## Energy Transferred Depends on Current, p.d. and Time

1) When an electrical charge goes through a change in potential difference, then energy is transferred (as work is done against resistance — p.185).

2) Energy is supplied to the charge at the power source to 'raise' it through a potential.

3) The charge gives up this energy when it 'falls' through any potential drop in components elsewhere in the circuit.

4) To find the energy transferred to an electrical component, you can use the equation:

$$E = I \times V \times t$$

Where $E$ is energy transferred in joules (J), $I$ is current in amps (A), $V$ is p.d. in volts (V) and $t$ is time in seconds (s).

Charges gaining energy at the battery

+6V

+6V

+3V

0V

0V

Charges releasing energy in resistors

*This equation comes from combining two of the equations from the next page.*

5) The larger the current through, or p.d. across, a component, the more energy is transferred to it.

## Energy is Transferred from Cells and Other Sources

1) Electrical appliances are designed to transfer energy to components in the circuit when a current flows.

Kettles transfer energy electrically from the mains a.c. supply to the thermal energy store of the heating element inside the kettle.

Energy is transferred electrically from the battery of a handheld fan to the kinetic energy store of the fan's motor.

2) Of course, no appliance transfers all energy completely usefully. The higher the current, the more energy is transferred to the thermal energy stores of the components (and then the surroundings).

3) This heating usually increases the resistance of the components, like you saw on page 185.

## Heating a Circuit isn't Always Bad

1) Heating up a component generally reduces its efficiency (p.158) — less energy is transferred to useful energy stores because more of it is being transferred to the thermal energy store of the component.

2) If the temperature gets too high, this can cause components in the circuit to melt — which means the circuit will stop working, or not work properly.

*More on fuses on p.193.*

3) Fuses use this effect to protect circuits — they melt and break the circuit if the current gets too high.

4) The heating effect of an electric current can have other advantages. For example, it's ace if you want to heat something. Toasters contain a coil of wire with a really high resistance. When a current passes through the coil, its temperature increases so much that it glows and gives off infrared radiation. This radiation transfers energy to the bread and cooks it.

5) Filament bulbs and electric heaters work in a similar way.

## Have a break from all this work — or you'll have no energy left...

There's no escaping energy transfers I'm afraid. Practise using that equation then take a quick break to recharge.

Q1    A laptop charger is connected to a 230 V source for an hour. A current of 8.0 A flows through it.
Calculate the energy transferred by the laptop charger.                                    [2 marks]

# Power in Circuits

You know that electrical devices <u>transfer energy</u> — well, their <u>power</u> determines how <u>quickly</u> this happens.

## Energy Transferred Depends on Power

1) The <u>total</u> energy transferred by an appliance depends on <u>how long</u> the appliance is on for and its <u>power</u>.

2) The <u>power</u> of an appliance is the energy that it <u>transfers per second</u>. So the <u>more</u> energy it transfers in a given time, the <u>higher</u> its power.

3) The <u>power</u> of an appliance can be found using:

| Power (W) = Energy transferred (J) ÷ Time (s) |

$$P = \frac{E}{t}$$

4) Appliances are often given a <u>power rating</u> — they're labelled with the <u>maximum</u> safe power that they can operate at. You can usually take this to be their <u>maximum operating power</u>.

5) The power rating tells you the <u>maximum</u> amount of <u>energy</u> transferred between stores <u>per second</u> when the appliance is in use.

> Microwaves have a range of <u>power ratings</u>. A microwave with a power rating of 500 W will take <u>longer</u> to cook food than one with a power rating of 750 W. This is because the 500 W transfers <u>less</u> energy <u>per second</u> to the <u>thermal</u> energy store of the food, so it takes longer to cook.

6) This helps customers choose between models — the <u>lower</u> the power rating, the <u>less</u> electricity an appliance uses in a given time and so the <u>cheaper</u> it is to run.

7) But, a higher power <u>doesn't</u> necessarily mean that it transfers <u>more</u> energy <u>usefully</u>. An appliance may be <u>more powerful</u> than another, <u>but less efficient</u>, meaning that it might still only transfer the <u>same amount</u> of energy (or even <u>less</u>) to useful stores (see p.158).

## Power Also Depends on Current and Potential Difference

1) The <u>power transferred</u> by an appliance depends on the <u>potential difference</u> (p.d.) across it, and the <u>current</u> flowing through it.

2) The <u>p.d.</u> tells you how much <u>energy each unit of charge transfers</u> (p.185), and the <u>current</u> tells you <u>how much charge</u> passes per unit time. So <u>both</u> will affect the rate that <u>energy is transferred</u> to an appliance, and the rate at which it <u>transfers energy</u> to other stores.

3) The <u>power</u> of an appliance can be found with:

| Electrical power (W) = Current (A) × Potential difference (V) |   $P = IV$

4) You can use this equation to work out the fuse (p.193) that should be used in an appliance. To work out the size of the <u>fuse</u> needed, you need to work out the <u>current</u> that the item will normally use:

> **EXAMPLE:** A 1 kW hair dryer is connected to a 230 V supply. Find the fuse needed.
> 1) Use the equation to find the normal current.    $I = P \div V = 1000 \div 230 = 4.3$ A
> 2) A fuse is usually rated just a little    So a 5 amp fuse is needed.
>    higher than the normal current.

5) You can also find the power if you <u>don't know</u> the <u>potential difference</u>. To do this, stick $V = IR$ from page 185 into $P = IV$, which gives you:

$P = I^2R$    Where $P$ is the electrical power in watts (W), $I$ is current in amperes (A) and $R$ is the resistance in ohms ($\Omega$).

## You have the power — now use your potential...

I'm afraid the best way to learn all of this is to just practise using those equations again and again. Sorry.

Q1    Calculate the difference in the amount of energy transferred by a 250 W TV and a 375 W TV when they are both used for two hours.

[3 marks]

# Electricity in the Home

There are two types of electricity supply — <u>alternating</u> and <u>direct currents</u>. Read on for more about both...

## Mains Supply is a.c., Battery Supply is d.c.

1) There are two types of electricity supplies — <u>alternating current</u> (a.c.) and <u>direct current</u> (d.c.).

2) In <u>a.c. supplies</u> the current is <u>constantly</u> changing direction. <u>Alternating currents</u> are produced by <u>alternating voltages</u> (the <u>positive</u> and <u>negative</u> ends of the p.d. keep <u>alternating</u>).

3) The <u>UK mains supply</u> (the electricity in your home) is an a.c. supply at around <u>230 V</u>.

4) The frequency of the a.c. mains supply is <u>50 cycles per second</u> or <u>50 Hz</u> (hertz).

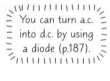
You can turn a.c. into d.c. by using a diode (p.187).

5) By contrast, cells and batteries supply <u>direct current</u> (d.c.).

6) <u>Direct current</u> is a current that is always flowing in the <u>same direction</u>. It's created by a <u>direct voltage</u> (a p.d. that is <u>only positive</u> or <u>negative</u>, not both).

## Most Cables Have Three Separate Wires

1) Most electrical appliances are connected to the mains supply by <u>three-core</u> cables. This means that they have <u>three wires</u> inside them, each with a <u>core of copper</u> and a <u>coloured plastic coating</u>.

2) The <u>colour</u> of the insulation on each cable shows its <u>purpose</u>.

3) The colours are <u>always</u> the <u>same</u> for <u>every</u> appliance. This is so that it's easy to tell the different wires <u>apart</u>.

1) <u>LIVE WIRE</u> — <u>brown</u>.
The live wire carries the voltage (potential difference, p.d.). It alternates between a <u>high +ve and −ve voltage</u> of about <u>230 V</u>.

2) <u>NEUTRAL WIRE</u> — <u>blue</u>.
The neutral wire <u>completes</u> the circuit — electricity normally flows <u>in</u> through the <u>live</u> wire and <u>out</u> through the <u>neutral</u> wire. The neutral wire is always at <u>0 V</u>.

3) <u>EARTH WIRE</u> — <u>green</u> and <u>yellow</u>.
The earth wire is for <u>safety</u> and <u>protecting</u> the <u>wiring</u>. It carries the current away if something goes <u>wrong</u> and stops the appliance casing becoming <u>live</u>. It's <u>also</u> at 0 V.

- The <u>p.d.</u> between the <u>live wire</u> and the <u>neutral wire</u> equals the <u>supply p.d.</u> (<u>230 V</u> for the mains).
- The <u>p.d.</u> between the <u>live wire</u> and the <u>earth wire</u> is also <u>230 V</u> for a mains-connected appliance.
- There is <u>no p.d.</u> between the <u>neutral wire</u> and the <u>earth wire</u> — they're both at 0 V.

4) <u>Plug sockets</u> have <u>switches</u> which are connected in the <u>live wire</u> of the circuit. This is so the circuit can be <u>broken</u> — the appliance becomes <u>isolated</u> and the risk of an <u>electric shock</u> is reduced.

## Touching the Live Wire Gives You an Electric Shock

1) Your <u>body</u> (just like the earth) is at <u>0 V</u>.

2) This means that if you touch the <u>live wire</u>, a <u>large potential difference</u> is produced across your body and a <u>current</u> flows through you.

3) This causes a large <u>electric shock</u> which could injure or even kill you.

4) Even if a plug socket or a light switch is turned <u>off</u> (i.e. the switch is <u>open</u>) there is still a <u>danger</u> of an electric shock. A current <u>isn't flowing</u>, but there is still a p.d. in the live wire. If you made <u>contact</u> with the live wire, your body would provide a <u>link</u> between the supply and the earth, so a <u>current</u> would flow <u>through you</u>.

5) <u>Any</u> connection between <u>live</u> and <u>neutral</u> can be <u>dangerous</u>. If the link creates a <u>low resistance</u> path to earth, a huge current will flow, which could result in a fire.

---

## Why are earth wires green and yellow — when mud is brown..?

Electricity is very useful, but it can also be very dangerous. Make sure you know the risks.

Q1   Explain the difference between a.c. and d.c. electricity supplies.          [2 marks]

# Fuses and Earthing

Fuses and circuit breakers are super important. And questions on them cover a whole barrel of fun — electrical current, resistance, potential difference... Read this page and make sure you've got it sussed.

## Earthing and Fuses Prevent Electrical Overloads

Surges (sudden increases) in current can occur because of changes in a circuit (e.g. an appliance suddenly switching off) or because of a fault in an electrical appliance. Current surges can lead to the circuits and wiring in your appliances melting or causing a fire, and faulty appliances can cause deadly electric shocks.

The earth wire and a fuse are included in electrical appliances to prevent this from happening. This is how they work:

1) If a fault develops in which the live wire somehow touches the metal case, then because the case is earthed, too great a current flows in through the live wire, through the case and out down the earth wire.

2) This surge in current melts the fuse when the amount of current is greater than the fuse rating. Fuses are connected to the live wire, so that breaking the fuse breaks the circuit and cuts off the live supply.

3) This isolates the whole appliance, making it impossible to get an electric shock from the case. It also prevents the risk of fire caused by the heating effect of a large current.

4) Fuses should be rated as near as possible but just higher than the normal operating current.

5) The larger the current, the thicker the cable you need to carry it (to stop the cable getting too hot and melting). That's why the fuse rating needed for cables usually increases with cable thickness.

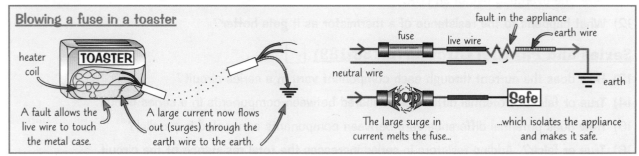

6) As well as the fuses in plugs, there are also household fuses (these are the ones that blow when a light bulb goes). These work in the same way, but protect the wiring in the house, not just in an appliance.

## Circuit Breakers are Even Safer Than Fuses

Circuit breakers can be used in the place of household fuses.

1) Instead of melting a fuse, a large current may instead 'trip' (turn off) a circuit breaker.

2) Circuit breakers turn off quicker than the time taken for a fuse to melt.

3) They can also be reset, which is much easier than having to replace a fuse.

4) However, circuit breakers are more expensive than fuses.

## Insulating Materials Make Appliances "Double Insulated"

1) All appliances with metal cases are usually "earthed" to reduce the danger of electric shock.

2) "Earthing" just means the case must be attached to an earth wire. An earthed conductor can never become live.

3) If the appliance has a plastic casing and no metal parts showing then it's said to be double insulated.

4) Anything with double insulation like that doesn't need an earth wire — just a live and neutral. Cables that only carry the live and neutral wires are known as two-core cables.

## Nothing shocks my mum — she's very down to earth...

Earthing is dead important, so make sure you understand it and the life-saving protection it provides.

Q1　　Which wire are fuses connected in?　　　　　　　　　　　　　　　　　　[1 mark]

# Revision Questions for Section 21

Well, that wraps up Section 21 — time to have a go at a few questions to see how much you can remember.

- Try these questions and tick off each one when you get it right.
- When you've done all the questions for a subtopic and are completely happy with it, tick off the topic.

## Circuit Basics (p.184-187) ☑

1) What is meant by potential difference and resistance in a circuit?
2) Define current and state an equation that links current, charge and time, with units for each.
3) Draw the circuit symbols for: a cell, a filament lamp, a diode, a motor and an LDR.
4) Give the equation that links energy transferred, charge moved and potential difference.
5) What is the equation that links potential difference, current and resistance?
6) Briefly explain why resistance increases with temperature for a resistor.
7) Explain how you would investigate how the current through a component affected its resistance.
8) True or false? An ammeter must be connected in parallel to the component being tested.
9) Name one linear component and one non-linear component.
10) Explain how the resistance of an LDR varies with light intensity.
11) Give one everyday use of an LDR.
12) What happens to the resistance of a thermistor as it gets hotter?

## Series and Parallel Circuits (p.188-189) ☑

13) How does the current through each component vary in a series circuit?
14) True or false? Potential difference is shared between components in a series circuit.
15) How does potential difference vary between components connected in parallel?
16) True or false? Adding resistors in series increases the total resistance of the circuit.
17) Does adding two resistors in parallel increase or decrease the total resistance of a circuit?

## Power and Energy Transfers in Circuits (p.190-191) ☑

18) Write down the equation that links energy transferred, current, potential difference and time.
19) Give two disadvantages of the heating effect in an electrical circuit.
20) Give two advantages of the heating effect in an electrical circuit.
21) Define power in terms of energy transferred.
22) What is a power rating?
23) State the equation that links electrical power, current and potential difference.
24) What is the third equation for electrical power, which links current and resistance?

## Electricity in the Home and Electrical Safety (p.192-193) ☑

25) True or false? Mains supply electricity is an alternating current.
26) What is the frequency of the UK mains supply?
27) Why are the three wires in a three-core cable colour coded?
28) Give the potential differences for the three wires in a three-core mains cable.
29) Explain why touching a live wire is dangerous.
30) Explain how a fuse protects you if a fault causes the live wire to touch the metal case of an appliance.
31) True or false? Circuit breakers must be replaced each time they 'trip'.

# Magnets and Magnetic Fields

I think magnetism is an <u>attractive</u> subject, but don't get <u>repelled</u> by the exam — <u>revise</u>.

## Magnets Produce Magnetic Fields

1) All magnets have <u>two poles</u> — <u>north</u> and <u>south</u>.

2) All magnets produce a <u>magnetic field</u> — a region where <u>other</u> <u>magnets</u> or <u>magnetic materials</u> (see next page) experience a <u>force</u>.

3) You can show a magnetic field by drawing <u>magnetic field lines</u>.

4) The lines always go from <u>north to south</u> and they show <u>which way</u> a force would act on a north pole at that point in the field.

5) The <u>closer together</u> the lines are, the <u>stronger</u> the magnetic field.

6) The <u>further away</u> from a magnet you get, the <u>weaker</u> the field is.

7) The magnetic field is <u>strongest</u> at the <u>poles</u> of a magnet. This means that the <u>magnetic forces</u> are also <u>strongest</u> at the poles.

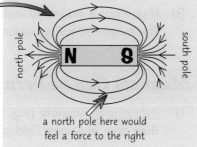

To see the shape of a magnetic field, place a piece of card over a magnet and sprinkle iron filings onto it. The filings line up with the field lines — but they won't show you the direction of the field.

north pole

south pole

a north pole here would feel a force to the right

## Magnetic Fields Cause Forces between Magnets

1) Between <u>two magnets</u> the magnetic force can be <u>attractive</u> or <u>repulsive</u>. Two poles that are the same (these are called <u>like poles</u>) will <u>repel</u> each other. Two <u>unlike</u> poles will <u>attract</u> each other.

2) Placing the north and south poles of two bar magnets <u>near</u> each other creates a <u>uniform field</u> between the two poles. The magnetic field is the <u>same strength</u> everywhere between the poles.

3) If you're asked to <u>draw</u> a uniform magnetic field, you need to draw <u>at least three</u> field lines, <u>parallel</u> to each other and all the <u>same distance</u> apart.

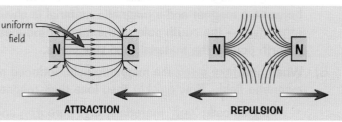

uniform field

**ATTRACTION**

**REPULSION**

Don't forget the arrows on your field lines.

## Plotting Compasses Show the Directions of Magnetic Fields

1) Inside a compass is a tiny <u>bar magnet</u> called a <u>needle</u>. A compass needle always <u>lines up</u> with the magnetic field it's in.

2) You can use a compass to build up a picture of what the field around a magnet <u>looks like</u>:

- Put the magnet on a <u>piece of paper</u> and <u>draw round it</u>.

- Place the compass on the paper <u>near</u> the magnet. The needle will point in the <u>direction</u> of the <u>field line</u> at this position.

- Mark the direction of the <u>compass needle</u> by drawing two dots — one at each end of the needle.

- Then <u>move</u> the compass so that the <u>tail end</u> of the needle is where the <u>tip</u> of the needle was in the <u>previous position</u> and put a dot by the tip of the needle. Repeat this and then <u>join up</u> the marks you've made — you'll end up with a <u>drawing</u> of one <u>field line</u> around the magnet.

- Repeat this method at different points around the magnet to get several field lines. Make sure you draw <u>arrows</u> from north to south on your field lines.

3) When they're not near a magnet, compasses always point towards the Earth's <u>North Pole</u>. This is because the <u>Earth</u> generates its own <u>magnetic field</u> (and the <u>North Pole</u> is actually a <u>magnetic south pole</u>). This shows the <u>inside</u> (<u>core</u>) of the Earth must be <u>magnetic</u>.

The compass follows the field lines and points towards the south pole of the bar magnet.

## Magnets are like farmers — surrounded by fields...

Magnetism is one of those things that takes a while to make much sense. Learn these basics — you'll need them.

Q1    Draw the magnetic field lines for a bar magnet. Label the areas where the field is strongest.    [3 marks]

Q2    Describe how to plot the magnetic field lines of a bar magnet using a compass.    [4 marks]

# Permanent and Induced Magnets

Magnetic fields don't just affect <u>magnets</u> — they affect a few special <u>magnetic materials</u> too.

## *Very Few Materials are Magnetic*

1) The main <u>three</u> magnetic elements are <u>iron</u>, <u>nickel</u> and <u>cobalt</u>.

2) Some alloys and compounds of these metals are also magnetic. For example, <u>steel</u> is magnetic because it contains <u>iron</u>.

3) If you put a magnetic material near a magnet, it is <u>attracted</u> to that magnet. The magnetic force between a magnet and a magnetic material is <u>always</u> attractive.

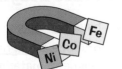

## *Magnets Can be Permanent or Induced*

1) <u>Permanent</u> magnets (e.g. bar magnets) produce their own magnetic field <u>all the time</u>.

2) <u>Induced</u> (or <u>temporary</u>) magnets only produce a magnetic field while they're <u>in</u> another <u>magnetic field</u>.

3) If you put any <u>magnetic material</u> into a magnetic field, it becomes an <u>induced</u> magnet.

4) This <u>magnetic induction</u> explains why the force between a magnet and a magnetic material is always <u>attractive</u> — the south pole of the magnet induces a north pole in the material, and vice versa.

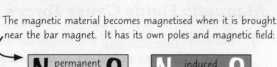

The magnetic material becomes magnetised when it is brought near the bar magnet. It has its own poles and magnetic field:

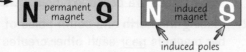

5) When you <u>take away</u> the magnetic field, induced magnets return to normal and <u>stop producing</u> a magnetic field. How <u>quickly</u> they lose their magnetism depends on the material they're made from.

- Magnetically '<u>soft</u>' materials, e.g. pure <u>iron</u> and <u>nickel-iron alloys</u>, lose their magnetism very quickly.
- Magnetically '<u>hard</u>' materials, e.g. <u>steel</u>, lose their magnetism more slowly. <u>Permanent magnets</u> are made from magnetically hard materials.

## *Magnetic Materials have Lots of Uses*

There are many different <u>uses</u> of <u>magnetic materials</u>, the number of which has grown since the invention of <u>electromagnets</u> (p.198). For example:

1) <u>Fridge doors</u> — there is a <u>permanent</u> magnetic strip in your fridge door to keep it closed.

2) <u>Cranes</u> — these use <u>induced</u> electromagnets to <u>attract</u> and <u>move</u> magnetic materials — e.g. moving <u>scrap metal</u> in scrap yards.

3) <u>Doorbells</u> — these use <u>electromagnets</u> which turn <u>on</u> and <u>off</u> rapidly, to repeatedly attract and release an arm which <u>strikes</u> the metal bell to produce a <u>ringing</u> noise.

4) <u>Magnetic separators</u> — these are used in recycling plants to <u>sort metal items</u> (like cans).

5) <u>Maglev trains</u> — these use <u>magnetic repulsion</u> to make trains <u>float</u> slightly above the track (to reduce losses from <u>friction</u>) and to <u>propel</u> them along.

6) <u>MRI machines</u> — these use magnetic fields to create <u>images</u> of the inside of your body without having to use <u>ionising radiation</u> (like X-rays, p.171).

7) <u>Speakers</u> — these use the <u>motor effect</u> (p.197) to make a <u>paper cone</u> move, creating a <u>sound wave</u>.

---

## *Attractive ~~end~~ with a magnetic personality — I'm a catch...*

Remember, induced magnets are also called temporary because they're only magnetic when in a magnetic field.

Q1     State three everyday uses of magnetic materials.                                         [3 marks]

Q2     Give two differences between permanent and induced magnets.                  [2 marks]

# Electromagnetism and the Motor Effect

On this page you'll see that a <u>magnetic field</u> is also found around a <u>wire</u> that has a <u>current</u> passing through it.

## A Moving Charge Creates a Magnetic Field

1) When a <u>current flows</u> through a <u>long, straight conductor</u> (e.g. a <u>wire</u>) a <u>magnetic field</u> is created <u>around</u> it.

2) The field is made up of <u>concentric circles</u> perpendicular to the wire, with the wire in the centre.

3) Changing the <u>direction</u> of the <u>current</u> changes the direction of the <u>magnetic field</u> — use the <u>right-hand thumb rule</u> to work out which way it goes. (In experiments, you can use a <u>plotting compass</u> to find its direction, p.195.)

4) The <u>larger</u> the current through the wire, or the <u>closer</u> to the wire you are, the <u>stronger</u> the field is.

<u>The Right-Hand Thumb Rule</u>
Using your right hand, point your thumb in the direction of current and curl your fingers. The direction of your fingers is the direction of the field.

## The Motor Effect — A Current in a Magnetic Field Experiences a Force

When a <u>current-carrying conductor</u> (e.g. a <u>wire</u>) is put between magnetic poles, the two <u>magnetic fields</u> interact. The result is a <u>force</u> on the wire.

This is an aerial view. The red dot represents a wire carrying current "out of the page" (towards you). (If it was a cross ('×') then that would mean the current was going into the page.)

→ Normal magnetic field of wire
→ Normal magnetic field of magnets
→ **Deviated magnetic field of magnets**

The wire also exerts an equal and opposite force on the magnet (from Newton's Third Law, see p.152) but we're just looking at the force on the wire.

1) To experience the <u>full force</u>, the <u>wire</u> has to be at <u>90°</u> (right angles) to the <u>magnetic field</u>. If the wire runs <u>along</u> the <u>magnetic field</u>, it won't experience <u>any force at all</u>. At angles in between, it'll feel <u>some</u> force.

2) The force always acts in the <u>same direction</u> relative to the <u>magnetic field</u> and the <u>direction of the current</u> in the wire. So changing the <u>direction</u> of either the <u>magnetic field</u> or the <u>current</u> will change the direction of the <u>force</u>.

→ Current
→ Magnetic field
→ Force

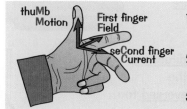

1) <u>Fleming's left-hand rule</u> is used to find the <u>direction of the force</u> on a current-carrying conductor.

2) Using your <u>left hand</u>, point your <u>First finger</u> in the direction of the <u>magnetic Field</u> and your <u>seCond finger</u> in the direction of the <u>Current</u>.

3) Your <u>thuMb</u> will then point in the direction of the <u>force</u> (Motion).

## You Can Find the Size of the Force Using F = BIl

The <u>force</u> acting on a <u>conductor</u> in a <u>magnetic field</u> depends on three things:

1) The <u>magnetic flux density</u> — how many <u>field</u> (<u>flux</u>) lines there are in a <u>region</u>. This shows the <u>strength</u> of the magnetic field (p.195).

2) The size of the <u>current</u> through the conductor.

3) The <u>length</u> of the conductor that's <u>in</u> the magnetic field.

When the current is at <u>90°</u> to the magnetic field it is in, the <u>force</u> acting on it can be found using the equation on the right.

Force (N)

$$F = B \times I \times l$$

Current (A)

Magnetic flux density (T, tesla or N/Am)

Length (m)

## *Left-hand rule for the motor effect — drive on the left...*

Learn the left-hand rule and use it — don't be scared of looking like a muppet in the exam.

Q1    A 35 cm long piece of wire is at 90° to an external magnetic field. The wire experiences a force of 0.98 N when a current of 5.0 A is flowing through it. Calculate the magnetic flux density of the field.    [2 marks]

# Solenoids and Electromagnetic Induction

Solenoids and electromagnetic induction both sound pretty horrible — but don't panic, they're not as bad as they first seem. Just take this page slowly and you should be fine...

## A Solenoid is a Long Coil of Wire

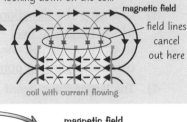

current    magnetic field

1) Around a single loop of current-carrying wire, the magnetic field looks like this:

2) You can increase the strength of the magnetic field produced by a length of wire by wrapping it into a long coil with lots of loops, called a solenoid.

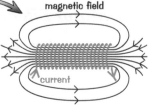

looking down on the coil:

magnetic field

field lines cancel out here

coil with current flowing

3) The field lines around each separate loop of wire line up.

- Inside the solenoid, you get lots of field lines pointing in the same direction. The magnetic field is strong and almost uniform.

- Outside the coil, the overlapping field lines cancel each other out — so the field is weak apart from at the ends of the solenoid.

4) You end up with a field that looks like the one around a bar magnet. The direction of the field depends on the direction of the current (p.197).

magnetic field

current

5) A solenoid is an example of an ELECTROMAGNET — a magnet with a magnetic field that can be turned on and off using an electric current.

6) You can increase the field strength of the solenoid even more by putting a block of iron in the centre of the coil. This iron core becomes an induced magnet (see p.196) whenever current is flowing.

## A Changing Magnetic Field Induces a Potential Difference in a Conductor

**Electromagnetic Induction:** The induction of a potential difference (and current if there's a complete circuit) in a wire which is experiencing a change in magnetic field.

*Induces is a fancy word for creates.*

1) There are two different situations where you get electromagnetic induction. The first is if an electrical conductor (e.g. a coil of wire) and a magnetic field move relative to each other.

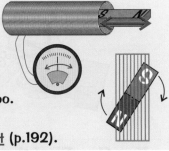

- You can do this by moving/rotating either a magnet in a coil of wire OR a conductor (wire) in a magnetic field (either way, you're "cutting" magnetic field lines and so inducing a p.d.).

- If you move or rotate the magnet (or conductor) in the opposite direction, then the p.d./current will be reversed. Likewise if the polarity of the magnet is reversed, then the potential difference/current will be reversed too.

- If you keep the magnet (or the coil) moving backwards and forwards, or keep it rotating in the same direction, you produce an alternating current (p.192).

2) You also get an induced p.d. when the magnetic field through an electrical conductor changes (gets bigger or smaller or reverses). This is what happens in a transformer.

3) You can increase the size of the induced p.d. by increasing the STRENGTH of the magnetic field, increasing the SPEED of movement/change of field or having MORE TURNS PER UNIT LENGTH on the coil of wire.

4) The induced p.d./current always opposes the change that made it:

- When a current is induced in a wire, that current produces its own magnetic field (p.197).

- The magnetic field created by an induced current always acts against the change that made it. Basically, it's trying to return things to the way they were.

NO MORE CHANGES

## Give me one good raisin why I should make the currant joke...

Motors and solenoids are used in loads of everyday things from speakers to alarm clocks.

Q1    Sketch the magnetic field in and around a solenoid.                    [3 marks]

# Transformers

Transformers use electromagnetic induction to make transferring electricity between places more efficient.

## Transformers Change the p.d. — but Only for Alternating Current

1) Transformers use induction to change the size of the potential difference of an alternating current.

2) They all have two coils of wire, the primary and the secondary coils, joined with an iron core.

3) When an alternating p.d. is applied across the primary coil, it produces an alternating magnetic field.

4) The iron in the core is a magnetic material (see p.196) that is easily magnetised and demagnetised. Because the coil is producing an alternating magnetic field, the magnetisation in the core also alternates.

5) This changing magnetic field induces a p.d. in the secondary coil.

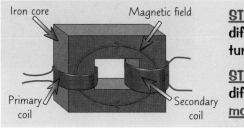

**STEP-UP TRANSFORMERS** step the potential difference up (i.e. increase it). They have more turns on the secondary coil than the primary coil.

**STEP-DOWN TRANSFORMERS** step the potential difference down (i.e. decrease it). They have more turns on the primary coil than the secondary.

6) Transformers are almost 100% efficient. So you can assume that the input power is equal to the output power. Using $P = I \times V$ (page 191), you can write this as:

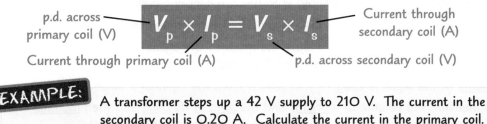

p.d. across primary coil (V)

$$V_p \times I_p = V_s \times I_s$$

Current through primary coil (A)

Current through secondary coil (A)

p.d. across secondary coil (V)

$V_p \times I_p$ is the power output at the primary coil. $V_s \times I_s$ is the power input at the secondary coil.

**EXAMPLE:** A transformer steps up a 42 V supply to 210 V. The current in the secondary coil is 0.20 A. Calculate the current in the primary coil.

1) Rearrange the transformer equation.  $V_p \times I_p = V_s \times I_s$ so $I_p = (V_s \times I_s) \div V_p$
2) Then stick in the values you have.  $I_p = (210 \times 0.20) \div 42 = 1.0$ A

## Transformers in the National Grid Produce a High p.d. and a Low Current

1) Once the electricity has been generated, it goes into the national grid — a network of wires and transformers that connects UK power stations to consumers (anyone who uses electricity).

2) The national grid has to transfer loads of energy each second, which means it transmits electricity at a high power (as power = energy transferred ÷ time taken, p.191).

3) Electrical power = current × potential difference ($P = IV$, p.191), so to transmit the huge amounts of power needed, you either need a high potential difference or a high current.

4) But a high current makes wires heat up, so loads of energy is wasted to thermal stores.

5) So to reduce these losses and make the national grid more efficient, high-voltage, low-resistance cables, and transformers are used.

6) Step-up transformers at power stations boost the p.d. up really high (400 000 V) and keep the current relatively low.

7) Step-down transformers then bring it back down to safe, usable levels at the consumers' end.

## Transformers — NOT robots in disguise...

Make sure you know how transformers work, and then take a stab at using that equation with this question.

Q1    A transformer has an input potential difference of 1.6 V. The output power is 320 W.
Calculate the input current.                                                    [2 marks]

# Density

Time for some <u>maths</u> I'm afraid.  But at least it comes with a fun experiment, so it's not all bad...

## Density is Mass per Unit Volume

<u>Density</u> is a measure of the '<u>compactness</u>' (for want of a better word) of a substance.  It relates the <u>mass</u> of a substance to how much <u>space</u> it <u>takes up</u>.

The symbol for density is a Greek letter rho ($\rho$) — it looks like a p but it isn't.

$$\text{Density} = \frac{\text{mass}}{\text{volume}}$$

The units of density are g/cm³ or kg/m³.

1) The density of an object depends on what it's made of.  Density <u>doesn't vary</u> with <u>size</u> or <u>shape</u>.

2) The average <u>density</u> of an object determines whether it <u>floats</u> or <u>sinks</u> — a solid object will <u>float</u> on a fluid if it has a <u>lower average density</u> than the fluid.

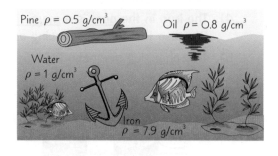

Pine $\rho = 0.5$ g/cm³     Oil $\rho = 0.8$ g/cm³
Water $\rho = 1$ g/cm³
Iron $\rho = 7.9$ g/cm³

## You Can Find the Density of Solids and Liquids

1) To <u>find</u> the density of a substance, measure its <u>mass</u> and <u>volume</u> and use the formula above.

2) The easiest way to find the <u>density</u> of a <u>liquid</u> is to use a <u>measuring cylinder</u>.

3) Use a <u>mass balance</u> (p.208) to measure the <u>mass</u> of the <u>empty</u> measuring cylinder.

4) Pour in the liquid you're investigating.  Measure the mass of the cylinder again — the <u>difference</u> in mass is equal to the <u>mass of the liquid</u>.

5) Finding the <u>volume</u> of the liquid is easy — just read it from the cylinder's scale.  <u>1 ml = 1 cm³</u>.

6) If you want to measure the volume of a <u>prism</u>, find the <u>area</u> of its <u>base</u> and then <u>multiply</u> it by its <u>height</u>.  For a <u>cube</u> this is dead easy — it's just length × width × height.

7) If your object <u>isn't</u> a regular shape, you can find its volume using the fact that an object <u>submerged</u> in water will displace a volume of water <u>equal</u> to its <u>own volume</u>.  One way of doing this is to use a <u>density bottle</u>:

1) Measure the <u>mass</u> ($m_1$) of the object using a mass balance.

2) <u>Fill</u> the bottle with a liquid of a <u>known density</u> (e.g. water).

3) Place the <u>stopper</u> into the bottle and <u>dry</u> the outside.

4) Measure the <u>mass</u> of the bottle ($m_2$).

5) <u>Empty</u> the bottle and place the <u>object</u> into the density bottle.  Repeat steps 2 and 3.  Measure the <u>mass</u> of the bottle ($m_3$).

6) Calculate the volume of displaced water:

- The <u>mass</u> of the <u>displaced water</u> = $m_2 - (m_3 - m_1)$

- You know the <u>density</u> of water, so you can use $V = m \div \rho$ to find the volume displaced.  This equals the <u>volume of the object</u>.

7) Calculate the density of the object using $\rho = m \div V$ with the <u>mass</u> you measured in <u>step 1</u> ($m_1$) and the <u>volume</u> you calculated in <u>step 6</u>.

**PRACTICAL**

50 ml

50 ml

Liquid is pushed up the tube in the stopper, so the volume inside the bottle is constant.

You can also use a eureka can and a measuring cylinder if you don't have access to density bottles.

## I'm feeling a bit dense after that lot...

Remember — density is all about how tightly packed the particles in a substance are.  Nice and simple really.

Q1    An object has a mass of 0.45 kg and a volume of 75 cm³.  Calculate its density in kg/m³.        [3 marks]

Q2    A cube has edges of length 1.5 cm and an average density of 3500 kg/m³.  What is its mass?    [3 marks]

# Kinetic Theory and States of Matter

According to kinetic theory, everything's made of <u>tiny little balls</u>. The table, this book, your Gran...

## *Kinetic Theory is a Way of Explaining Matter*

1) In kinetic theory, you can think of the particles that make up matter as <u>tiny balls</u>. You can explain the ways that matter behaves in terms of how these tiny balls <u>move</u>, and the <u>forces</u> between them.

2) <u>Three states of matter</u> are <u>solid</u> (e.g. ice), <u>liquid</u> (e.g. water) and <u>gas</u> (e.g. water vapour). The <u>particles</u> of a substance in each state are <u>the same</u> — only the <u>arrangement</u> and <u>energy</u> of the particles are <u>different</u>. If you <u>reverse</u> a change of state, the particles <u>go back</u> to how they were before.

3) So changes of state are <u>physical changes</u> (only the <u>form</u> of a substance changes). These are <u>different</u> from <u>chemical reactions</u>, where <u>new substances</u> are created by the reaction.

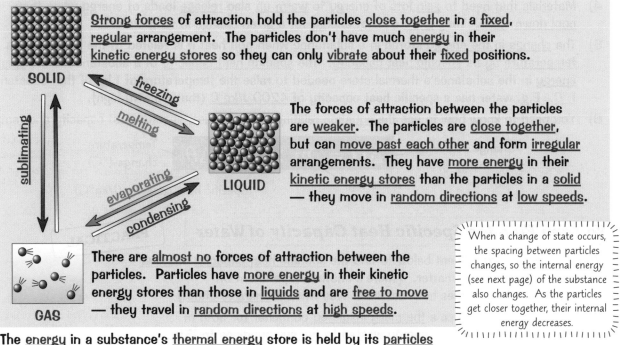

<u>Strong forces</u> of attraction hold the particles <u>close together</u> in a <u>fixed</u>, <u>regular</u> arrangement. The particles don't have much <u>energy</u> in their <u>kinetic energy stores</u> so they can only <u>vibrate</u> about their <u>fixed</u> positions.

**SOLID**

*freezing*

*melting*

*sublimating*

*evaporating*

*condensing*

**LIQUID**

The forces of attraction between the particles are <u>weaker</u>. The particles are <u>close together</u>, but can <u>move past each other</u> and form <u>irregular</u> arrangements. They have <u>more energy</u> in their <u>kinetic energy stores</u> than the particles in a <u>solid</u> — they move in <u>random directions</u> at <u>low speeds</u>.

**GAS**

There are <u>almost no</u> forces of attraction between the particles. Particles have <u>more energy</u> in their kinetic energy stores than those in <u>liquids</u> and are <u>free to move</u> — they travel in <u>random directions</u> at <u>high speeds</u>.

> When a change of state occurs, the spacing between particles changes, so the internal energy (see next page) of the substance also changes. As the particles get closer together, their internal energy decreases.

4) The <u>energy</u> in a substance's <u>thermal energy</u> store is held by its <u>particles</u> in their <u>kinetic energy</u> stores — this is what the thermal energy store actually is.

5) When you <u>heat</u> a liquid, the <u>extra energy</u> is transferred into the particles' <u>kinetic energy stores</u>, making them <u>move faster</u>. Eventually, when enough of the particles have enough energy to overcome their attraction to each other, big bubbles of <u>gas</u> form in the liquid — this is <u>boiling</u>.

6) It's similar when you heat a <u>solid</u>. The extra energy makes the <u>particles vibrate faster</u> until eventually the forces between them are <u>partly overcome</u> and the particles start to move around — this is <u>melting</u>.

## *Density of a Substance Varies with State but Mass Doesn't*

1) Provided you're working with a <u>closed system</u> (i.e. no particles can escape, and no new particles can get in) the <u>mass</u> of a substance <u>isn't affected</u> when it changes <u>state</u>. This makes sense — the <u>mass of a substance</u> is the <u>mass of its particles</u>, and the particles aren't changing, they're just being rearranged.

2) However, when a substance changes state its <u>volume does change</u>. The particles in most substances are <u>closer together</u> when they're a <u>solid</u> than a <u>liquid</u> (ice and water are an exception), and are closer together when they're a <u>liquid</u> than a <u>gas</u> (see the diagrams above).

3) Since <u>density = mass ÷ volume</u> (p.200), then density must change too. Generally, substances are <u>most dense</u> when they're <u>solids</u> and <u>least dense</u> when they're <u>gases</u>.

---

## *Physics — it's really about state of mind...*

Remember, the mass of a substance just comes from the particles, not the spaces between them. So as something expands or contracts, its volume changes but its mass stays the same.

Q1    Explain how the density of a typical substance changes as it changes from solid to liquid to gas.  [3 marks]

# Specific Heat Capacity

The temperature of something isn't quite the same thing as the energy stored in the substance's thermal energy store. That's where specific heat capacity comes in...

## Specific Heat Capacity Relates Temperature and Energy

1) Heating a substance increases the energy in its thermal energy store (or the kinetic energy stores of its particles, see p.156). You may sometimes see this referred to as the internal energy of a substance.

> Internal energy is actually the sum of the energy in the kinetic and potential stores of the particles. You can usually ignore energy in potential stores though.

2) So in kinetic theory, temperature is a way of measuring the average internal energy of a substance.

3) However, it takes more energy to increase the temperature of some materials than others. E.g. you need 4200 J to warm 1 kg of water by 1 °C, but only 139 J to warm 1 kg of mercury by 1 °C.

4) Materials that need to gain lots of energy to warm up also release loads of energy when they cool down again. They store a lot of energy for a given change in temperature.

5) The change in the energy stored in a substance when you heat it is related to the change in its temperature by its specific heat capacity. The specific heat capacity of a substance is the change in energy in the substance's thermal store needed to raise the temperature of 1 kg of that substance by 1 °C. E.g. water has a specific heat capacity of 4200 J/kg°C (that's pretty high).

6) You need to know how to use the equation relating energy, mass, specific heat capacity and temperature.

Change in thermal energy (J) —— $$\Delta Q = m \times c \times \Delta \theta$$ —— Temperature change (°C)

Mass (kg) —— Specific heat capacity (J/kg°C)

> $\Delta$ just means 'change in'.

## You can Find the Specific Heat Capacity of Water

**PRACTICAL**

You can use the experiment below to find the specific heat capacity of water — or any liquid for that matter. (There's another experiment on page 203 that investigates how water behaves when it changes state.)

If you can, you should use a thermally insulated container for both of these experiments to reduce energy wasted to the surroundings (p.159).

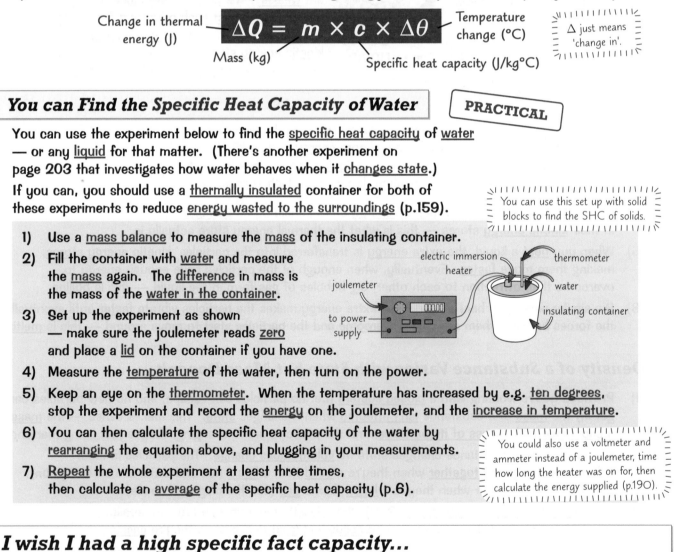

> You can use this set up with solid blocks to find the SHC of solids.

1) Use a mass balance to measure the mass of the insulating container.

2) Fill the container with water and measure the mass again. The difference in mass is the mass of the water in the container.

3) Set up the experiment as shown — make sure the joulemeter reads zero and place a lid on the container if you have one.

joulemeter — to power supply — electric immersion heater — thermometer — water — insulating container

4) Measure the temperature of the water, then turn on the power.

5) Keep an eye on the thermometer. When the temperature has increased by e.g. ten degrees, stop the experiment and record the energy on the joulemeter, and the increase in temperature.

6) You can then calculate the specific heat capacity of the water by rearranging the equation above, and plugging in your measurements.

> You could also use a voltmeter and ammeter instead of a joulemeter, time how long the heater was on for, then calculate the energy supplied (p.190).

7) Repeat the whole experiment at least three times, then calculate an average of the specific heat capacity (p.6).

---

## I wish I had a high specific fact capacity...

Make sure you practise using that equation — it's a bit of a tricky one.

Q1 If a metal has a specific heat capacity of 420 J/kg°C, calculate how much the temperature of a 0.20 kg block of the metal will increase by if 1680 J of energy are supplied to it. [2 marks]

Q2 Describe an experiment you could do to find the specific heat capacity of water. [4 marks]

# Specific Latent Heat

If you heat up a pan of water on the stove, the water never gets any hotter than 100 °C. You can <u>carry on heating it up</u>, but the <u>temperature won't rise</u>. How come, you say? It's all to do with <u>latent heat</u>...

## You Need to Put In Energy to Break Intermolecular Bonds

1) Remember, when you <u>heat</u> a solid or liquid, you're transferring <u>energy</u> to the kinetic energy stores of the particles in the substance, making the particles <u>vibrate</u> or <u>move faster</u> (p.156).

2) When a substance is <u>melting</u> or <u>boiling</u>, you're still putting in <u>energy</u>, but the energy's used for <u>breaking intermolecular bonds</u> rather than raising the temperature.

3) When a substance is <u>condensing</u> or <u>freezing</u>, bonds are <u>forming</u> between particles, which <u>releases</u> energy. This means the <u>temperature doesn't go down</u> until all the substance has turned into a liquid (condensing) or a solid (freezing).

4) You can see this by doing this simple <u>experiment</u>:

**PRACTICAL**

1) Fill a <u>beaker</u> with <u>crushed ice</u>.
2) Place a <u>thermometer</u> into the beaker and record the <u>temperature</u> of the ice.
3) Using the Bunsen burner, <u>gradually heat</u> the beaker full of ice.
4) Every twenty seconds, record the <u>temperature</u> and the <u>current state</u> of the ice (e.g. partially melted, completely melted).
5) Continue this process until the water begins to <u>boil</u>.
6) Plot a graph of <u>temperature against time</u> for your experiment.

thermometer
beaker
ice
stand
Bunsen burner

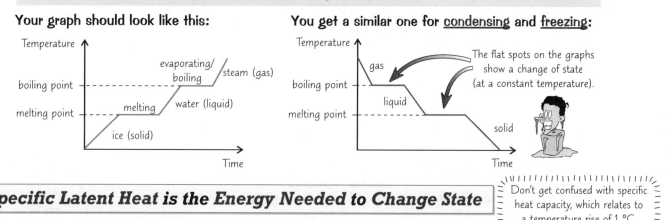

Your graph should look like this:

You get a similar one for <u>condensing</u> and <u>freezing</u>:

The flat spots on the graphs show a change of state (at a constant temperature).

## Specific Latent Heat is the Energy Needed to Change State

*Don't get confused with specific heat capacity, which relates to a temperature rise of 1 °C.*

1) The <u>specific latent heat</u> (SLH) of a <u>change of state</u> of a substance is the <u>amount of energy</u> needed to <u>change 1 kg</u> of it from <u>one state to another without changing its temperature</u>.

2) For <u>cooling</u>, specific latent heat is the energy <u>released</u> by a change in state.

3) Specific latent heat is <u>different</u> for <u>different materials</u>, and for changing between <u>different states</u>.

4) The specific latent heat for changing between a <u>solid</u> and a <u>liquid</u> (<u>melting</u> or <u>freezing</u>) is called the <u>specific latent heat of fusion</u>. The specific latent heat for changing between a <u>liquid</u> and a <u>gas</u> (<u>evaporating</u>, <u>boiling</u> or <u>condensing</u>) is called the <u>specific latent heat of vaporisation</u>.

5) You can work out the <u>energy needed</u> (or <u>released</u>) when a substance of mass $m$ changes state using this <u>formula</u>:

Thermal Energy ($Q$) = Mass ($m$) × Specific Latent Heat ($L$)

Thermal energy is given in <u>joules</u> (J), mass is in <u>kg</u> and SLH is in <u>J/kg</u>.

## Breaking Bonds — Blofeld never quite manages it...

Fun fact: this stuff explains how sweating cools you down — the energy that builds up in your body when you exercise is used to change liquid sweat into gas, rather than increasing your temperature. Nice...

Q1 Sketch a graph showing how the temperature of a sample of water will change over time as it's heated from −5 °C to 105 °C.

[3 marks]

# Particle Motion in Gases

Gas particles fly around, bump into things and exert forces on them. This is happening to you right now
— the air around you is exerting pressure on you (unless you're somehow reading this in space).

## Colliding Gas Particles Create Pressure

1) According to kinetic theory, all matter is made up of very small, constantly moving particles.

2) In a gas, these particles are free to move around in completely random directions.
Particles in a gas hardly take up any space. Most of the gas is empty space.

3) As gas particles move about, they randomly bang into each other and
whatever else gets in the way, like the walls of their container.

4) Gas particles are very small, but they still have a mass.
When they collide with something, they exert a force on it.

5) All these collisions cause a net force acting outwards on the inside surface
of the container. The force acting per unit area is the pressure.

6) The more particles there are in a given volume, the more often they'll
collide with the walls of the container, and with each other, so the higher the pressure will be.

## Increasing the Temperature Increases the Pressure

1) The pressure a gas exerts on its container also depends on how
fast the particles are going and how often they hit the walls.

2) If you hold a gas in a sealed container with a fixed mass and volume and heat it, energy
is transferred to the kinetic energy stores of the gas particles and they move faster.
This means the particles hit the container walls harder and more often, creating more pressure.

3) If the gas is cooled, the particles have less energy and move less quickly.
The particles hit the walls with less force and less often, so the pressure is reduced.

> A sealed container is an
> example of a closed system —
> no matter can get in or out.

## Absolute Zero is as Cold as Stuff Can Get — 0 kelvin

1) If you increase the temperature of something, you give its particles more
energy — they move about more quickly or vibrate more. In the same way,
if you cool a substance down, you're reducing the energy of the particles.

2) In theory, the coldest that anything can ever get is -273 °C — this temperature
is known as absolute zero. At absolute zero, the particles have as little energy
in their kinetic stores as it's possible to get — they're pretty much still.

3) Absolute zero is the start of the Kelvin scale of temperature.

4) A temperature change of 1 °C is also a change of 1 kelvin. The two scales
are pretty similar — the only difference is where the zero occurs.

5) To convert from degrees Celsius to kelvins, just add 273.
And to convert from kelvins to degrees Celsius, just subtract 273.

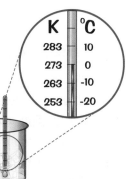

|  | Absolute zero | Freezing point of water | Boiling point of water |
|---|---|---|---|
| Celsius scale | −273 °C | 0 °C | 100 °C |
| Kelvin scale | 0 K | 273 K | 373 K |

> There's no degree
> symbol when you write
> a temperature in kelvins.
> Just write K, not °K. OK.

## Gas particles need to watch where they're going...

Remember, the more gas particles there are, and the faster they travel, the higher the pressure. Simple...

Q1     Find the value of 25 °C in kelvin.                                                    [1 mark]

Q2     Explain how a gas exerts pressure on its container.                                    [2 marks]

# Forces and Elasticity

And now for something a bit more fun — <u>squishing</u>, <u>stretching</u> and <u>bending</u> stuff.

## Stretching, Compressing or Bending Transfers Energy

1) When you apply a force to an object you may cause it to <u>stretch</u>, <u>compress</u> or <u>bend</u>.

2) To do this, you need <u>more than one</u> force acting on the object (otherwise the object would simply <u>move</u> in the direction of the <u>applied force</u>, instead of changing shape).

3) An object has been <u>elastically distorted</u> if it can <u>go back</u> to its <u>original shape</u> and <u>length</u> after the force has been removed.

4) Objects that can be elastically distorted are called <u>elastic objects</u> (e.g. a spring).

5) An object has been <u>inelastically distorted</u> if it <u>doesn't</u> return to its <u>original shape</u> and <u>length</u> after the force has been removed.

6) The <u>elastic limit</u> is the point where an object <u>stops</u> distorting <u>elastically</u> and <u>begins</u> to distort <u>inelastically</u>.

7) <u>Work is done</u> when a force stretches or compresses an object and causes energy to be transferred to the <u>elastic potential energy</u> store of the object. If it is <u>elastically distorted</u>, <u>ALL</u> this energy is transferred to the object's <u>elastic potential energy store</u> (see p.206).

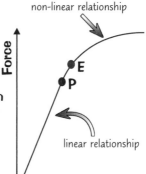

Elastic objects — useful for passing exams and scaring small children

## Extension is Directly Proportional to Force...

If a spring is supported at the top and then a weight is attached to the bottom, it <u>stretches</u>.

1) The <u>extension</u> of a stretched spring (or other elastic object) is <u>directly</u> <u>proportional</u> to the load or <u>force</u> applied — so $F \propto x$.

2) This means that there is a <u>linear</u> relationship between force and extension. (If you plotted a <u>force-extension</u> graph for the spring, it would be a <u>straight line</u>.)

3) This is the equation:

$$F = k \times x$$

where $F$ is the applied force in N, $k$ is the spring constant in N/m and $x$ is the extension in m.

4) The <u>spring constant</u> depends on the <u>material</u> that you are stretching — a <u>stiffer</u> spring has a <u>greater</u> spring constant.

5) The equation also works for <u>compression</u> (where $x$ is just the <u>difference</u> between the <u>natural</u> and <u>compressed</u> lengths — the <u>compression</u>).

*For a linear relationship, the gradient of an object's force-extension graph is equal to its spring constant.*

## ...but this Stops Working when the Force is Great Enough

There's a <u>limit</u> to the amount of force you can apply to an object for the extension to keep on increasing <u>proportionally</u>.

1) The graph shows <u>force against extension</u> for an elastic object.

2) There is a <u>maximum</u> force above which the graph <u>curves</u>, showing that extension is <u>no longer</u> proportional to force. The relationship is now <u>non-linear</u> — the object <u>stretches more</u> for each unit increase in force. This point is known as the <u>limit of proportionality</u> and is shown on the graph at the point marked **P**.

3) The <u>elastic limit</u> (see above) is marked as **E**. Past this point, the object is <u>permanently stretched</u>.

non-linear relationship

Force

E
P

linear relationship

Extension

---

## I could make a joke, but I don't want to stretch myself...

That equation is pretty simple, but that doesn't mean you can skip over it. Have a go at the question below.

Q1    A spring is fixed at one end and a force of 1 N is applied to the other end, causing it to stretch. The spring extends by 2 cm. Calculate the spring constant of the spring.    [2 marks]

# Investigating Elasticity

You can do an easy experiment to see exactly how adding masses to a spring causes it to stretch.

## You Can Investigate the Link Between Force and Extension | PRACTICAL

Set up the apparatus as shown in the diagram. Make sure you have plenty of extra masses, then measure the mass of each (with a mass balance) and calculate its weight (the force applied) using $W = mg$ (p.150).

You could do a quick pilot experiment first to find out what size masses to use.

- Using an identical spring to the one you will be testing, load it with masses one at a time and record the force (weight) and extension each time.
- Plot a force-extension graph and check that you get a nice straight line for at least the first 6 points. If it curves too early, you need to use smaller masses.

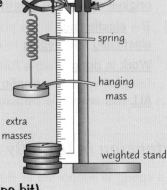

1) Measure the natural length of the spring (when no load is applied) with a millimetre ruler clamped to the stand. Make sure you take the reading at eye level and add markers (e.g. thin strips of tape) to the top and bottom of the spring to make the reading more accurate.

2) Add a mass to the spring and allow the spring to come to rest. Record the mass and measure the new length of the spring. The extension is the change in length.

3) Repeat this process until you have enough measurements (no fewer than 6).

4) Plot a force-extension graph of your results. It will only start to curve if you exceed the limit of proportionality, but don't worry if yours doesn't (as long as you've got the straight line bit).

You should find that a larger force causes a bigger extension. You can also think of this as more work needing to be done to cause a larger extension. The force doing work is the gravitational force and for elastic distortions, this force is equal to $F = kx$.

You can find the work done for a particular forces (or energy stored — see below) by calculating the area under the linear section of your force-extension graph up to that value of force.

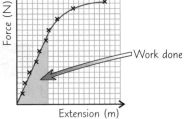

## You Can Calculate Work Done for Linear Relationships

1) Look at the graph on the previous page. The elastic limit is always at or beyond the limit of proportionality. This means that for a linear relationship, the distortion is always elastic — all the energy being transferred is stored in the spring's elastic potential energy store.

2) So, as long as a spring is not stretched past its limit of proportionality, work done to the spring is equal to the energy stored in its elastic potential energy store.

3) For a linear relationship, the energy in the elastic potential energy store (and so the work done) can be found using:

Energy transferred in stretching (J) — $$E = \tfrac{1}{2} \times k \times x^2$$

Spring constant (N/m)

Extension$^2$ (m$^2$)

## Time to spring into action and learn all this...

Remember that you can only use the gradient to find the spring constant if the graph is linear (a straight line).

Q1     A spring with a spring constant of 40 N/m extends elastically by 2.5 cm. Calculate the amount of energy stored in its elastic potential energy store.     [2 marks]

# Revision Questions for Sections 22 and 23

And you've reached the end of <u>Section 23</u>, woohoo — time to give your old grey matter a work out.

- Try these questions and <u>tick off each one</u> when you <u>get it right</u>.
- When you've done <u>all the questions</u> for a topic and are <u>completely happy</u> with it, tick off the topic.

## <u>Magnetism (p.195-196)</u> ☑

1) What is a magnetic field? In which direction do magnetic field lines point?
2) Sketch the field lines around a bar magnet.
3) Explain the behaviour of a plotting compass that is far away from a magnet.
4) Give three examples of magnetic materials.
5) What is the difference between a permanent magnet and an induced magnet?

## <u>Electromagnetism and the Motor Effect (p.197)</u> ☑

6) Describe the magnetic field around a current-carrying wire.
7) Explain why a current-carrying conductor in a magnetic field experiences a force.
8) What is Fleming's left-hand rule?
9) Name two ways you could decrease the force on a current-carrying wire in a magnetic field.

## <u>Solenoids, Electromagnetic Induction and Transformers (p.198-199)</u> ☑

10) Explain the shape and strength of the magnetic field inside and outside a solenoid.
11) Give two ways you could reverse the direction of an induced current.
12) True or false? Induced currents create magnetic fields that oppose the change that made them.
13) What kind of current are transformers used with?
14) True or false? Step-down transformers have more coils on their primary coil than on their secondary.
15) Explain how transformers are used to improve efficiency when transmitting electricity.

## <u>Density and the Kinetic Theory of Matter (p.200-203)</u> ☑

16) What is the formula for density? What are the units of density?
17) For each state of matter, describe the arrangement of the particles.
18) Is a change of state a physical change or a chemical change?
19) True or false? Mass stays the same when a substance changes state.
20) Define specific heat capacity.
21) Define specific latent heat. Give a formula for specific latent heat.

## <u>Particle Motion (p.204)</u> ☑

22) Define gas pressure for a sealed container.
23) What happens to the pressure of a gas in a sealed container of fixed volume when it is heated? Explain why this happens.
24) What is absolute zero? What value does it have in kelvin?

## <u>Stretching, Compressing and Bending (p.205-206)</u> ☑

25) Explain why you need more than one force acting on an object to cause it to stretch.
26) How do you find the spring constant from a linear force-extension graph?
27) What is the limit of proportionality?
28) Give the equation used to find the energy transferred in stretching an object.

# Apparatus and Techniques

Safety specs out, lab coats on — it's time to find out about the skills you'll need in <u>experiments</u>. Finally time to look like a real scientist... hurrah! But you also need to know about this stuff in your exams... boooo...

## Solids Should Be Measured Using a Balance

1) To weigh a solid, start by putting the <u>container</u> you're weighing your substance <u>into</u> on the <u>balance</u>.

2) Set the balance to exactly <u>zero</u> and then start weighing out your substance.

3) It's <u>no good</u> carefully weighing out your solid if it's not all transferred to your reaction vessel — the amount in the <u>reaction vessel</u> won't be the same as your measurement. Here's a couple of methods you can use to make sure that none gets left in your weighing container...

> - If you're <u>dissolving</u> the solid in a solvent to make a <u>solution</u>, you could <u>wash</u> any remaining solid into the new container using the <u>solvent</u>. This way you know that <u>all</u> the solid you weighed has been transferred.
>
> - You could <u>reweigh</u> the weighing container <u>after</u> you've transferred the solid. This lets you can work out <u>exactly</u> how much you added to your experiment.

*You can also weigh the mass of liquids with balances.*

## Three Ways to Measure Liquids

There are a few methods you might use to measure the volume of a liquid. Whichever method you use, always read the volume from the <u>bottom of the meniscus</u> (the curved upper surface of the liquid) when it's at <u>eye level</u>.

Read volume from here — the bottom of the meniscus.

pipette filler

> <u>Pipettes</u> are long, narrow tubes that are used to suck up an <u>accurate</u> volume of liquid and <u>transfer</u> it to another container. A <u>pipette filler</u> attached to the end of the pipette is used so that you can <u>safely control</u> the amount of liquid you're drawing up. Pipettes are often <u>calibrated</u> to allow for the fact that the last drop of liquid stays in the pipette when the liquid is ejected. This reduces <u>transfer errors</u>.

> <u>Burettes</u> measure from top to bottom (so when they're filled to the top of the scale, the scale reads zero). They have a tap at the bottom which you can use to release the liquid into another container (you can even release it drop by drop). To use a burette, take an <u>initial reading</u>, and once you've released as much liquid as you want, take a <u>final reading</u>. The <u>difference</u> between the readings tells you <u>how much</u> liquid you used.

*If you only want a couple of drops of liquid, and don't need it to be accurately measured, you can use a dropping pipette to transfer it.*

> <u>Measuring cylinders</u> are the most common way to measure out a liquid. They come in all different <u>sizes</u>. Make sure you choose one that's the right size for the measurement you want to make. It's no good using a huge 1000 cm³ cylinder to measure out 2 cm³ of a liquid — the graduations will be too big, and you'll end up with <u>massive errors</u>. It'd be much better to use one that measures up to 10 cm³.

## Gas Syringes Measure Gas Volumes

Gases can be measured with a gas syringe. They should be measured at <u>room temperature and pressure</u> as the <u>volume</u> of a gas <u>changes</u> with temperature and pressure. You should also use a gas syringe that's the <u>right size</u> for the measurement you're making. Before you use the syringe, you should make sure it's <u>completely sealed</u> (so that no gas can escape, making any results inaccurate) and that the plunger moves smoothly.

*You could also count the bubbles of gas released. But the bubbles released could be different sizes and if they're produced quickly you might miss some. So this method is less accurate.*

1) There are times when you might want to <u>collect</u> the gas produced by a reaction. For example, to investigate the <u>rate</u> of reaction.

2) The most accurate way to measure the volume of a gas that's been produced is to collect it in a <u>gas syringe</u> (see page 128).

3) You could also collect it by <u>displacing water</u> from a measuring cylinder.

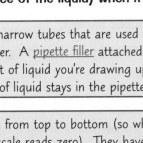

delivery tube

collected gas

gas syringe

reaction mixture

# Apparatus and Techniques

## Measure Temperature and Time Accurately

TEMPERATURE: You can use a <u>thermometer</u> to measure the temperature of a substance:

1) Make sure the <u>bulb</u> of your thermometer is <u>completely submerged</u> in any substance you're measuring.

2) If you're taking an initial reading, you should wait for the temperature to <u>stabilise</u> first.

3) Read your measurement off the <u>scale</u> on a thermometer at <u>eye level</u> to make sure it's correct.

TIME: You should use a <u>stopwatch</u> to <u>time</u> most experiments — they're more <u>accurate</u> than regular watches.

1) Always make sure you <u>start</u> and <u>stop</u> the stopwatch at exactly the right time. Or alternatively, set an <u>alarm</u> on the stopwatch so you know exactly when to stop an experiment or take a reading.

2) In physics, you might be able to use a <u>light gate</u> (p.210). This will <u>reduce errors</u> in your experiment.

## Measure pH to Find Out How Acidic or Alkaline a Solution Is

1) <u>Indicators</u> are dyes that <u>change colour</u> depending on whether they're in an <u>acid</u> or an <u>alkali</u>. You use them by adding a couple of drops of the indicator to the solution you're interested in. <u>Universal indicator</u> is a <u>mixture</u> of indicators that changes colour <u>gradually</u> as pH changes. It's useful for <u>estimating</u> the pH of a solution based on its colour.

2) <u>Indicator paper</u> is useful if you don't want to colour the entire solution that you're testing. It <u>changes colour</u> depending on the pH of the solution it touches. You can also hold a piece of <u>damp indicator paper</u> in a <u>gas sample</u> to test its pH.

Blue litmus paper turns <u>red</u> in acidic conditions and red litmus paper turns <u>blue</u> in alkaline conditions.

3) <u>pH probes</u> are attached to pH meters which have a <u>digital display</u> that gives a <u>numerical</u> value for the pH of a solution. They're used to give an <u>accurate value</u> of pH. (See p.105 for more on pH.)

## Measure Most Lengths with a Ruler

1) In most cases, a <u>centimetre ruler</u> can be used to measure <u>length</u>. It depends on what you're measuring though — <u>metre rulers</u> or <u>long measuring tapes</u> are good for <u>large</u> distances, and <u>micrometers</u> are used for measuring tiny things, like the <u>diameter of a wire</u>.

Length can be measured in different units (e.g. mm, cm, m). Smaller units have a higher degree of accuracy.

2) The ruler should always be <u>parallel to</u> what you want to measure.

3) If you're dealing with something where it's <u>tricky</u> to measure just <u>one</u> accurately (e.g. water ripples, p.165), you can measure the length of <u>ten</u> of them and then <u>divide</u> to find the <u>length of one</u>.

4) If you're taking <u>multiple measurements</u> of the <u>same</u> object (e.g. to measure changes in length) then make sure you always measure from the <u>same point</u> on the object. It can help to put a <u>marker</u> or <u>pointer</u> onto the object to line up your ruler against.

5) Make sure the ruler and the object are always at <u>eye level</u> when you take a reading.

Sometimes you'll need to calculate the area of something. If you need to, here's how:

1) First, you'll need to take <u>accurate measurements</u> of its dimensions (see above for measuring lengths).

2) Then you can <u>calculate</u> its <u>area</u>.

Area of a <u>rectangle</u> = <u>length</u> × <u>width</u>. So, if you're measuring the area of a field that's 30 m by 55 m, the <u>area</u> would be 30 × 55 = <u>1650 m²</u>.

Here are some examples of other area formulas that may come in useful:
Area of a triangle = ½ × base × height
Area of a circle = πr²

## Use a Protractor to Find Angles

1) First align the <u>vertex</u> (point) of the angle with the mark in the <u>centre</u> of the protractor.

2) Line up the <u>base line</u> of the protractor with one line that forms the <u>angle</u> and then measure the angle of the other line using the scale on the <u>protractor</u>.

3) If the lines creating the angle are very <u>thick</u>, align the protractor and measure the angle from the <u>centre</u> of the lines. Using a <u>sharp pencil</u> to trace light rays or draw diagrams helps to <u>reduce errors</u> when measuring angles.

4) If the lines are <u>too short</u> to measure easily, you may have to <u>extend</u> them.

Practical Skills

# Apparatus and Techniques

## *There Are a Couple of Ways to Measure Potential Difference and Current*

### Voltmeters Measure Potential Difference

1) If you're using an analogue voltmeter, choose the voltmeter with the most appropriate unit (e.g. V or mV). If you're using a digital voltmeter, you'll most likely be able to switch between them.

2) Connect the voltmeter in parallel (p.188) across the component you want to test. The wires that come with a voltmeter are usually red (positive) and black (negative). These go into the red and black coloured ports on the voltmeter.

3) Then simply read the potential difference from the scale (or from the screen if it's digital).

### Ammeters Measure Current

1) Just like with voltmeters, choose the ammeter with the most appropriate unit.

2) Connect the ammeter in series (p.188) with the component you want to test, making sure they're both on the same branch. Again, they usually have red and black ports to show you where to connect your wires.

3) Read off the current shown on the scale or by the screen.

### Multimeters Measure Both

1) Instead of having a separate ammeter and voltmeter, many circuits use multimeters.

2) These are devices that measure a range of properties — usually potential difference, current and resistance.

3) If you want to find potential difference, make sure the red wire is plugged into the port that has a 'V' (for volts).

4) To find the current, use the port labelled 'A' or 'mA' (for amps).

5) The dial on the multimeter should then be turned to the relevant section, e.g. to 'A' to measure current in amps. The screen will display the value you're measuring.

## *Light Gates Measure Velocity and Acceleration*

1) A light gate sends a beam of light from one side of the gate to a detector on the other side. When something passes through the gate, the beam of light is interrupted. The light gate then measures how long the beam was undetected.

2) To find the velocity of an object, connect the light gate to a computer. Measure the length of the object and input this using the software. It will then automatically calculate the velocity of the object as it passes through the beam.

3) To measure acceleration, use an object that interrupts the signal twice in a short period of time, e.g. a piece of card with a gap cut into the middle.

4) The light gate measures the velocity for each section of the object and uses this to calculate its acceleration. This can then be read from the computer screen.

Light gate

Beam of light

Card interrupts the beam

Have a look at page 151 for an example of a light gate being used.

## *I set up my apparatus — they had a blind date at the cinema...*

That's three pages filled high with apparatus and techniques that you need to know for your exams and for your practicals too. In the exam, you might be asked to comment on how an experiment's been set up. So get learning.

# Heating Substances

Heating a reaction isn't as simple as wrapping it up in a lumpy wool jumper and a stripy scarf...

## Bunsen Burners Have a Naked Flame

Bunsen burners are good for heating things quickly.  You can easily adjust how strongly they're heating.  But you need to be careful not to use them if you're heating flammable compounds as the flame means the substance would be at risk of catching fire.

### Here's how to use a Bunsen burner...

- Connect the Bunsen burner to a gas tap, and check that the hole is closed.  Place it on a heat-proof mat.
- Light a splint and hold it over the Bunsen burner.  Now, turn on the gas.  The Bunsen burner should light with a yellow flame.
- The more open the hole is, the more strongly the Bunsen burner will heat your substance.  Open the hole to the amount you want.  As you open the hole more, the flame should turn more blue.
- The hottest part of the flame is just above the blue cone, so you should heat things here.
- If your Bunsen burner is alight but not heating anything, make sure you close the hole so that the flame becomes yellow and clearly visible.
- If you're heating something so that the container (e.g. a test tube) is in the flame, you should hold the vessel at the top, furthest away from the substance (and so the flame) using a pair of tongs.
- If you're heating something over the flame (e.g. an evaporating dish), you should put a tripod and gauze over the Bunsen burner before you light it, and place the vessel on this.

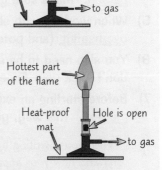

## The Temperature of Water Baths & Electric Heaters Can Be Set

1) A water bath is a container filled with water that can be heated to a specific temperature.  A simple water bath can be made by heating a beaker of water over a Bunsen burner and monitoring the temperature with a thermometer.  However, it can be hard to keep the temperature of the water constant.

2) An electric water bath will monitor and adjust the temperature for you.  It's a much easier way of keeping the temperature of a reaction mixture constant.  Here's how you use one:

- Set the temperature on the water bath, and allow the water to heat up.
- Place the vessel containing your substance in the water bath using test tube holders or tongs.  The level of the water outside the vessel should be just above the level of the substance inside the vessel.
- The substance will then be warmed to the same temperature as the water.  As the substance in the vessel is surrounded by water, the heating is very even.
- Water boils at 100 °C, so you can't use a water bath to heat something to a higher temperature than this — the water won't get hot enough.

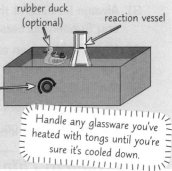

Handle any glassware you've heated with tongs until you're sure it's cooled down.

3) Electric heaters are often made up of a metal plate that can be heated to a certain temperature.  The vessel containing the substance you want to heat is placed on top of the hot plate.  You can heat substances to higher temperatures than you can in a water bath but, as the vessel is only heated from below, you'll usually have to stir the substance inside to make sure it's heated evenly.

## A bath and an electric heater — how I spend my January nights...

You know, I used to have a teacher who'd play power ballads when the Bunsen burners were alight and sway at the front of the class like he was at a gig.  You might think that I just made that up...  But it's true...

# Safety and Experiments

Labs are <u>dangerous places</u>, so here's a page on things you can do to keep yourself and others <u>safe</u>.

## Be Careful When You Do Experiments

1) There are always hazards in any experiment, so <u>before</u> you start an experiment you should read and follow any <u>safety precautions</u> to do with your method or the apparatus you're using.

2) Stop masses and equipment falling by using <u>clamp stands</u>. Make sure masses are of a <u>sensible weight</u> so they don't break the equipment they're used with, and use <u>pulleys</u> of a sensible <u>length</u>.

3) When <u>heating</u> materials, make sure to let them <u>cool</u> before moving them, or wear <u>insulated gloves</u> while handling them. If you're using an <u>immersion heater</u> to heat liquids, you should always let it <u>dry out</u> in air, just in case any liquid has leaked inside the heater.

4) If you're using a <u>laser</u>, there are a few safety rules you must follow. Always wear <u>laser safety goggles</u> and never <u>look directly into</u> the laser or shine it <u>towards another person</u>. Make sure you turn the laser <u>off</u> if it's not needed to avoid any accidents.

5) When working with electronics, make sure you use a <u>low</u> enough <u>voltage</u> and <u>current</u> to prevent wires <u>overheating</u> (and potentially melting) and avoid <u>damage to components</u>, like blowing a filament bulb.

6) You also need to be aware of <u>general safety</u> in the lab — handle <u>glassware</u> carefully so it doesn't <u>break</u>, don't stick your fingers in sockets and avoid touching frayed wires. That kind of thing.

7) Before starting an experiment, you should write out a <u>detailed risk assessment</u> (see page 77) and <u>method</u>. This way, you can make sure you carry out your experiment accurately and safely.

When you're writing out a <u>method</u> for your experiment, it's always a good idea to draw a <u>labelled diagram</u> showing how your apparatus will be <u>set up</u>. The easiest way to do this is to use a scientific drawing, where each piece of apparatus is drawn as if you're looking at its <u>cross-section</u>. For example:

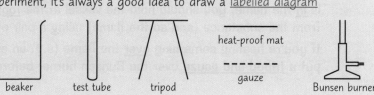

beaker    test tube    tripod    heat-proof mat / gauze    Bunsen burner

## Make Sure you Work Safely Around Hazardous Chemicals

1) The substances used in chemical reactions are often <u>hazardous</u>. For example, they might catch fire easily (they're flammable), or they might irritate or burn your skin if you come into contact with them.

2) Whenever you're doing an experiment, you should wear a <u>lab coat</u>, <u>safety goggles</u> and <u>gloves</u>. Also, make sure that you're wearing <u>sensible clothing</u> when you're in the lab (e.g. open shoes won't protect your feet from spillages).

3) Always be careful that the chemicals you're using aren't flammable before you go lighting any Bunsen burners, and make sure you're working in an area that's <u>well ventilated</u>.

4) If you're doing an experiment that might produce nasty <u>gases</u> (such as chlorine), you should carry out the experiment in a <u>fume hood</u> so that the gas can't escape out into the room you're working in.

5) Never directly touch any chemicals (even if you're wearing gloves). Use a <u>spatula</u> to transfer <u>solids</u> between containers. Carefully <u>pour</u> liquids between different containers, using a <u>funnel</u> to avoid spillages.

6) Be careful when you're <u>mixing</u> chemicals, as a reaction might occur.

## You Need to Think About Ethical Issues In Your Experiments

Any <u>organisms</u> involved in your investigations need to be treated <u>safely</u> and <u>ethically</u>. <u>Animals</u> need to be treated <u>humanely</u> — they should be <u>handled carefully</u> and any wild animals captured for studying should be <u>returned to their original habitat</u>. Any animals kept in the lab should also be <u>cared for</u> in a humane way, e.g. they should not be kept in conditions that are <u>too hot</u>. If you are carrying out an experiment involving other <u>students</u>, they should not be forced to participate <u>against their will</u> or feel <u>pressured</u> to take part.

## Proper lab attire includes golden fur and a waggy tail...

The stuff on this page is all for your own good. It will help you in the exam, and make sure you stay safe in the lab.

# Answers

**p.11 — Cells**

**Q1 a)** Contains genetic material that controls the activities of the cell *[1 mark]*.

**b)** Where most of the reactions for respiration take place *[1 mark]*.

**c)** Involved in translation of genetic material in the synthesis of proteins *[1 mark]*.

**p.12 — Specialised Cells**

**Q1 a)** To transport the male's DNA to the female's egg *[1 mark]*.

**b)** Any two from: they have a long tail *[1 mark]* to allow the sperm cell to swim to the egg cell *[1 mark]*. / They contain lots of mitochondria *[1 mark]* to provide energy for swimming *[1 mark]*. / The acrosome contains enzymes *[1 mark]* that can digest the membrane of the egg cell to deliver the DNA into the egg cell *[1 mark]*. They have a haploid nucleus *[1 mark]* so that when the sperm cell and egg cell combine at fertilisation, the resulting cell has the right number of chromosomes *[1 mark]*.

**p.13 — Microscopy**

**Q1** Select the lowest-powered objective lens *[1 mark]* and move the stage up so the slide is just underneath the objective lens *[1 mark]*. Looking through the lens, move the stage downwards until the specimen is nearly in focus *[1 mark]*. Adjust the height of the stage with the fine adjustment knob until the image is in focus *[1 mark]*.

**p.14 — More Microscopy**

**Q1** real size = image size ÷ magnification
= $7 \times 10^{-1}$ mm (or 0.7 mm) ÷ 400 *[1 mark]*
= 0.00175 mm *[1 mark]*
× 1000 = 1.75 μm *[1 mark]*

**p.15 — Enzymes**

**Q1** If the pH is too high or too low, it can interfere with the bonds holding the enzyme together. This changes the shape of the active site *[1 mark]* and denatures the enzyme *[1 mark]*.

**p.16 — More on Enzymes**

**Q1** 33 ÷ 60 = 0.55 cm$^3$ s$^{-1}$ *[1 mark]*

**p.17 — Enzymes in Breakdown and Synthesis**

**Q1 a)** simple sugars *[1 mark]*

**b)** amino acids *[1 mark]*

**p.18 — Diffusion, Osmosis and Active Transport**

**Q1** E.g. active transport requires energy and diffusion is passive *[1 mark]*. Active transport moves substances against a concentration gradient whereas diffusion is the movement of substances down a concentration gradient *[1 mark]*.

**p.19 — Investigating Osmosis**

**Q1** percentage change = $\frac{11.4 - 13.3}{13.3} \times 100$
= −14.3% *[2 marks for correct answer, 1 mark for correct answer without minus sign]*

**p.20 — Mitosis**

**Q1** The cell grows and increases the amount of subcellular structures it has *[1 mark]*. It also duplicates its DNA *[1 mark]*.

**p.21 — Cell Division and Growth**

**Q1 a)** cell elongation *[1 mark]*

**b)** Cell elongation makes a plant's cells expand so the cells get bigger (and the plant grows) *[1 mark]*.

**p.22 — Stem Cells**

**Q1** The tips of plant shoots contain meristem tissue *[1 mark]*. Meristems produce unspecialised cells that are able to divide and form any cell type in the plant *[1 mark]*. This means the plant is able to produce all the different specialised cells it needs in order to grow into a new plant *[1 mark]*.

**p.23 — The Nervous System**

**Q1** A sensory neurone has one long dendron and one short axon *[1 mark]* with a cell body in the middle *[1 mark]*. The function of a sensory neurone is to carry nerve impulses from receptor cells to the CNS *[1 mark]*.

**p.24 — Synapses and Reflexes**

**Q1** Impulses are sent from receptors in his hand along a sensory neurone to the CNS *[1 mark]*. The impulse is transferred across a synapse to a relay neurone *[1 mark]* via the release of neurotransmitters *[1 mark]*. It is then transferred across another synapse to a motor neurone *[1 mark]* and travels along the motor neurone to the effector (a muscle in his arm) *[1 mark]*.

**p.26 — Sexual Reproduction and Meiosis**

**Q1** 24 chromosomes *[1 mark]*

**Q2** When the cell divides, some of the chromosomes from the organism's father and some of the chromosomes from the organism's mother go into each new cell *[1 mark]*. The mixing up of the chromosomes/genes creates genetic variation *[1 mark]*.

**p.27 — DNA**

**Q1** A and T *[1 mark]*.
C and G *[1 mark]*.

**Q2** The salt helps the DNA to stick together *[1 mark]*.

**p.28 — Genetic Diagrams**

**Q1** Your genotype is the combination of alleles you have *[1 mark]*. Your phenotype is the characteristics you have *[1 mark]*.

**p.29 — More Genetic Diagrams**

**Q1** Ff and ff *[1 mark]*.

**p.30 — Variation**

**Q1** It results in new combinations of alleles in offspring *[1 mark]*.

**p.31 — The Human Genome Project**

**Q1** A person's genes can be used to help predict what diseases they're most at risk of developing *[1 mark]*. This means that they could be given lifestyle and diet advice to help prevent them from getting the diseases *[1 mark]*.

**p.32 — Natural Selection and Evidence for Evolution**

**Q1** Arranging fossils in chronological/date order shows gradual changes/development in organisms *[1 mark]*.

**p.34 — Fossil Evidence for Human Evolution**

**Q1 a)** That they belong to a more recent species, like *Homo neanderthalis* / *Homo sapiens* *[1 mark]*.

**b)** E.g. using stratigraphy. / Using carbon-14 dating to date any carbon-containing material found with the tools. *[1 mark]*

**p.35 — Classification**

**Q1** E.g. genetic analysis showed that Archaea and Bacteria were less closely related than first thought *[1 mark]*.

**p.36 — Selective Breeding**

**Q1** E.g. selective breeding reduces the gene pool *[1 mark]*. This can cause an increased chance of organisms inheriting harmful genetic defects *[1 mark]*. There is also an increased chance that a population could be wiped out by a new disease *[1 mark]*.

**p.37 — Genetic Engineering**

**Q1** It can improve the yield of the crop *[1 mark]*, because herbicide-resistant crops can be sprayed with herbicides to kill weeds without the crop being damaged *[1 mark]*.

**p.39 — Health and Disease**

**Q1** *Vibrio cholerae* is spread via contaminated water sources *[1 mark]*. Its spread can be prevented by ensuring that people have access to clean water supplies *[1 mark]*.

**p.40 — STIs**

**Q1** An STI is a sexually transmitted infection / an infection which is spread via sexual contact *[1 mark]*.

**Q2** Any two from: e.g. wearing a condom when having sex / avoiding sharing needles / taking medication to reduce the risk of passing the virus on *[1 mark for each correct answer, up to 2 marks]*

**p.41 — Fighting Disease**

**Q1** They have cells that produce mucus to trap pathogens *[1 mark]*. They have cells with cilia *[1 mark]*, which waft the mucus up to the back of the throat where it can be swallowed *[1 mark]*.

**Q2** A type of white blood cell that is involved in the specific immune response/produces antibodies *[1 mark]*.

**p.42 — Memory Lymphocytes and Immunisation**

**Q1** Memory lymphocytes are produced in response to a foreign antigen and remain in the body for a long time *[1 mark]*. So when the pathogen enters the body again, there are more cells that recognise it and can produce antibodies against it *[1 mark]*.

**p.43 — Antibiotics and Other Medicines**

**Q1** In a double-blind trial, patients are randomly put into two groups — some receive the drug and some receive a placebo *[1 mark]*. Neither the patient nor the doctor knows whether the patient is getting the drug or a placebo until all of the results have been gathered *[1 mark]*.

**p.44 — Non-Communicable Diseases**

**Q1** E.g. smoking / diet high in saturated fat / drinking too much alcohol / not enough exercise / obesity *[1 mark]*.

**p.45 — Measures of Obesity**

**Q1 a)** Beginning: 76.0 kg ÷ 1.58 m$^2$
= 30.4 kg m$^{-2}$ *[1 mark]*
End: 73.0 kg ÷ 1.58 m$^2$ = 29.2 kg m$^{-2}$ *[1 mark]*

**b)** Before: moderately obese *[1 mark]*
After: overweight *[1 mark]*

**p.46 — Treatments for Cardiovascular Disease**

**Q1** E.g. having heart surgery is a major procedure with a risk of bleeding, blood clots and infection *[1 mark]*. If making lifestyle changes or taking medicines are an option, then these are much less risky *[1 mark]*.

**p.47 — Photosynthesis**

**Q1** Photosynthesis produces glucose *[1 mark]*, which is used to make larger, complex molecules that make up the mass of the plant's living material/the plant's biomass *[1 mark]*.

**Q2** Temperature, light intensity and carbon dioxide concentration *[1 mark for each]*.

**p.48 — Limiting Factors in Photosynthesis**

**Q1** The rate of photosynthesis increases with increasing light intensity/is directly proportional to light intensity *[1 mark]* up to a point at which the rate levels off *[1 mark]*.

**p.49 — Transport in Plants**

**Q1** Water is lost from a plant's leaves by evaporation and diffusion *[1 mark]*. This creates a slight shortage of water in the leaves, so more water is drawn up through the xylem vessels to replace it *[1 mark]*. This in turn means there's more water drawn up from the roots, so there's a constant transpiration stream through the plant *[1 mark]*.

### p.50 — Stomata and Transpiration
**Q1** In low light conditions, the stomata begin to close *[1 mark]*. This means that very little water can escape *[1 mark]*, so the rate of transpiration and therefore the rate of water uptake by the plant decreases *[1 mark]*.

### p.52 — Hormones
**Q1** testes *[1 mark]*

### p.53 — Adrenaline and Thyroxine
**Q1** thyroid gland *[1 mark]*

**Q2** TRH stimulates the pituitary gland to release thyroid stimulating hormone/TSH *[1 mark]*. TSH stimulates the thyroid gland to release thyroxine, so the blood thyroxine level rises *[1 mark]*.

### p.54 — The Menstrual Cycle
**Q1** LH stimulates the release of an egg/ovulation *[1 mark]*. It also stimulates the remains of the follicle to develop into a corpus luteum *[1 mark]*, which secretes progesterone *[1 mark]*.

### p.55 — Controlling Fertility
**Q1** FSH *[1 mark]* and LH *[1 mark]* are given before egg collection to stimulate egg production *[1 mark]*.

### p.56 — Homeostasis — Control of Blood Glucose
**Q1** Insulin *[1 mark]* is secreted by the pancreas into the bloodstream *[1 mark]*. The insulin causes glucose to move into the liver and muscle cells, so the concentration in the blood returns to normal *[1 mark]*.

### p.57 — Diabetes
**Q1** Type 1 diabetes is caused when the pancreas produces little or no insulin *[1 mark]*.

**Q2** E.g. body mass index/BMI *[1 mark]*, waist-to-hip ratio *[1 mark]*.

### p.59 — Exchange of Materials
**Q1** Surface area:
$(1 × 1) × 2 = 2$
$(4 × 1) × 4 = 16$
$2 + 16 = 18$ $\mu m^2$ *[1 mark]*
Volume:
$1 × 1 × 4 = 4$ $\mu m^3$ *[1 mark]*
So the surface area to volume ratio is $18 : 4$, which is $9 : 2$ in its simplest form *[1 mark]*.
(In this question the ratio has been simplified down to the smallest whole numbers. It's not in the form $n : 1$ because then $n$ would not be a whole number.)

### p.60 — Specialised Exchange Surfaces — the Alveoli
**Q1** Any one from: e.g. they have a large surface area. / They have a moist lining for dissolving gases. / They have very thin walls. / They have a good blood supply *[1 mark]*.

### p.61 — Circulatory System — Blood
**Q1** They help the blood to clot at a wound, to stop blood pouring out/microorganisms getting in *[1 mark]*.

**Q2** They have a large surface area for absorbing oxygen *[1 mark]*. They don't have a nucleus, which allows more room for carrying oxygen *[1 mark]*. They contain haemoglobin, which can combine with oxygen in the lungs and release it in body tissues *[1 mark]*.

### p.62 — Circulatory System — Blood Vessels
**Q1** They have a big lumen to help the blood flow despite the low pressure *[1 mark]* and they have valves to keep the blood flowing in the right direction *[1 mark]*.

**Q2** It increases the rate of diffusion of substances across them between the blood and cells *[1 mark]*.

### p.63 — Circulatory System — The Heart
**Q1** stroke volume = cardiac output ÷ heart rate
= 4221 cm³ min⁻¹ ÷ 67 bpm
= 63 cm³ *[2 marks for the correct answer, or 1 mark for the correct calculation]*

### p.64 — Respiration
**Q1** The leg muscles didn't get enough oxygen during the sprint, so began to use anaerobic respiration *[1 mark]*. This resulted in the production of lactic acid *[1 mark]*. The build up of lactic acid in the muscles caused cramp *[1 mark]*.

### p.65 — Investigating Respiration
**Q1 a)** E.g. a test tube with glass beads / boiled/dead beans *[1 mark]*.

**b)** A series of water baths each set to a different temperature *[1 mark]*.

### p.67 — Ecosystems and Interactions Between Organisms
**Q1** Any two from: temperature / amount of water / light intensity / levels of pollutants *[1 mark for each correct answer, up to 2 marks]*

### p.68 — Investigating Ecosystems
**Q1** Quadrats could be placed in a line across the habitat, forming a belt transect *[1 mark]*. Data could then be collected from the quadrats *[1 mark]*. These two steps should be repeated in the same area and a mean should be calculated for each quadrat *[1 mark]*.

### p.69 — Human Impacts on Biodiversity
**Q1** Non-indigenous species may out-compete indigenous species for resources, so that the indigenous species decreases in number or dies out *[1 mark]*. Non-indigenous species can also bring new diseases to a habitat, which can infect and kill the indigenous species *[1 mark]*.

### p.70 — Conservation and Biodiversity
**Q1** Reforestation increases biodiversity in deforested areas *[1 mark]* because it increases the number of tree species in an area *[1 mark]*, which provide food and shelter for animal species *[1 mark]*.

### p.71 — The Carbon Cycle
**Q1** Microorganisms in the carbon cycle are decomposers *[1 mark]*. They break down dead organisms and waste products *[1 mark]* and release $CO_2$ through respiration as they do so *[1 mark]*.

### p.72 — The Water Cycle
**Q1** Energy from the Sun makes water from the sea evaporate, turning it into water vapour *[1 mark]*. The water vapour is carried upwards, as warm air rises *[1 mark]*. When it gets higher up, it cools and condenses to form clouds *[1 mark]*. Water then falls from the clouds as precipitation, usually as rain *[1 mark]*.

### p.73 — The Nitrogen Cycle
**Q1** Decomposers turn proteins in dead leaves into ammonia *[1 mark]*. Then nitrifying bacteria turn the ammonia into nitrites *[1 mark]* and then into nitrates *[1 mark]*.

### p.75 — Chemical Equations
**Q1** $2Fe + 3Cl_2 \rightarrow 2FeCl_3$ *[1 mark]*

**Q2 a)** water → hydrogen + oxygen *[1 mark]*

**b)** $2H_2O \rightarrow 2H_2 + O_2$
*[1 mark for correct reactants and products, 1 mark for a correctly balanced equation]*

### p.76 — Chemical Equations Involving Ions
**Q1** $H^+_{(aq)} + OH^-_{(aq)} \rightarrow H_2O_{(l)}$ *[1 mark]*

### p.77 — Hazards and Risk
**Q1** The student should wear gloves, a lab coat and goggles when handling chemical A / should only use low concentrations of chemical A *[1 mark]*. When handling chemical B, the student should take care to keep it away from naked flames *[1 mark]*.

### p.78 — The History of the Atom
**Q1** During the gold foil experiment, alpha particles were fired at a thin sheet of gold *[1 mark]*. The plum pudding model predicted that the alpha particles would pass straight through the sheet, or only be deflected slightly *[1 mark]*. Though most of the particles did pass straight through, a few were deflected more than expected and a small number were deflected straight back *[1 mark]*. This suggested that most of the atom is made up of empty space, with a positive nucleus in the centre *[1 mark]*.

**Q2** E.g.

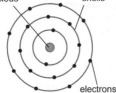

nucleus          shells

electrons

*[1 mark for correct structure, 1 mark for correct labels]*

### p.79 — The Atom
**Q1** electrons = 19 *[1 mark]*, protons = 19 *[1 mark]*, neutrons = 39 − 19 = 20 *[1 mark]*

### p.80 — Isotopes and Relative Atomic Mass
**Q1** $(79 × 51) + (81 × 49) = 7998$ *[1 mark]*
$7998 ÷ 100 = 79.98 = 80$ *[1 mark]*

### p.81 — The Periodic Table
**Q1** Potassium and sodium are both in Group 1. Potassium and calcium are in different groups. So the properties of potassium should be closer to those of sodium than calcium *[1 mark]*, because elements in the same group have similar properties *[1 mark]*.

### p.82 — Electronic Configurations
**Q1** 2.8.3 or

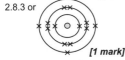

*[1 mark]*

**Q2** Group 2 *[1 mark]*
Period 4 *[1 mark]*

### p.83 — Ions
**Q1** $Li_2O$ *[1 mark]*

### p.84 — Ionic Bonding
**Q1** Each sodium atom loses an electron to form an $Na^+$ ion *[1 mark]*. Each chlorine atom gains an electron to form a $Cl^-$ ion *[1 mark]*. The oppositely charged ions are attracted to each other by electrostatic attraction *[1 mark]*.

**Q2**

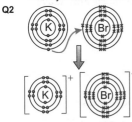

*[1 mark for arrow showing electron transferred from potassium to bromine, 1 mark for both ions having correct electron configurations, 1 mark correct charges on ions]*

### p.85 — Ionic Compounds
**Q1** A lot of energy is needed to break the strong attraction between the ions/the strong ionic bonds *[1 mark]*.

### p.86 — Covalent Bonding
**Q1** The intermolecular forces between molecules of $O_2$ are weak and don't need much energy to break *[1 mark]*. This gives $O_2$ a low boiling point (so it's a gas at room temperature) *[1 mark]*.

**Q2** $N_2$ molecules aren't charged/don't contain any free electrons or ions *[1 mark]*.

### p.87 — Giant Covalent Structures and Fullerenes
**Q1** E.g. graphite can be used as a lubricant because it's soft and slippery / can be used to make electrodes because it conducts electricity *[1 mark for any correct use of graphite, 1 mark for a property of graphite that makes it suitable for the stated use.]*

## p.88 — Metallic Bonding

**Q1** Copper is a good electrical conductor *[1 mark]* as it contains delocalised electrons which are able to carry an electrical current *[1 mark]*.

**Q2** Sample A is likely to be the metal *[1 mark]*. Metals can conduct electricity as a solid as the metallic structure contains delocalised/free electrons that are able to carry a charge *[1 mark]*. Metals are also generally shiny *[1 mark]*.

## p.89 — Conservation of Mass

**Q1** The mass of the container is likely to decrease over the course of the reaction *[1 mark]* as one of the products is a gas *[1 mark]*. Since the container isn't sealed, the gas will be lost from the reaction vessel and so its mass won't be measured *[1 mark]*.

## p.90 — Relative Masses and Chemical Formulas

**Q1** $(2 \times 12) + (5 \times 1) + 16 + 1 = 46$ *[1 mark]*

**Q2** $C_2H_4Cl$ *[1 mark]*

## p.91 — Moles

**Q1** moles = mass ÷ $M_r$
= 90 ÷ 18 = 5.0 moles *[1 mark]*

**Q2** $3.5 \times 6.02 \times 10^{23} = 2.107 \times 10^{24}$ *[1 mark]*

**Q3** moles = mass ÷ $M_r$
= 81.4 ÷ 74 = 1.1 moles *[1 mark]*
$1.1 \times 6.02 \times 10^{23} = 6.622 \times 10^{23}$ *[1 mark]*
In one particle of $Ca(OH)_2$, there are 5 atoms, so in 1.1 moles there are:
$6.622 \times 10^{23} \times 5 = 3.311 \times 10^{24}$ atoms *[1 mark]*

## p.92 — More Calculations

**Q1** mass = moles × $M_r$
= 0.200 × 119 = 23.8 moles *[1 mark]*

**Q2** $M_r$ = mass ÷ moles = 87.0 ÷ 0.500
= 174 *[1 mark]*

**Q3** 200 cm³ = (200 ÷ 1000) dm³ = 0.2 dm³ *[1 mark]*
mass = concentration × volume
= 55 × 0.2 = 11 g *[1 mark]*

## p.93 — Calculating Empirical Formulas

**Q1** mass of oxygen = 45.6 − 13.9 = 31.7 g *[1 mark]*
moles = mass ÷ $M_r$
moles of oxygen = 31.7 ÷ 16 = 1.98125
moles of nitrogen = 13.9 ÷ 14 = 0.99... *[1 mark]*
Divide by the smallest number (0.99...).
oxygen = 1.98125 ÷ 0.99... = 2
nitrogen = 0.99... ÷ 0.99... = 1
Ratio of O : N = 2 : 1.
So empirical formula = $NO_2$ *[1 mark]*

## p.94 — Limiting Reactants

**Q1** $M_r$(KBr) = 39 + 80 = 119
$M_r$($Br_2$) = 80 × 2 = 160 *[1 mark]*
moles of KBr = mass ÷ $M_r$ = 23.8 ÷ 119
= 0.200 moles *[1 mark]*
From the equation, 2 moles of KBr react to produce 1 mole of $Br_2$. So 0.200 moles of KBr will produce (0.200 ÷ 2) = 0.100 moles of $Br_2$ *[1 mark]*.
So mass of $Br_2$ = 0.100 × 160
= 16.0 g *[1 mark]*

## p.95 — Balancing Equations using Masses

**Q1** mass of element Y present
= 52.00 − 17.92 = 34.08 g *[1 mark]*
moles = mass ÷ $M_r$ (or $A_r$)
moles of Fe = 17.92 ÷ 56 = 0.32 moles
moles of product = 52.00 ÷ 162.5 = 0.32 moles *[1 mark]*
moles of $Y_2$ = 34.08 ÷ 71 = 0.48 *[1 mark]*
So ratio of Fe : $Y_2$ : product
= 0.32 : 0.48 : 0.32.
Divide them all by 0.32:
Ratio of Fe : $Y_2$ : product = 1 : 1.5 : 1.
Multiply by 2 to get everything to the nearest whole number:
Ratio of Fe : $Y_2$ : product = 2 : 3 : 2 *[1 mark]*
So balanced equation: 2Fe + 3$Y_2$ → 2(product)
To make the equation balance, the product must contain 1 atom of Fe and 3 atoms of Y.
So the balanced equation is:
2Fe + 3$Y_2$ → 2Fe$Y_3$ *[1 mark]*

## p.97 — States of Matter

**Q1** gas, liquid, solid *[1 mark]*

**Q2** In a gas, there's almost no force of attraction between the particles *[1 mark]*. The particles move constantly with random motion *[1 mark]*, travel in straight lines and only interact when they collide *[1 mark]*.

## p.98 — Changes of State

**Q1** From a gas to a liquid *[1 mark]*.

**Q2** A — gas *[1 mark]*, B — solid *[1 mark]*,
C — liquid *[1 mark]*.

## p.99 — Purity

**Q1** Under the scientific definition, a pure substance is a substance completely made up of a single element or compound *[1 mark]*. Orange juice is not chemically pure, since it is a mixture (of water, sugars and other compounds) *[1 mark]*.

**Q2** No, I do not agree with Glyn. Since the sample he has is a pure chemical, it should have a sharp melting point *[1 mark]*.

## p.100 — Distillation

**Q1** Methanol will be collected in the first fraction *[1 mark]*, because it has the lowest boiling point of the three compounds in the mixture *[1 mark]*.

## p.101 — Filtration and Crystallisation

**Q1** Slowly heat the solution to evaporate off some of the water *[1 mark]*. Stop heating once some of the water has evaporated / once copper sulfate crystals start to form *[1 mark]*. Allow the solution to cool until copper sulfate crystals form *[1 mark]*. Filter the crystals out of the solution and dry them in a warm place / desiccator / drying oven *[1 mark]*.

## p.102 — Chromatography

**Q1** A piece of filter paper *[1 mark]*.

**Q2** Chemical A will end up closer to the solvent front than B *[1 mark]*. A is more soluble in the solvent, so it will spend more time dissolved in the mobile phase, and move further up the paper *[1 mark]*.

## p.103 — Interpreting Chromatograms

**Q1** $R_f$ of Y = distance travelled by Y ÷ distance travelled by solvent front
= 3.6 cm ÷ 6.0 cm *[1 mark]* = 0.60 *[1 mark]*

## p.104 — Water Treatment

**Q1** The water is first filtered through a wire mesh to filter out large objects and through gravel and sand to filter out smaller solid objects *[1 mark]*. Then, a sedimentation process is used. This involves adding aluminium sulfate / iron sulfate to the water, causing fine particles to clump together and settle at the bottom *[1 mark]*. Finally, chlorine gas is bubbled through the water to kill harmful bacteria *[1 mark]*.

**Q2** Tap water could contain other ions that might interfere with the reaction *[1 mark]*. He should use deionised water instead *[1 mark]*.

## p.105 — Acids and Bases

**Q1** acidic *[1 mark]*

## p.106 — Strong and Weak Acids

**Q1** A strong acid ionises/dissociates almost completely in water *[1 mark]*. A weak acid only ionises/dissociates a small amount in water *[1 mark]*.

**Q2** It increased *[1 mark]* by a factor of 1000 *[1 mark]*.

## p.107 — Reactions of Acids

**Q1** 2HCl + $CaCO_3$ → $CaCl_2$ + $H_2O$ + $CO_2$
*[1 mark for correct reactants and products, 1 mark for a correctly balanced equation]*

## p.108 — Making Insoluble Salts

**Q1 a)** soluble *[1 mark]*
**b)** insoluble *[1 mark]*
**c)** insoluble *[1 mark]*
**d)** soluble *[1 mark]*

**Q2** E.g. barium nitrate/barium chloride and copper sulfate *[1 mark for any soluble barium salt and 1 mark for any soluble sulfate]*

## p.109 — Making Soluble Salts

**Q1** E.g. add the base/iron oxide to warmed acid *[1 mark]*. Keep on adding base until all the acid has been neutralised. At this point, no more base will react and it will sink to the bottom of the flask *[1 mark]*. Filter out the excess solid using filter paper *[1 mark]*. Evaporate off some of the water from the salt solution and leave it until salt crystals form *[1 mark]*. Filter off the crystals and leave them to dry *[1 mark]*.

## p.110 — Electrolysis

**Q1** anode *[1 mark]*

## p.111 — Predicting Products of Electrolysis

**Q1** $2Br^- \rightarrow Br_2 + 2e^-$ *[1 mark for correct formulas, 1 mark for balancing]*

## p.112 — Electrolysis of Copper Sulfate

**Q1** The anode is a big lump of impure copper *[1 mark]* and the cathode is a thin piece of pure copper *[1 mark]*. During the electrolysis, the electrical supply pulls electrons off copper atoms at the impure copper anode so they dissolve and form copper ions *[1 mark]*. These copper ions migrate to the cathode where they accept electrons to reform copper atoms, and coat the cathode with a pure layer of copper *[1 mark]*.

## p.114 — The Reactivity Series

**Q1** H / hydrogen *[1 mark]*

**Q2** Calcium is more easily oxidised as it's higher up the reactivity series/it's more reactive *[1 mark]*.

## p.115 — Reactivity of Metals

**Q1 a)** Metal B, Metal C, Metal A *[1 mark]*
**b)** Metal A is copper. Metal B is magnesium. Metal C is zinc *[1 mark for all three correct]*.

## p.116 — Displacement Reactions

**Q1** Silver would not displace iron from iron chloride solution, because it's lower down than iron in the reactivity series/less reactive than iron *[1 mark]*.

**Q2** Lithium would displace zinc from zinc sulfate solution, as it's higher than zinc in the reactivity series/it's more reactive than zinc *[1 mark]*.

## p.117 — Extracting Metals Using Carbon

**Q1** Tin is less reactive than carbon *[1 mark]* so you could extract tin from its ore by reducing it with carbon *[1 mark]*.

**Q2** E.g. 2ZnO + C → 2Zn + $CO_2$
*[1 mark for correct reactants and products, 1 mark for balanced equation]*

## p.118 — Other Methods of Extracting Metals

**Q1** Aluminium would be more expensive to extract than iron *[1 mark]* as aluminium is more reactive than carbon, so has to be extracted using electrolysis, whereas iron can be extracted by reduction with carbon *[1 mark]*. Extracting metals using electrolysis is much more expensive than using reduction with carbon as it requires high temperatures to melt the metal ore which is expensive/there are costs associated with using electricity, whereas reduction using carbon is much cheaper *[1 mark]*.

## p.119 — Recycling

**Q1** E.g. Metals are non-renewable, so recycling metals is important to conserve finite resources of the metal *[1 mark]*. Also, non-recycled material has to be disposed of in landfill sites, which take up space and can pollute the surroundings *[1 mark]*.

## p.120 — Life Cycle Assessments

**Q1** Any four from, e.g. the energy required to extract the raw materials / whether the raw materials are renewable or not / whether other harmful emissions (e.g. CO/HCl) are produced / whether the waste products are harmful or not / how environmentally friendly the cars are to dispose of *[1 mark for each]*.

## p.121 — Dynamic Equilibrium

**Q1** A reversible reaction is one where the products can react with each other to produce the reactants *[1 mark]*.

**Q2** Dynamic equilibrium occurs when the forward and backward reactions in a reversible reaction occur at the same time *[1 mark]* and at the same rate *[1 mark]*, so there is no change in concentration of the reactants or the products *[1 mark]*.

## p.122 — Le Chatelier's Principle

**Q1** The position of equilibrium will shift to the right (towards the products) *[1 mark]*. The forward reaction is endothermic, so when the temperature is increased the equilibrium position will move to the right to absorb the excess heat *[1 mark]*.

**Q2** Decreasing the pressure would shift the equilibrium position to the left (towards the reactants) *[1 mark]* as there are more moles of gas on the reactant side than on the product side *[1 mark]*. So the yield of $SO_3$ would decrease *[1 mark]*.

## p.123 — Group 1 — Alkali Metals

**Q1** The lithium should move around the surface of the water, fizzing vigorously, then dissolve *[1 mark]*.

**Q2** $2K + 2H_2O \rightarrow 2KOH + H_2$ *[1 mark for correct products and reactants and 1 mark for correct balancing]*

## p.124 — Group 7 — Halogens

**Q1** $2Na + Br_2 \rightarrow 2NaBr$ *[1 mark for correct products and reactants and 1 mark for correct balancing]*

## p.125 — Halogen Displacement Reactions

**Q1** He should add a few drops of the solution to a bromine salt solution (e.g. potassium bromide) *[1 mark]*. If the solution turns orange, the halogen solution contains chlorine. If there is no reaction, the halogen solution contains bromine *[1 mark]*.

## p.126 — Group 0 — Noble Gases

**Q1** Any melting point between −150 °C and 80 °C *[1 mark]*.

## p.128 — Reaction Rates

**Q1** E.g. put a conical flask on a mass balance and add your reactants *[1 mark]*. As gas is produced from the reaction, measure how quickly the reading on the balance drops until the balance stops changing *[1 mark]*. Plot the results in a graph of change in mass against time *[1 mark]*.

**Q2** E.g. the result is subjective *[1 mark]*.

## p.129 — Rate Experiments Involving Gases

**Q1** E.g. place a measured volume of hydrochloric acid of a known concentration in a conical flask. Add a known mass of calcium carbonate in the form of marble chips *[1 mark]*. Immediately add a gas syringe. Take readings of the volume of gas produced at regular time intervals *[1 mark]*. Repeat the experiment with the same volume and concentration of acid and the same mass of calcium carbonate but increase the surface area of magnesium by crunching the marble up. Repeat again with the same mass of powdered chalk *[1 mark]*.

## p.130 — Rate Experiments Involving Precipitation

**Q1** The time taken would decrease *[1 mark]*.

## p.131 — Calculating Rates

**Q1** E.g.

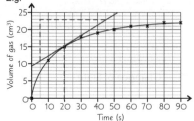

*[1 mark]*

Change in $y$ = 23 − 11 = 12
Change in $x$ = 45 − 5 = 40
Gradient = 12 ÷ 40 = 0.30 $cm^3\ s^{-1}$
*[1 mark for a rate between 0.25 $cm^3\ s^{-1}$ and 0.40 $cm^3\ s^{-1}$]*

## p.132 — Collision Theory

**Q1** The energy transferred during a collision (particles must collide with enough energy for the collision to be successful) *[1 mark]* and the collision frequency *[1 mark]*.

**Q2** Breaking a solid into smaller pieces will increase the surface area to volume ratio *[1 mark]*. This means that particles of the other reactant will have more area to work on *[1 mark]*. This increases the frequency of collisions and speeds up the rate of reaction *[1 mark]*.

## p.133 — Catalysts

**Q1** A catalyst is a substance which increases the rate of reaction *[1 mark]*, without being chemically changed or used up *[1 mark]*.

**Q2** The manganese dioxide is not chemically changed or used up so only a tiny amount is needed to catalyse a large quantity of reactant *[1 mark]*.

**Q3** Enzymes are biological catalysts *[1 mark]*. They speed up chemical reactions inside living cells *[1 mark]*.

## p.134 — Endothermic and Exothermic Reactions

**Q1** The products are at a higher energy than the reactants so the reaction must be endothermic *[1 mark]*. This means the reaction mixture must have decreased in temperature *[1 mark]*.

## p.135 — Measuring Temperature Changes

**Q1** They help to insulate the reaction mixture, limiting the energy transferred to or from the surroundings and by evaporation *[1 mark]*.

## p.136 — Bond Energies

**Q1** Energy required to break original bonds:
$(1 \times N\equiv N) + (3 \times H-H)$
= 941 + (3 × 436) = 941 + 1308
= 2249 kJ $mol^{-1}$ *[1 mark]*
Energy released by forming new bonds:
$(6 \times N-H)$
= 6 × 391 = 2346 kJ $mol^{-1}$ *[1 mark]*
Overall energy change:
= 2249 − 2346 = −97 kJ $mol^{-1}$ *[1 mark]*

## p.137 — Fractional Distillation

**Q1** Crude oil is heated until most of it turns into a gas *[1 mark]*. The gases enter a fractionating column and the liquid part/bitumen is drained off at the bottom *[1 mark]*. There's a temperature gradient in the column — the column is hot at the bottom and cooler at the top *[1 mark]*. The longer hydrocarbons with high boiling points turn back into liquids and drain out lower down the column *[1 mark]*. Shorter hydrocarbons have lower boiling points so turn into liquids and are drained off higher up the column *[1 mark]*.

## p.138 — Hydrocarbons

**Q1** $C_9H_{20} + 14O_2 \rightarrow 9CO_2 + 10H_2O$
*[1 mark for correct formulas, 1 mark for balancing]*

## p.139 — Pollutants

**Q1** Carbon monoxide *[1 mark]* and soot *[1 mark]*.

## p.140 — Cracking

**Q1** Cracking involves breaking strong covalent bonds within alkane molecules *[1 mark]*.

**Q2** $C_{12}H_{26}$ *[1 mark]*

## p.141 — The Atmosphere

**Q1** A lot of the early $CO_2$ dissolved into the oceans *[1 mark]*. Green plants evolved and removed $CO_2$ from the atmosphere through photosynthesis *[1 mark]*. Much of the $CO_2$ got locked up in fossil fuels and sedimentary rocks *[1 mark]*.

## p.142 — The Greenhouse Effect

**Q1** A gas in the atmosphere that can absorb and reflect heat radiation *[1 mark]*.

**Q2** Any two from, e.g. more people means more $CO_2$ given out from respiration / more energy needed for day to day living e.g. lighting, transport and cooking — this energy comes mainly from burning fossil fuels which releases $CO_2$ / space made for houses and farming through deforestation means that less $CO_2$ is taken out of the atmosphere by photosynthesis *[1 mark for each correct answer]*.

## p.143 — Climate Change

**Q1** Global warming is a type of climate change where the Earth's average temperature has increased *[1 mark]*. Increased human activity is believed to have caused increased levels of greenhouse gases in our atmosphere which has resulted in an enhanced greenhouse effect *[1 mark]*.

**Q2** Any two from, e.g. walk or cycle instead of drive / turn your central heating down / use more renewable energy *[1 mark for each correct answer]*.

## p.145 — Distance, Displacement, Speed and Velocity

**Q1 a)** Any two from: e.g. speed / distance / mass / temperature *[2 marks]*

**b)** Any two from: e.g. displacement / momentum / force / acceleration / velocity *[2 marks]*

**Q2** $s = d \div t$ = 200 ÷ 25 *[1 mark]* = 8 m/s *[1 mark]*

## p.146 — Acceleration

**Q1** $u$ = 0 m/s, $v$ = 5 m/s, $a$ = $g$ = 10 $m/s^2$,
$x = (v^2 - u^2) \div 2a$ = (25 − 0) ÷ (2 × 10) *[1 mark]*
= 1.25 m *[1 mark]*

## p.147 — Distance/Time Graphs

**Q1** E.g.

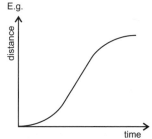

*[1 mark for a continuous line that initially curves upwards, and which curves downwards at the end until it becomes horizontal, 1 mark for a straight middle section.]*

## p.148 — Velocity/Time Graphs

**Q1 a)**

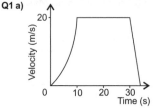

*[1 mark for an upwards curved acceleration line to 20 m/s, 1 mark for a straight line representing steady speed, 1 mark for a straight line representing deceleration]*

**b)** $a$ = gradient of the line
= change in vertical ÷ change in horizontal
= (0 − 20) ÷ (34 − 30) *[1 mark]*
= −20 ÷ 4 = −5 $m/s^2$
So the deceleration is 5 $m/s^2$ *[1 mark]*

## p.149 — Newton's First and Second Laws

**Q1** $F = ma$ = (80 + 10) × 0.25 *[1 mark]*
= 22.5 N *[1 mark]*

## p.150 — Weight and Circular Motion

**Q1 a)** $W = mg = 25 \times 10$ *[1 mark]* $= 250$ N *[1 mark]*

**b)** $W = 25 \times 1.6$ *[1 mark]* $= 40$ N *[1 mark]*

## p.151 — Investigating Motion

**Q1** E.g. it removes human error for timings *[1 mark]*

## p.152 — Inertia and Newton's Third Law

**Q1** An object with a smaller mass (in this case the empty trolley) will have a smaller inertial mass, so less force is needed to stop it *[1 mark]*.

## p.153 — Momentum

**Q1** $p = mv = 60 \times 3$ *[1 mark]* $= 180$ kg m/s *[1 mark]*

**Q2** Before the gun fires the bullet, the total momentum is zero (neither the gun nor the bullet are moving) *[1 mark]*. When the bullet leaves the gun, it has momentum in one direction *[1 mark]*. The gun moves backwards, and has an equal but opposite momentum to the bullet *[1 mark]*. This means that the total momentum after the bullet has been fired is still zero. Momentum has been conserved *[1 mark]*.

## p.154 — Changes in Momentum

**Q1** First, convert quantities to the correct units:
58 g = 0.058 kg
11.6 ms = 0.0116 s *[1 mark]*
$F = [(m \times v) - (m \times u)] \div t$
$= [(0.058 \times 34) - (0.058 \times 0)] \div 0.0116$
*[1 mark]*
$F = 170$ N *[1 mark]*

## p.155 — Stopping Distances and Reaction Times

**Q1** If you're tired, e.g. from a long journey, your reaction time is likely to be longer *[1 mark]*, which would increase thinking distance and so stopping distance *[1 mark]*. This would make an accident more likely if you needed to brake suddenly *[1 mark]*.

## p.156 — Energy Stores

**Q1** The change in height is 5 m.
So the energy transferred from the gravitational potential energy store is:
$\Delta$GPE $= m \times g \times \Delta h = 2 \times 10 \times 5$ *[1 mark]*
$= 100$ J *[1 mark]*
This is transferred to the kinetic energy store of the object, so KE = 100 J *[1 mark]*
KE $= \frac{1}{2} \times m \times v^2$ so $v^2 = (2 \times \text{KE}) \div m$
$= (2 \times 100) \div 2$ *[1 mark]*
$= 100$ m/s$^2$
$v = \sqrt{100} = 10$ m/s *[1 mark]*

## p.157 — Transferring Energy

**Q1** Energy in the chemical energy store of the wood is transferred by heating to the thermal energy stores of the surroundings *[1 mark]*. The rest of the energy is transferred away by light waves *[1 mark]*.

## p.158 — Efficiency

**Q1** Useful energy transferred by device
$= 500 - 420 = 80$ J *[1 mark]*
Efficiency $= \dfrac{\text{useful energy transferred by device}}{\text{total energy supplied to device}}$
$= 80 \div 500 = 0.16$ *[1 mark]*
$0.16 \times 100 = 16\%$ *[1 mark]*

## p.159 — Reducing Unwanted Energy Transfers

**Q1** E.g. lubricate moving parts *[1 mark]*.

## p.160 — Energy Resources

**Q1** Any two from: e.g. bio-fuels / wind power / the Sun/solar power / hydro-electricity / the tides *[2 marks]*

## p.161 — More Energy Resources

**Q1** E.g. wind farms produce no pollution, which is much better for the environment than burning coal. They are also cheap to run, as there are no fuel costs and minimal running costs.
You would need a lot of space to put the wind farm on, as you need lots of turbines to get the same power as a coal power station. People nearby also might dislike the wind farm, because wind farms spoil the view and can be noisy.
*[4 marks — 1 mark for each correct advantage, up to 2 marks, 1 mark for each correct disadvantage, up to 2 marks]*.

## p.162 — Trends in Energy Resource Use

**Q1** Any two from: e.g. building new power plants is expensive / people don't want to live near new power plants / renewable energy resources are less reliable than non-renewable energy resources / hybrid cars are more expensive than equivalent petrol cars *[2 marks]*.

## p.164 — Wave Basics

**Q1** $7.5 \div 100 = 0.075$ m *[1 mark]*
$v = f\lambda$, so $f = v \div \lambda$
$= 0.15 \div 0.075$ *[1 mark]*
$= 2$ Hz *[1 mark]*

## p.165 — Measuring Waves

**Q1** E.g. attach a signal generator to a dipper and place it in a ripple tank filled with water to create some waves. Place a screen underneath the ripple tank, then turn on a strobe light and dim the other lights in the room *[1 mark]*. Adjust the frequency of the strobe light until the ripples appear to freeze *[1 mark]*. Measure the distance between the shadows on the screen beneath the tank — this is equal to the wavelength of the ripples *[1 mark]*.

## p.166 — Wave Behaviour at Boundaries

**Q1** The light will bend away from the normal *[1 mark]*.

## p.167 — Investigating Refraction

**Q1 a)** Draw around a glass block onto a piece of paper. Shine a light ray from a ray box into the block *[1 mark]*. Trace the incident ray and mark where the ray emerges from the block. Remove the block and join these up with a straight line *[1 mark]*. Measure the angle of incidence and angle of refraction *[1 mark]*. Repeat this experiment for different materials, keeping the angle of incidence constant and seeing how the angle of refraction changes with the material *[1 mark]*.

**b)** So you can easily trace the light ray to measure the angle between the ray and the normal *[1 mark]*.

## p.168 — Electromagnetic Waves

**Q1** E.g. gamma rays are ionising so they can cause tissue damage and cancer, but visible light isn't ionising *[1 mark]*. They carry more energy than visible light, so their potential for damage is higher *[1 mark]*.

## p.169 — EM Waves for Communication

**Q1** They can pass easily through the Earth's watery atmosphere without being absorbed *[1 mark]*.

## p.170 — Microwaves and Infrared

**Q1** Any three from: e.g. burglar alarms / thermal imaging / short range communication / cooking / optical fibres *[3 marks]*

## p.171 — More Uses of EM Waves

**Q1** Any two from: e.g. fluorescent lamps / security pens / detecting forged bank notes / sterilising water *[2 marks]*

**Q2** E.g. you don't have to freeze it/cook it/preserve it to keep it fresher for longer *[1 mark]*

## p.172 — The Model of the Atom

**Q1 a)** The centre of an atom is a tiny, positively charged nucleus *[1 mark]*. This is made up of protons and neutrons and is the source of most of the atom's mass *[1 mark]*. Most of the atom is empty space *[1 mark]*. Electrons orbit the nucleus at set energy levels *[1 mark]*.

**b)** The radius of a nucleus is about 10 000 times smaller than the radius of the atom *[1 mark]*.

## p.173 — Electron Energy Levels

**Q1** A positive ion is an atom that has lost one or more electrons *[1 mark]*. A positive ion is formed when an outer electron absorbs enough energy that it leaves the atom *[1 mark]*.

## p.174 — Isotopes and Nuclear Radiation

**Q1** E.g. a thin sheet of paper will absorb alpha particles *[1 mark]*. Aluminium that's about 5 mm thick will absorb beta-minus particles *[1 mark]*. Thick sheets of lead or many metres of concrete will absorb gamma rays *[1 mark]*.

## p.175 — Nuclear Equations

**Q1** Beta-minus particle *[1 mark]*

**Q2** $^{219}_{86}\text{Rn} \rightarrow \, ^{215}_{84}\text{Po} + \, ^{4}_{2}\alpha$
*[1 mark for correct layout, 1 mark for correct symbol for an alpha particle, 1 mark for total atomic and mass numbers being equal on both sides]*

## p.176 — Half-Life

**Q1** The number of half-lives in 240 hours is
$240 \div 60 = 4$ half-lives *[1 mark]*
Initial count = 480
after 1 half-life = $480 \div 2 = 240$
after 2 half-lives = $240 \div 2 = 120$
after 3 half-lives = $120 \div 2 = 60$
after 4 half-lives = $60 \div 2 = 30$
So the activity after 240 hours = 30 Bq *[1 mark]*

## p.177 — Background Radiation and Contamination

**Q1** E.g. rocks *[1 mark]*, cosmic rays *[1 mark]* and fallout from nuclear explosions *[1 mark]*

## p.179 — Energy Transfers and Systems

**Q1** The wind does work on the windmill *[1 mark]* causing it to turn and transferring energy to the kinetic energy store of the windmill *[1 mark]*.

## p.180 — Work Done and Power

**Q1** $E = F \times d = 20 \times 0.2$ *[1 mark]* $= 4$ N *[1 mark]*

**Q2** $P = E \div T = 6000 \div 30$ *[1 mark]*
$= 200$ W *[1 mark]*

## p.181 — Forces

**Q1** E.g.

*[2 marks for all forces correctly drawn, 1 mark for three forces correctly drawn — weight and normal contact force arrows should be the same length, the arrow for the driving force should be longer than the weight arrow and the arrow for the resistive force should be shorter]*

## p.182 — Forces and Vector Diagrams

**Q1** E.g.

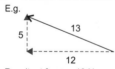

Resultant force = 13 N
*[1 mark for a correct scale drawing, 1 mark for correct resultant force]*

## p.184 — Current and Circuits

**Q1** $Q = I \times t$, so
$t = Q \div I = 120 \div 2.5$ *[1 mark]*
$= 48$ s *[1 mark]*

## p.185 — Potential Difference and Resistance

**Q1** $E = Q \times V$, so
$V = E \div Q = 360 \div 75$ *[1 mark]*
$= 4.8$ V *[1 mark]*

**Q2** $V = I \times R$, so
$R = V \div I = 4.25 \div 0.25$ *[1 mark]*
$= 17 \, \Omega$ *[1 mark]*

## p.186 — Investigating Components

**Q1**

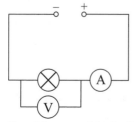

*[1 mark for a complete circuit with a variable d.c. power supply in series with a filament lamp, 1 mark for correct circuit symbols for all components, 1 mark for a voltmeter connected across the filament lamp and an ammeter connected in series with the filament lamp.]*

## p.187 — Circuit Devices

**Q1 a)** E.g. automatic night lights — a light automatically turns on when it gets dark *[1 mark]*.

**b)** E.g. thermostats — the heating automatically turns on/off at a certain temperature *[1 mark]*.

## p.188 — Series and Parallel Circuits

**Q1** 0.5 A *[1 mark]*

**Q2** E.g.

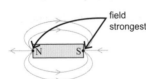

*[1 mark for the correct circuit symbols, 1 mark for two bulbs connected in parallel, 1 mark for both switches being on the same branches as the lamps]*

## p.189 — More on Series and Parallel Circuits

**Q1** $R = 2 + 3 + 7 = 12\ \Omega$ *[1 mark]*
$I = V \div R = 12 \div 12$ *[1 mark]* $= 1$ A *[1 mark]*

## p.190 — Energy in Circuits

**Q1** $E = I \times V \times t = 8.0 \times 230 \times (60 \times 60)$ *[1 mark]*
$= 6\ 624\ 000$ J *[1 mark]*

## p.191 — Power in Circuits

**Q1** $E = P \times t = 250 \times (2 \times 60 \times 60)$
$= 1\ 800\ 000$ J *[1 mark]*
$E = 375 \times (2 \times 60 \times 60) = 2\ 700\ 000$ J *[1 mark]*
So difference in the energy transferred is
$2\ 700\ 000 - 1\ 800\ 000 = 900\ 000$ J *[1 mark]*

## p.192 — Electricity in the Home

**Q1** In alternating current supply, the current is constantly changing direction *[1 mark]*. In a direct current supply, the current always travels in the same direction *[1 mark]*.

## p.193 — Fuses and Earthing

**Q1** The live wire *[1 mark]*.

## p.195 — Magnets and Magnetic Fields

**Q1**

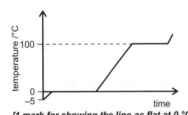

*[1 mark for at least two lines from north to south, 1 mark for an arrow on a line pointing from north to south, 1 mark for an indication of the field being strongest at the poles]*

**Q2** Put the magnet on a piece of paper and put a compass next to it, making a mark on the paper at each end of the needle *[1 mark]*. Then move the compass so that the tail of the compass needle is where the tip of the needle was previously, and mark again where the needle is pointing *[1 mark]*. Repeat this several times and then join up the markings for a complete sketch of a field line around the magnet *[1 mark]*. Do this several times for different points around the magnet to get several field lines *[1 mark]*.

## p.196 — Permanent and Induced Magnets

**Q1** Any three from: e.g. fridge doors / speakers / microphones / doorbells / cranes *[3 marks]*

**Q2** E.g. permanent magnets produce their own magnetic fields but induced magnets become magnets when they're in a magnetic field *[1 mark]*. The force between an induced magnet and a permanent magnet is always attractive, but between two permanent magnets it can be attractive or repulsive *[1 mark]*.

## p.197 — Electromagnetism and the Motor Effect

**Q1** Rearrange $F = B \times I \times l$
for the magnetic flux density, $B$:
$B = F \div (I \times l)$
$= 0.98 \div (5.0 \times 0.35)$ *[1 mark]*
$= 0.56$ T (or N/Am) *[1 mark]*

## p.198 — Solenoids and Electromagnetic Induction

**Q1**

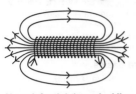

*[1 mark for tightly packed lines inside the coil, 1 mark for parallel lines inside the coil, 1 mark for field similar to a bar magnet outside of coil]*

## p.199 — Transformers

**Q1** $V_p \times I_p = V_s \times I_s = 320$ W
$I_p = 320 \div V_p = 320 \div 1.6$ *[1 mark]*
$= 200$ A *[1 mark]*

## p.200 — Density

**Q1** volume in $m^3 = 75 \div (100^3)$
$= 7.5 \times 10^{-5}\ m^3$ *[1 mark]*
density = mass ÷ volume
$= 0.45 \div (7.5 \times 10^{-5})$ *[1 mark]*
$= 6000\ kg/m^3$ *[1 mark]*

**Q2** First find the cube's volume:
$0.015 \times 0.015 \times 0.015 = 3.375 \times 10^{-6}\ m^3$ *[1 mark]*
The cube's density is $3500\ kg/m^3$.
$m = \rho \times V = 3500 \times (3.375 \times 10^{-6})$ *[1 mark]*
$= 0.01181...\ kg = 12$ g (to 2 s.f.) *[1 mark]*

## p.201 — Kinetic Theory and States of Matter

**Q1** As a typical substance changes from solid to liquid to gas, its density will decrease *[1 mark]* as its mass will stay the same *[1 mark]* but its volume will increase as the particles have more energy to overcome the forces between them *[1 mark]*.

## p.202 — Specific Heat Capacity

**Q1** $\Delta Q = mc\Delta\theta$, so:
$\Delta\theta = \Delta Q \div (m \times c)$
$= 1680 \div (0.20 \times 420)$ *[1 mark]*
$= 20\ °C$ *[1 mark]*

**Q2** E.g. measure the mass of an empty insulating container. Pour water into the container and measure the mass again. Use this to determine the mass of the water *[1 mark]*. Using an immersion heater connected to a joulemeter, heat the water *[1 mark]*. Use a thermometer to monitor the temperature of the water. Once the temperature of the water has increased by 10 °C, turn off the immersion heater *[1 mark]*. Use the reading from the joulemeter and the equation $\Delta Q = mc\Delta\theta$ to find the specific heat capacity *[1 mark]*.

## p.203 — Specific Latent Heat

**Q1**

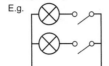

*[1 mark for showing the line as flat at 0 °C, 1 mark for showing the line as flat at 100 °C. 1 mark for drawing the line as straight, with a positive gradient, for temperatures below 0 °C, between 0 and 100 °C, and above 100 °C.]*

## p.204 — Particle Motion in Gases

**Q1** $25 + 273 = 298$ K *[1 mark]*

**Q2** When gas particles collide with the walls of their container, they exert a force on it *[1 mark]*. Across many particles, this force acting on the container causes an outward pressure *[1 mark]*.

## p.205 — Forces and Elasticity

**Q1** $k = F \div x = 1 \div 0.02$ *[1 mark]* $= 50$ N/m *[1 mark]*

## p.206 — Investigating Elasticity

**Q1** $E = \frac{1}{2}kx^2 = \frac{1}{2} \times 40 \times (0.025)^2$ *[1 mark]*
$= 0.0125$ J *[1 mark]*

# Index

# Index